TECTONICS

A Series of Geology Texts

EDITORS: James Gilluly and A. O. Woodford

TECTONICS

By JEAN GOGUEL

Professor of the School of Mines in Paris
Director of the Geological Map Service
of France

English translation from the French Edition of 1952

By HANS E. THALMANN

Stanford University, California

W. H. Freeman and Company

SAN FRANCISCO AND LONDON

Author's Preface to the English Edition

THIS ENGLISH TRANSLATION of my book *Traité de Tectonique* (Paris, 1952) has, to some degree, an advantage over the French Edition in that pertinent literature to 1957 could be discussed. However, no change has been made in the original aim or content of the book.

Most of the examples used were chosen either from France or from neighboring western European countries. Since these examples are intended to illustrate general theories rather than to give a systematic description of a certain region, I have not replaced them with examples from the United States or the western hemisphere, nor do I regard them to be of inconvenience to the American reader. I hope, however, that these examples will be of value to geologists in the Western Hemisphere who wish to become more intimately familiar with European geology, and, in particular, with Alpine geology.

The reader is encouraged to search for analogous examples in American geology. This, in my opinion, is the best way in which the information presented can be put to use and applied by the American student of tectonics.

JEAN GOGUEL

March 1962

CONTENTS

CHAPTER ONE

Introduction

Historical character of geology—Definition of tectonics—Methods to be applied—Plan of the work—Fundamental observations.

AT FIRST GLANCE geology seems to have as its object the study and description of the rocky masses that make up the solid part of the earth. Such practical applications of geology as are employed in mineral exploitation, ground-water exploration, tunnel driving, and the study of artificial construction stability require that both the state and arrangement of rocks be known. In comparison with the activities of man, or in contrast with the freely moving air or surface waters, rocks are the very image of stability and permanence.

Although the descriptive approach is entirely insufficient for promoting an understanding of the nature and disposition of rocks, all becomes clear when a historical point of view is taken and when an attempt is made to reconstruct the genesis of the rocky masses. By considering an initial phase of such historical reconstruction, we can predict their long-term effects. Thus, the comparatively short-term effects of erosion by a brook enable us to comprehend the scooping out of a valley, just as the deposition of a thin film of mud is analogous to the filling in of a sedimentary basin. To make such extrapolations, we need only use our imagination: sea-level variations, the existence of volcanoes in regions where their activity is no longer evident, or the former extension of glaciers much beyond their present size. Comparison of certain areas with other regions furnishes us with another basis for such historical reconstruction.

However, if we wish to extend our reconstruction to explain, for example, the formation of mountains, it is necessary to visualize phenomena that are completely different from anything it is possible to actually observe. Rocks have been stretched and twisted, and hundreds of kilometers have undergone upheavals of an extraordinary amplitude. It is only after having reconstructed these deformations, by analyzing the forms they have given to the rocks, that it has been realized that the changes were not essentially different from certain

1

changes recognized after earthquakes, or from gradual changes in elevation due to uplift or subsidence.

Tectonics is concerned with the examination of these deformations and with the study of the present forms of deformed rock masses. As is characteristic of geology in general, tectonics is principally a historical science, inasmuch as its object is the reconstruction of past phenomena. Only this sort of reconstruction can furnish the key to the interpretation of geologic structures.

For the determination of the present form of rock masses, we have only very fragmentary data concerning parts that are not masked by recent formations; these data concern only the surface produced by erosion at the heart of the deformed mass. However, the indications provided by a historical reconstruction of the deformation are too meager to permit formulation of a hypothesis regarding the disposition of deformed rock masses. Even if we were only concerned with understanding the present disposition of the rocks, a historical reconstruction would be indispensable in order to make the most of our observations. In many instances, precise knowledge concerning the disposition of deformed rocks is of sufficient economic importance to justify a very profound study along these lines.

The deformations undergone by rocks, the tempests in the solid crust of the globe, deserve an intense study, if only to acquire knowledge of the earth, without regard to practical applications. The geometric analysis of forms evidently constitutes a first phase of this study; these forms are both among the essential data at our disposal, and at the same time one of the results to be obtained. However, a geometric analysis should be supplemented by a study of the chronology. The description of the process of deformation constitutes a problem in kinematics—that is, a problem in analysis of motion. The forces that have deformed the rocks must also be considered, thus bringing dynamics into play. This obliges us to consider the mechanics of deformable solids, thus implying the use of a certain mathematical apparatus. However, we shall leave this out of consideration for the moment, thus avoiding mathematical calculations and limiting ourselves to the point of view of the naturalist. The inquisitive reader eager to investigate more thoroughly the mechanical and mathematical aspects of these questions, or even simply to seek proof of the results cited, is referred to an earlier work of the author.[1]

The successive phases of the analysis that we have just outlined—geometric, kinematic, dynamic—can be applied on different scales. Even the deformation of a small fragment of rock presents problems outside common experience. Moreover, this deformation may strikingly modify the properties of the rock. Then we shall have to show how the deformations undergone by the rock can be analyzed in detail. And finally, we should seek the laws according to which the deformations should be grouped and classified, both in space and in time.

When we attempt to date tectonic deformations in the general history of the earth, insofar as stratigraphy enables us to reconstruct it, it becomes obvious that they are by no means mere chance happenings. Quite the contrary; great paroxysms of tectonic deformation constitute major events in the history of the globe. Except for the evolution of the living world, which seems to have been uninfluenced by tectonic deformations, all other phenomena coordinate themselves around these great crises. The nature and extent of sediments depend upon the corresponding paleogeography—that is, upon the form and extent of the lands and seas that resulted from earlier deformations as well as from contemporaneous deformations. The activity of volcanoes, as well as the deep recrystallizations that have given birth to the plutonic rocks, also appear closely related to tectonic paroxysms. These paroxysms evidently constitute the surface manifestation of a sort of life—an internal pulsation of the globe. The information supplied by tectonics is, then, of primary importance in geophysics. Various methods have been developed within this discipline that provide us with information about the internal structure of the earth. The hypotheses formulated to coordinate these indications should also permit us to explain the deformations observed at the surface. Inversely, geophysical data are essential to an understanding of deformations.

Any author of a treatise on geology is faced with a dilemma: Should he insist, above all, upon methods and general laws, or should he, on the contrary, systematically describe the objects of his study, enumerating the results obtained? When it is a question of stratigraphy, the second alternative seems best. Here we have felt it best to insist upon method, while endeavoring, especially through the choice of illustrations, to base our methods on concrete examples.

However, neither a systematic presentation of results nor an overall description of principal mountain chains will be found here. Since the space available prevents extensive local descriptions, the syntheses we might present would necessarily be somewhat dogmatic. This we preferred to avoid, for even the most classic syntheses may, and should, change. As with many of the laws formulated in geology, the emphasis should be on establishing them, rather than on applying them.

In this investigation of the movements of the earth's crust, the subject matter of tectonics, we shall begin by examining the methods of analysis and then go on to the interpretation of the observations—that is, to the detailed reconstruction of crustal movements. Beginning with Chapter 16, we shall offer a more synthetic point of view and shall attempt to view the tectonic phenomenon as a whole (though there will be no description of the "face of the earth" as shaped by these deformations) and in relation to other phenomena.

In a final chapter, we shall examine what hypotheses may be formulated regarding the internal structure of the globe in order to account for the tectonic observations made at its surface.

Doubtless there would be no better introduction to the study of tectonics than the reading of *Voyages dans les Alpes*[2] by Horace Benedict de Saussure. In this book, we see how an excellent observer, with practically no previous theoretical experience, through his acute observations of natural phenomena, conceived two essential ideas. While contemplating Mont Blanc, from the top of the Grammont (II, p. 341), and later, standing before the Matterhorn (IV, p. 414), he declares that erosion, "by the waters of the snows and rains," scooped out the valleys, leaving behind the mountains as fragments of a formerly unbroken mass. While observing the Vallorsine conglomerates, whose beds are vertical (II, p. 100), or the bend outlined by the beds of Tithonic limestone at the Nant d'Arpenaz Falls, on the right bank of the Arve (IV, p. 414), de Saussure recognized that the layers, today tilted up on edge, or bent, must have been formed horizontally; so there is the proof of the deformation of the rocky mass.

Those are the two essential notions upon which the study of tectonics is based, proven with a care no longer to be found in later authors, who consider them evident. Terrestrial surface relief has been carved out by the erosion of a formerly unbroken mass. In certain regions, especially in most mountains, this mass is formed of rocks that have undergone deformation. We are going to seek to analyze this deformation.

Notes and References

1. Goguel, J., *Introduction à l'étude mécanique des déformations de l'Écorce Terrestre,* Mém. Carte géol. France, 2nd ed., Paris, 1948.

2. Neuchâtel, 4 vols., 1779–1796.

CHAPTER TWO

Morphology and Tectonics

Role of morphology in the study of the form of rock masses—Successive cycles of erosion or of deposition—Eustatic movements—Deformation of erosional or alluvial surfaces—Morphological role of recent faults—Movements verified through earthquakes—Other present movements.

THERE IS NO *a priori* difference between the present epoch and the geologic periods of the past; consequently, tectonic movements may now be studied at least in certain regions. If these movements are too slow to be directly perceptible, they may possibly be recognized by comparing the forms of the terranes with those that would have resulted through the simple action of erosion.

However, it must be recognized that many geographers have acquired the habit of analyzing relief forms, assuming more or less implicitly, that they result from the action of erosion upon an immobile rocky mass. According to all evidence, this is an approximation, sound only in regions unaffected by recent movements. In order to explain the formation of terraces, for instance, we must assume movement of the entire continent relative to sea level, or the reverse (eustatic movement).

However, in certain zones, the morphology can only be explained by postulating a deformation at a more or less recent epoch. The more ancient the erosion from which the erosion forms result, the more they manifest the trace of such movements.

Before examining the manner in which morphology indicates either wholly vertical movements or true folding, we should indicate the role it plays, even where the tectonic movements to be studied are older than the shaping of relief by erosion.

For the geologist who proposes simply to determine the form of the various rock masses, morphology is an indispensable complement to the direct observation of outcrop lithology. For a statement of the laws of erosion and of the resultant relations between land forms and the nature of rocks, we refer to specialized treatises.[1] A geologist with a good command of these laws can verify his working hypothesis about rock distribution by examining the terranes, and can sometimes be put on the trail of a geologic peculiarity by an apparently inexplicable morphologic feature.

The study of morphology begins with the topographic map, but no matter how detailed and precise it may be, the topographic map alone would obviously not suffice. Morphologic studies should be made during the observation of outcrops. In mountains, where the view is very extensive, morphologic analysis can often be conducted quite rapidly if the observation points are varied so as to avoid errors due to perspective.

Direct observation may be supplemented by the study of stereoscopic photographs, taken either on the ground (from the ends of a relatively long base) or from the air. It is often suggested that the length of the base on the ground should be one tenth of the distance to the nearest feature. Stereoscopic observation then gives unexaggerated relief, corresponding to a model that would be in our scale. If n and f are the distances to the nearest and farthest points, a base up to $nf/10(f - n)$ may be chosen, with the risk of producing an exaggerated relief, which is always the case with air photos.

Except when the nature of an outcrop is discernible on the photographs (either directly or through the nature of the vegetation), we should keep in mind that the photographs reveal only morphologic data, which is altogether insufficient for a tectonic interpretation. The ease with which air photographs can be used tempts us to make premature interpretations that are insufficiently supported or insufficiently verified by the direct study of outcrops. A number of errors have resulted from this vicious method of work, and it may be that the list is still open.

Whether an understanding of morphology results from direct examination, from map study, or from observation of stereoscopic photographs, it is known that hard rocks are characterized by steeper slopes than less resistant rocks. This "hardness" is something entirely relative; it characterizes the relative resistance to erosion of rocks within a particular climate and does not correspond directly to any physical qualities of the rocks.

Certain rocks are readily interpreted in terms of morphology: such, for example, are the limestones, whose solution by infiltrating waters produces the easy to recognize karst forms; gypsum is often riddled with funnel-shaped holes. In general, the depressions characteristic of soluble rocks may be sought on the air photo or on the ground. Besides the resistance to the erosion agents, permeability is shown in the topographic forms by the density of the hydrographic network, which is sometimes very characteristic.

But the use of morphologic analysis to distinguish rock types (often an unconscious process) involves grave risks of error. We must be able to distinguish successive related cycles of erosion, whose limits are marked (even in a homogeneous terrain) by changes in slope, from traces of hard horizontal

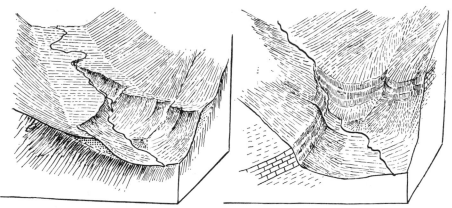

FIGURE 1. *Right, change of slope and discontinuity of longitudinal profile, determined by the presence of a hard bed. This situation should not be confused with that shown on the left, the nesting of an erosion cycle into a
cycle of alluvial deposition.*

beds; this applies both to valley cross profile and longitudinal profiles (Fig. 1).

There is also a danger of committing serious errors in interpreting recent
depositional forms (moraines, talus piles, and so on) as erosional forms on bed
rock. The best way to avoid such errors is to study the depositional forms
themselves, try to understand their genesis and distribution, and plot their
boundaries as exactly as possible. At the same time, in this manner, the zones
in which there is little hope of observing outcrops are defined.

To sum up, superficial morphologic analysis may involve grave errors, but
even a thorough analysis merely furnishes suggestions that should be verified
by the direct study of outcrops. It is mainly a way of making a sort of rough
draft of the work and of determining the zones within which our observation
should be focused.

There is, however, one case in which morphologic study furnishes results
that might escape direct observation; we refer to mass landslips. Especially

FIGURE 2. *Relationships that may develop on a slope by the slipping of calcareous
masses resting on a clayey formation (see also Fig. 52).*

in places where calcareous beds rest upon a marly series, we very frequently find that a large mass (perhaps several hundred meters across) has slipped progressively down slope (Fig. 2). The outcrops within the affected area may not appear to be lowered, and the dip may be only slightly changed. Very often, morphologic analysis will put us on the right track and prevent an erroneous interpretation of the outcrop pattern as being due to deep-seated displacement.

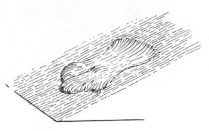

FIGURE 3

Elementary slip on a slope in clayey strata.

Forms more or less approximating a slip will be observed to have a bulge at the base and a small depression toward the top (Fig. 3). Similarly, the surface undulations on a marly slope reveal the presence of slips that may involve rocks below outcrop level. Real landslips, whose masses were notably displaced, are recognized through topographic forms, but their interpretation is confirmed in a decisive manner through examination of the slipped mass.

Morphology enables us to identify the cycles of erosion and alluvial deposition in a given region, the most recent of which are represented by alluvial terraces. The succession of these cycles records the changes in erosion processes, the causes of which must be analyzed: a change in elevation above sea level, for example, may either be the result of local upwarping, regional uplift, or even of variation in local base level (due to a landslip or to a cut off meander). Finally, the variations in climate may completely modify the conditions under which erosion takes place, both through variations in stream discharge and in modifications of the vegetal cover.

It is important to be able to recognize the succession of alluvial cycles due to such causes, in order to avoid making incorrect interpretations regarding continental deformation or sea-level variations. Figure 4 shows an example of terraces that were formed after a landslip barred the valley, causing a change in local base level.

The importance of climatic factors in the formation of terraces has been vigorously supported by certain recent geographic research findings.[2] The profile toward which a water course tends, which represents only a temporary equilibrium, depends both upon the flow (especially the flow at flood) and the proportion of solids carried by running waters; the destruction of vegetal covering enormously increases erosion and completely modifies the runoff.

At the eastern foot of the Andes, near Mendoza, for example, at the edge of the plains, there is a whole system of terraces not found in the plains themselves. It is impossible to assume that they record variation in sea level, since

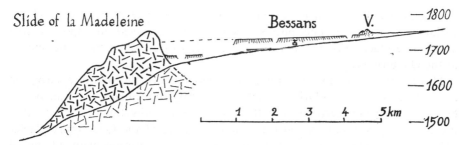

FIGURE 4. *An example of strictly local terraces in a section of the Arc River, upstream from Lansbourg (Savoie). The landslip of la Madeleine has barred the valley and caused the deposition of alluvial fill, which formed the Bessans terraces. The river has excavated a gorge through the slip and increased the slope of its profile. The frontal moraine of the Villaron (at V) rests upon the terrace, indicating the maximum extension of the glacier after the slip, which occurred after the warm period.*

this would imply recent erosion of earlier alluvium over a width of 1500 km. Nor is it necessary to assume an uplift of the chain corresponding to each of the terraces or erosion levels. Alluvial cones were probably formed during a period of heavy deposition and were subsequently cut through when the torrents began to erode more than they deposited. This example is rendered very striking by the considerable distance that separates the sea from the mountains in this part of the Argentine. Such changes in the behavior of torrents may have played a similar part in other countries.

It is no less a fact that the terrace steps downstream in a fluvial valley (especially when they correspond to raised beaches) indicate variations in sea level. The negative phases are difficult to date exactly, but may be indicated by the flooding of topographical forms, such as meander valleys.

It is customary to contrast orogenic movements, revealed by true deformation, with epeirogenic movements, which imply a vertical displacement of an entire land mass. The latter should, in turn, be distinguished from eustatic movements, resulting from changes in sea level.

Among the causes of eustatic movements in the Quaternary Period, the most important is certainly the accumulation of ice in the great glacial ice caps, which greatly decreased the volume of water in the oceans. Estimates of the corresponding fall of sea level vary greatly. Shepard[3] has proposed a figure of 1800 m, but this figure seems far too high and does not even suffice to explain the formation of submarine canyons by subaerial erosion, since some of them are as deep as 4000 m. Other estimates vary between 40 and 300 m. Moreover, owing to the changes produced in the terrestrial gravitational field as a result of mass displacements, the depressed oceans were not everywhere at a uniform distance below the present level, even in the absence of deformation.[4]

Glaciation is not the only possible cause of eustatic movements; in principle, the tectonic deformation of a marine zone may very well produce a global variation in sea level. This phenomenon may have played an important role during interglacial periods, but it is impossible to prove that the same applies to the Quaternary.

Having made an allowance for eustatic movements, the role of epeirogenic movements seems singularly restricted. The only movements that can be established with any certainty are those of isostatic adjustment, such as that undergone by Scandinavia since the disappearance of the Quaternary glacier (Chap. 16). This movement is revealed by the arrangement of raised beaches, which increase in elevation from south to north along the shores of the Baltic and are characterized by different shells (*Yoldia, Ancylus, Littorina, Lymnaea, Mya*).

Except for such passive isostatic readjustments, it is very difficult to discriminate between epeirogenic and orogenic movements. It must be admitted that the amplitude of the former may vary gradually from one location to another. On the other hand, the first consequence of a slight orogenic movement (or of an orogenic movement of short duration) should be a local change in elevation.

The variations of altitude of a given marine level, whether marked by raised beaches or by the terraces of lateral valleys, should then be interpreted as evidence of a deformation of the earth's crust. But when applying this principle, we must be sure that we are tracing the same bed. Too often, unfortunately, beds (observed bits of which it was hoped would fit into the picture) have been identified solely on the basis of their elevations. Errors of identification can be very serious in alluvial terraces. In raised beaches, paleontologic evidence may make identification possible if the beaches are old enough (Pleistocene and Pliocene). In the Baltic, important variations in the salinity have brought about a series of striking changes in the Recent fauna; thus the paleontologic record is particularly useful for such identification.

We might be tempted to introduce as evidence the variations of altitude of alluvial terraces, which, at the time of their deposition, followed the profile of a water course. But it is very difficult to discern what the former gradient of the water course was. Depending on the nature of the material transported, the discharge, and the flood regime, the equilibrium profile could vary greatly. Thus we cannot postulate that deformation followed deposition of the terrace alluvium, unless the terrace elevation increases downstream, or at least remains constant for a considerable distance. According to Rigo,[5] such would be the case for the Meuse above Mézieres; that is, at the point where the Meuse penetrates the Ardenne Massif.

The best known example of tectonically deformed alluvium is the low terrace of the Rhine, north of Mulhouse. This terrace slopes progressively downward, from an elevation 10 m above the present alluvium to stream level at a point 90 km downstream. Were this peculiarity isolated, it might be interpreted as due other than to tectonic deformation, but Jung[6] has shown the existence of surface upwarpings on the order of 2 m, which are directly above salt plugs that were located by geophysical prospecting. We would certainly have hesitated to interpret such slight surface irregularities as the result of tectonic deformation, if analogous deformations of much greater amplitude, which affected the base of the alluvium, had not been previously identified. The formation of this level, which began in the early Quaternary, was evidently much earlier than that of the low terrace, although the deformation was cumulative and extended over a much longer time. The sinking of the low terrace to the level of the present alluvial surface was accompanied by a sinking of the bottom of the alluvium, which drops to 44 m below sea level at Vieux Brisach but rises again to an elevation of 57 m above sea level downstream at Karlsruhe.[7] Above the Hettenschlag salt plug, the uplift of the base of the alluvium, relative to the surrounding regions, reaches 150 m in places.

By studying the base of the alluvium, known here through numerous borings, we avoid the causes of error introduced by erosion in the study of alluvial terraces. By itself, the comparison with a surface of the early Quaternary permits us to say that the very slight deformations of a relatively recent surface, such as that of the low terrace, are of tectonic origin. In Alsace, these tectonic deformations result from the superposition of two phenomena: the continued subsidence of the Rhenish trench, which represents the last action of a very ancient movement; and the local uplift of the salt plugs.

We shall have occasion to come back to the action of the salt plugs (Chaps. 10 and 13), whose upheaval may develop without the intervention of external forces. In the Gulf Coast region of Texas, there are numerous examples of upwarping of the alluvial plain (called "mounds"), which conceal salt plugs whose movements have continued until a quite recent epoch.

In certain regions, which are, in general, seismically active, tectonic movements can be inferred from faults, which may break the surface of the soil, interrupt the course of a stream, thus forming a lake, and so on. Fault scarps are rapidly altered by erosion, but the topographic forms resulting from very recent faulting are nevertheless characteristic. They have been abundantly described in California and in New Zealand,[8] but they are found in other active seismic regions (Japan, Assam, and elsewhere). Fractures of this type, changes in the level of Recent moraines, and bounding lakes have recently been described in the south of the Aar Massif (Grisons, Switzerland).[9]

Except within regions where faulting may be observed, there is evidently a better chance to prove tectonic deformation of an erosion surface the older the surface is. In Basse Provence, for instance, certain erosion surfaces are covered in places by Miocene sediments, which elsewhere are very clearly tilted. However, it is quite unusual to observe a definitely tilted erosion surface, inasmuch as a tilted surface is easily attacked by erosion, and as soon

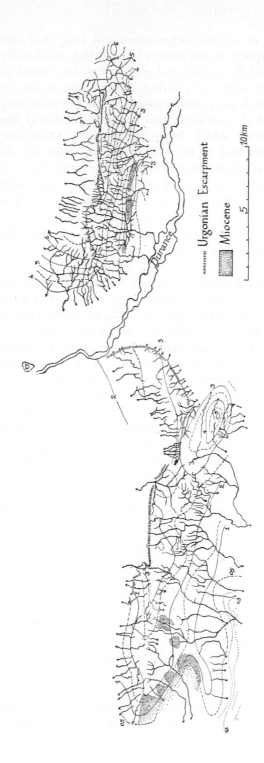

FIGURE 5. *Example of reconstruction, by morphology, of the present character of an old erosion surface. Map of the Alpilles and the Luberon (Bouches-du-Rhône and Vaucluse). The contour lines indicate the elevation in hectometers of the culminating points, the corresponding surface being deeply cut by many channels. Some Miocene remnants are to be found on this surface. (Reduced from a map drawn to a scale of 1:20,000.)*

as the protecting sediments are removed, it is soon reduced to shreds. But regular variations in the elevation of surface remnants may indicate that they formerly belonged to the same surface. In the Alpilles, and in the Luberon, we can confirm such an interpretation and can show that the present hydrographic network is everywhere orthogonal to the contours of the reconstructed surface. (See Fig. 5.) Obviously the bits of surface that remain horizontal cannot be correlated by their heights, since their vertical displacements must vary.

However, many geographers have distinguished between successive cycles of erosion on the basis of a comparison of the altitudes of old erosion surfaces. In the absence of positive arguments one way or the other, the choice between the two methods of interpretation is largely subjective. One method assumes the absence of deformation and the succession of erosion cycles whereas the other attempts to follow the deformations of an erosion surface. A quite striking example of the analysis of the movements by reconstruction of old, deformed erosion surfaces is found in the Besançon region, French Jura.[10]

In the absence of originally horizontal erosion surfaces, the analysis of a more complex relief may at times enable us to identify the trace of deformation. The very form of Lake Kioga in Central Africa shows that it is the product of warping, which affected a system of valleys and reversed the slope of the stream, thus producing a lake that discharges toward the Nile through what was originally one of its affluent branches.

In a remarkable study of the relief of Belgium,[11] Stevens has deliberately chosen the second method. His conclusions, however, are not accepted by all geographers. In the absence of well preserved erosion surfaces, he has made special use of the courses of streams and the altitudes of certain points, which do not seem to be in accordance with the nature of the rocks of which they are constituted, in order to reconstruct recent movements that would have modified the course of streams or caused captures. Such an approach may have to be fruitful, but in order to remove the uncertainties that exist, *it must be carried out in an extremely rigorous manner.*

As is shown by J. Bourcart,[12] the Dinarides folding actually continues throughout the more external chains, which make up the line of the Dalmatian Islands. Archeological investigations have proved that the site of Durazzo has, since ancient times, undergone warping, which has been found to correspond to the characteristics of the folds. The strings of islands separated from the coast by straits were, in general, probably formed as a result of this accentuation of folding. Through a study of the Tertiary sediments in Albania, Bourcart has shown that folding continued during sedimentation. Thus, Bourcart's stratigraphic arguments with respect to Dalmatia tend to confirm the morphologic indications, which are based, in part, upon the existence of archeological remains. In general, it is quite difficult to demonstrate, through simple morphologic considerations, recent tectonic movements, that is, movements that occur after erosion or contemporaneous with erosion.

The doctrine of uniformitarianism, so essential in geology, generally implies the preliminary study of present phenomena, which should enlighten us regarding the role of past phenomena, which we are seeking to reconstruct. This method hardly applies to the study of tectonic deformations, since the number of cases in which we have been able to demonstrate a movement directly is very limited.

Horizontal fault displacements have often been recorded during earthquakes. The best known and most studied example is that of the San Andreas fault, which was responsible for the San Francisco earthquake of 1906; but similar examples have been described in other parts of California and in Japan, Alaska, Assam, and elsewhere. At the time of the earthquake of November 10, 1946, in Peru, such a fault fractured the surface for a length of 18 km with a displacement of as much as 3.5 m.[13] Arnold Heim has published impressive photographs of it.[14] The question might arise as to whether the fractures are not secondary consequences of the shock; in Japan certain fissures have been seen to form only after the quake. However, it seems well established that, in the majority of cases, fault action is the phenomenon responsible for the earthquake. It has been demonstrated that progressively increasing strain is followed by sharp faulting. Residual strains—those that result from the fact that the inertia of the moving fault blocks causes them to pass the position of equilibrium—are relieved during aftershocks. An earthquake is essentially due to the vibratory phenomenon through which the energy is dissipated. Observation thus brings us direct information concerning the way in which this type of faulting usually occurs.

It is much more difficult to demonstrate movements that are probably very slow, and which were made possible by the plastic deformation of rocks. Doubtless the most interesting example of movements of this kind is that of the Buena Vista Hills oil field, in California.[15] In about 1933, it was noticed that casing breaks, recorded in wells, formed an angle of 25° with the horizontal. The intersection of this plane with the surface is marked by an escarpment, which had not previously attracted attention, but which seems due to action of the fault. Electric wires that crossed the escarpment were slackened, pipe-lines were bowed up, and the road was fissured, indicating an overthrust movement. This movement is progressing at about 1 inch per year. The horizontal component of displacement has been about 1 foot; the accompanying vertical component has reached 7 inches, which corresponds to a vertical displacement of about 4 feet per century. No earthquake was recorded, and it seems evident that the movement is progressing slowly but continuously. It is easy to realize how such a displacement could have escaped observation, although susceptible of producing very significant overthrusts in a time length on the order of geologic periods (2 m per century). Moreover, when analogous or more rapid movements are recorded, they are often explained as being due to purely superficial phenomena, such as landslips, settling after mining exploitation, dissolution in depth, and others.

It has often been proposed that special bench marks be set up in order to measure future tectonic displacements. In California, geodetic bench marks have been set up, which permit the displacements corresponding to earthquakes to be recorded in opposite directions on both sides of faults. Duclaux and Biget[16] have shown that it would be possible to record displacements as small as a few millimeters in magnitude on a straight line of 20 km. But in France, I do not know of any point where there is reason to assume an active horizontal movement, and the method does not seem to have been applied. Vertical movements may be recorded by the repetition of measurements upon systems of precise levelling, and in this way, numerous movements have been studied, in California and in Japan, following earthquakes.

In order to record a continuous deformation, it is tempting to take a levelling that is as ancient as possible as a standard of comparison, but care must be taken to avoid incorporating errors that may have been made in early measurements. In the work quoted above, Gilluly cites France as an example of recent movement, taking as a basis the divergence between the levellings of Bourdaloue (1857–1864) and Lallemand (1884–1893), a divergence reaching 80 cm at Cherbourg, but which was due, in fact, to errors in the first operation. (No later change has been recorded.) However, if such movements are still active in places, geodetic operations—triangulation and levelling—will record them in the long run. Again, allowance must be made for the normal subsidence of recent sediments and for the rapid subsidence that results from a depression of the water table, in regions where ground waters are greatly exploited. (For example, in certain interior basins in California, where the subsidence reaches 2 m, and in the region of Douai, northern France, where a subsidence of some 15 cm may well be assigned to such a cause, as distinguished from subsidence due to mining exploitations.)[17]

Notes and References

1. Noë, Géneral G. de la et Margerie, Em. de, *Les formes du terrain,* Paris, 1888.
Martonne, Em de, *Traité de géographie physique,* Vol. II, 5th ed., Armand Colin, Paris, 1934.
Macar, Paul, *Principes de géomorphologie normale,* Vaillant Carmanne and Masson, Liège and Paris, 1946.

2. Tricart, J., *Méthode d'études des terrasses,* Bull. Soc. géol. France, 5 sér., vol. 17, pp. 559–575, 1947.

3. Shepard, F. P., *Submarine Geology,* Harper, New York, 1948.

4. Goguel, J., *Contribution à l'étude des variations glaciaires du niveau des mers* (in preparation).

5. Rigo, M., *Etude des terraines fluviatiles sur le versant sud de l'Ardenne,* Ann. Soc. géol. Belgique, vol. 59, pp. M 1–30, 1935–1936.

6. Jung, J., Schlumberger, C. and M., *Soulèvement des alluvions du Rhin par les intrusions salines diapires de la Haute-Alsace,* Bull. Serv. géol. Alsace et Lorraine, vol. 3, pp. 77–86, 1936.

7. Théobald, M., *Carte de la base des formations alluviales dans le sud du fossé rhénan,* Mém. Serv. Carte géol. Alsace et Lorraine, no. 9, 1948.

8. Cotton, C. A., *Geomorphology,* 4th ed., Whitcomb and Tombs, Auckland, 1945.

————, Revival of Major Faulting in New Zealand, Geol. Mag., vol. 84, pp. 79–88, 1947.

9. Jäckli, Heinrich, *Verwerfung jungquartären Alters im südlichen Aarmassiv bei Somvix-Rabius* (Graubünden), Eclogae geol. Helv., vol. 44, pp. 332–337, 1951.

10. Dreyfuss, M., and Glangeaud, L., *La vallée du Doubs et l'évolution morphotectonique de la région bisontine,* Ann. Scient. Univ. Besançon, vol. 5, 1950.

11. Stevens, Ch., *Le relief de la Belgique,* Mém. géol., Univ. Louvain, vol. 12, 1938.

12. Bourcart, J., *Géographie des fonds des mers,* Payot, Paris, 1949. See especially pp. 92 ff.

13. Rüegg, Werner, *Le tremblement de terre d'Ancash (Perou) du 1ᵉ Novembre, 1946 et ses causes géotectoniques,* Institut Franç. Etudes Andines, Trav., vol. 2, pp. 153–166, Paris-Lima, 1950.

14. Heim, Arnold, *Observaciones geologicas en la region del terremoto de Ancash de Noviembre 1946,* Soc. geol. Peru, Vol. Jubilar., pt. 2, fasc. 6, pp. 1–28, Lima, 1949. One of Heim's photographs is reproduced in J. Coulomb, *La constitution physique de la Terre* (Fig. 1, p. 13), Paris, 1952.

15. Gilluly, J., Distribution of Mountain Building in Geologic Time, Bull. Geol. Soc. America, vol. 60, pp. 561–590, 1949.

McMasters, J. H., Analysis and Effects of Current Movements on an Active Fault in Buena Vista Hills Oil Field, Bull. California State Div. Mines, no. 118, pp. 517–518, 1943.

16. Duclaux, Jacques and Biget, Mlle., *Méthode d'observation des déformations de l'écorce terrestre,* Ann. de Géophys., vol. 1, fasc. 2, pp. 113–120, 1944–1945.

17. Regarding the question of Recent and present-day tectonic movements, reference is made to: *Geologische Rundschau,* vol. 43, no. 1, 1955, in which the papers presented at the spring, 1954 meeting of the Deutsche Geologische Gesellschaft in Mainz are assembled (Living Tectonics). See especially the article by E. Wegmann, *Vue d'ensemble, Tectonique Vivante,* pp. 273–306, in which he gives the history and overall analysis of working methods, the conclusions reached, and an extensive bibliography.

CHAPTER THREE

Stratigraphy and Tectonics

The two uses of stratigraphy in tectonics—Reconstruction of conditions of sedimentation—Determination of the age of movements by unconformities or by the detrital character of sediments—Subsidence—Detailed analysis of vertical movements—The geosynclinal idea—Example of Alpine sediments; cordilleras; flysch and molasse—Reworking of detrital sediments; Piedmont gravels—Character of Pyrenean or Provencal sediments—Influence of the action of faults, volcanic eruptions, and earthquakes upon stratigraphy.

AS DO OTHER branches of geology, stratigraphy has two aspects: historical and descriptive. On the one hand, it traces the history of the conditions that prevailed during the deposition of sediments; on the other hand, it describes the present mineral masses. Both of these aspects are involved in the study of tectonic events. Inasmuch as it is possible to reconstruct the original disposition of deformed beds, we are thus able to study the mode of deformation in sedimentary terranes in an incomparably more accurate manner than in eruptive or metamorphic terranes. In the following chapters, we shall discuss in detail the manner in which the precise data furnished by the successive stratigraphic horizons are used.

At times, the stratigraphy of an area may furnish indications that enable us to gather data in the horizontal direction, owing to lateral facies variations, or to a transgression of one stage relative to preceding stages, each of which can exist only in a limited area. Although such data are infinitely less precise than are data in the vertical direction, they have been put to reliable use in the Alps (see Chap. 6). Intrusive rock masses that cut across older terrains often furnish useful data on horizontal displacements; it was by correlating the disjointed fragments of a granitic block, thought to have been united originally, that the horizontal displacements on the transverse fault of Villefort

(Fig. 43) and the Great Glen Fault in Scotland (Fig. 154) were determined.

Aside from its essential role in tectonics—that is, enabling us to identify originally horizontal relationships—stratigraphy also furnishes other very important information. The careful analysis (petrographic as well as paleontologic) of succesive deposits indicates the conditions of their deposition; the nature of terrigenous sediments that came from them; the degree of volcanic activity (even of seismic activity); the possibility of marine communications and exchanges of fauna, and so forth. Such study also permits us to trace the variation of these diverse factors with time. It is evident that tectonic deformations directly influenced certain of these factors; consequently, stratigraphic investigations should furnish some information about the nature of the deformations.

The most important evidence concerns the age of these movements. It is well known that we seek to arrange the events whose history we are retracing on the basis of the succession of marine faunas. It is especially necessary to date tectonic deformations with reference to the deposition of successive beds. This may be effected by following two methods which correspond to the twofold relation between tectonics and stratigraphy. Since we know that the strata were originally horizontal, we can place the time of deformation between the time of deposition of the deformed beds and that of the undeformed beds.

If the later beds were deposited horizontally upon beds that had been more or less tilted or displaced, an unconformity will have been formed. Even if subsequent deformation occurs, tilting the most recent beds, the resulting unconformity will remain recognizable. Thus, it is possible to distinguish several successive phases of deformation. This is the classic unconformity method whose importance was demonstrated by Elie de Beaumont more than a century ago. However, if deformation took place during or prior to a period of emergence, a considerable interval of time may have passed between deposition of the youngest of the deformed beds and deposition of the oldest of the undeformed beds; thus, the age of the movements is poorly determined.

Much more accurate data can be obtained by the second method: in a given succession of sediments, each phase of deformation of the adjacent regions is expressed in certain traceable modifications. In a more general way, all such variations in the nature of the deposits or in the paleogeography, except those that stem from changes in fauna or climate, indicate deformation, largely of tectonic origin. After reviewing the different kinds of sediments that are characteristic of the various phases of deformation, we shall explain how they are grouped, using the Alpine chain as an example. A special chapter will be devoted to the analysis of the nature of deformations on the basis of stratigraphic evidence.

If the nature of a deposit is such that we can determine precisely under what depth of water it was formed, we can then determine it has undergone vertical displacement by comparing the thickness of the beds with the variation of the depth of formation of the deposit. In general, subsidence may very closely compensate for the accumulation of sediments. As early as 1848,[1] Elie de Beaumont noted that various beds in the Paris Basin (*Gryphaea*-limestone, Bathonian, Coral-Rag, Kimmeridgian with *Exogyra virgula*) present a uniform facies and, in general, seem to have been formed at a depth of less than 100 m. Since these Jurassic beds are several hundred meters thick, he concluded that there had been a "gradual sinking of the bottom of the basin, a sinking perhaps determined by the gradually increasing weight of the sediments being superposed." The term subsidence was selected much later to denote such a sinking. The explanation of this sinking under the weight of the sediments, suggested by Elie de Beaumont, has often been repeated later. However, the results of modern geodetic investigations, based on the principle of isostatic compensation, show that this explanation is not sufficient (Chap. 16). Whatever hypothesis is chosen for the calculation, isostatic sinking only accounts for about two-thirds of the thickness of the deposited beds. Subsidence, then, does not represent a simple, passive adaptation of the earth's crust to the weight of the sediments; it constitutes a true deformation of the crust. Moreover, we shall see later that this deformation (of a progressively variable magnitude in the Paris Basin) could have been produced elsewhere in connection with faults, with the result that subsiding sections (in which deposits were accumulating) were separated from other sections that had remained continually emerged.

This pattern has been well shown in the Franco–Belgian coal basin, where

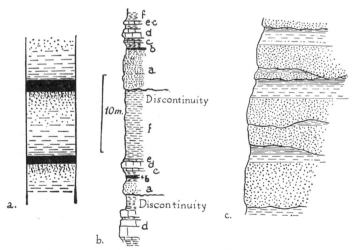

FIGURE 6. (*a*) *Character of the coal beds in the Nord Basin.* [*After P. Pruvost.*] (*b*) *Typical succession of cyclothems in Kansas, Pennsylvania; a = non-marine sandstones, b = coal, c = limestones containing littoral fossils, d = limestones containing nonlittoral fossils, e = limestones containing algae, f = shales, either brackish or fresh water.* [*After Moore.*] (*c*) *Diagram of a succession of cyclothems in the Swiss Aquitanian molasse.* (*Horizontal distances much reduced.*) [*After Bersier.*]

the sediments accumulated to a great thickness.[2] The footwall of each coal bed (Fig. 6)—more than 400 are known in about 2000 m thickness—contains vegetational soil pierced by roots, indicating that the water depth at the time of formation was a few decimeters at the maximum. The hanging walls of the beds (of a much more regular sedimentation) were on the other hand deposited under a certain thickness of water; each bed, then, marks a sharp deepening, marked in some cases by a brief invasion of the sea into the lacustrine basin. The subsequent deposition of sandstones and shales gradually reduced the depth until a marsh vegetation was re-established.

Owing to very precise observations made in the coal fields, Pruvost was able to show that successive basinwide sinkings, which affected sediments as far as Westphalia, were always considerably stronger to the east than to the west, the ratio remaining almost constant at each point. Pebbles from almost all of the earlier beds are found in most beds of the coal series, showing that outside the belt of sinking (in which the sediments that we are studying were deposited), other belts were being uplifted and subsequently eroded.

In certain parts of the basin, faults exist whose throw diminishes progressively toward the surface until it completely disappears. These faults may be considered to have permitted the zones to subside at different rates. However, the actual edges of the basin are generally unknown, most likely because they were removed by erosion following an uplift at the time of a subsequent phase. The situation differs only in the Bruay beds, which appear in this locality under a normal facies of sandstones and shales and which include some coal. At Roucourt,[3] the same stage is represented by a conglomerate of boulders of all sizes, derived from all levels of the Paleozoic. Some boulders weigh several tons. This conglomerate could only have been deposited at the foot of a scarp. It is locally preserved in connection with faults and is unconformable with the earlier beds. Thus, the movements proved by the presence of coal-bearing sediments are quite a different thing from simple subsidence of the basin. These movements were continuous over a long period, and have also involved uplifts. These uplifts were immediately attacked by erosion, which affected all the Paleozoic strata. This gives us an idea of their importance. The detailed study of certain mine workings shows that these deformations produced folds as well as faults.

Analogous rhythmic movements have also been recorded in other regions, notably in the Carboniferous of the United States and in the Swiss Molasse basin.[4] The term "cyclothem" has been created to designate the series of beds corresponding to each period of such a movement. The series of deposits that constitutes a cyclothem may, however, be incomplete. In some cyclothems, the coal may be lacking, or as is more often the case, the marine limestone beds, which at times mark the phase of maximum subsidence in the coal basins, may be missing. It seems that not only was subsidence discontinuous, but in addition, the movement of the floor was virtually oscillatory in nature.

In any event, the positive movement produced, in certain zones, erosion of the shales, which are channeled by coarser beds (sandstone).

The very progressive consolidation of the sediments (the muds or vegetal matter that have become shales or coals), which greatly decreased their thickness, apparently imposed a practically continuous sinking movement upon the truly oscillatory deformations of the bottom of the basin.

Bersier considers that, in the Swiss Aquitanian molasse, 3000 to 5000 years were required for the formation of a cyclothem 5 m thick (based on the thickness of annual beds that are identifiable in places). He notes that these periods of duration must vary, however, and suggests that the rhythmic movements thus demonstrated might correspond to the tectonic movements in the Alps. By any less sensitive method of recording, these movements would seem continuous.

Moreover, we must not lose sight of the fact that, in a deltaic formation, for example, the displacements of the arms of the river and of the corresponding sedimentation zones may involve channeling of muds by sandstones, without there being any movement other than the progressive sinking of the sediments. Only in the coal-bearing formations do we have stratigraphic knowledge (gained from their exploitation) precise enough to enable us to affirm that successive cyclothems are individualized throughout long distances and hence correspond to overall movements. The soils in the coal basin are exceptionally favorable markers. Usually, however, we have to rely on less precise markers.

Positive movements that culminated in emergence can always be recognized. However, we must avoid confusing lacunas due to emergence with those due to other causes. In the latter case, hard surfaces may have been formed, which are sometimes perforated by lithophages or worms (whose U-shaped holes should not be confused with the ramified perforations of roots, which would indicate an emergence). Thin ferruginous deposits may occur, which sometimes contain fossils from several zones or successive stages. For example, near Privas,[5] sedimentation lacunas occur at the top of the Toarcian and the Bajocian. The ferruginous crust that marks them runs laterally into an exploited iron ore, which has furnished ammonites varying from Aalenian to Bathonian. Farther on, these stages are represented by a continuous series of marls and limestones.

An emergence can produce a superficial alteration. Such alterations are especially distinct in the presence of such continental formations as plant-bearing or lignitic sandstones intercalated in the series. Coral formations indicate shallow-water conditions, but the development of coral reefs depends on a whole set of ecological conditions; thus their disappearance may be due to something other than an increase in depth. A drop in temperature or a current-borne clayey deposit may be responsible. The faunas of the marly or clayey formations in the Paris Basin, which alternate with reef or oolitic limestones, do not indicate a much greater depth.

Cayeux has interpreted the phosphate beds and the oolitic iron ores as indicating a shoals regime. It is thought that glauconite is formed at depths between 200 and 2000 m. Often, however, all the transitions between glauconite and oolitic iron are found. In either case, one of the essential conditions for formation is perhaps the absence of rapid sedimentation, in that sufficient time would not be available, under such conditions, for the chemical reactions to take place on the sea bottom.

In contrast to deposits containing phosphates, oxides of iron, and glauconite (which indicate a relatively moderate depth), the very deep deposits, corresponding to the red clay of the great depths, are characterized by their content of manganese nodules. Sedimentary rocks that can be compared with such deposits are extremely rare: it is possible to cite only a few upper Cretaceous beds on Timor, which are formed of red clay and contain manganese nodules and shark teeth.[24] Among the explanations for this scarcity of abyssal sediments, we should certainly include the fact that their formation takes place at an extremely slow rate, which is indicated by their very slight thickness.

Radiolarites, common in certain internal zones of the Alps, are sometimes compared with the radiolarian muds present in deep-sea sediments, but their alternation with limestones (certainly deposited at moderate depths) would imply repeated variations of depth of great amplitude, which is difficult to conceive. Thus, radiolarites, at least in some cases, have probably been formed at moderate depths.

Variations of depth indicated by facies changes should be compared stage by stage in order to reconstruct the sinking or uplift movements of each epoch. The persistence of paleogeographic conditions that such a comparison reveals is striking. Certain regions persist in their tendency toward subsidence, while others remain immobile or even undergo uplift. Movements that produce marine transgressions or overall emergence disturb but do not conceal the overall character of the affected regions. A marine regression, for example, would be less marked in a zone that had previously shown a tendency to sink than it would be elsewhere.

The classic concept of the geosyncline expresses the characteristics of the sediments that form in a zone destined to undergo tectonic deformation. If we could actually assign constant characters to sediments subsequently deformed, this would be the expression of one of the most important laws governing the evolution of the terrestrial globe.

Unfortunately, the geosynclinal concept, which we can trace back to James Hall (1859) and to Dana, who created the term in 1872, is difficult to define precisely. In Chap. 17 we shall discuss the various aspects of this problem. For the moment, it will be sufficient to indicate that we should make an objective analysis in each individual case of the character of the sedimentary series, study the variations in thickness of each stage, and endeavor to deduce therefrom the displacements of the bottom of the basin. The use of the term "geosynclinal" should be avoided at the analysis stage, since it implies, *a priori,* certain ill-defined characteristics, which vary from one author to another.

In a synthesis, if we wish to emphasize the overall characters of the sedimentary materials implied in an orogenic build-up (which corresponds to one of the meanings given to the term "geosynclinal"), then we should define these characters in a precise manner. Owing to the absence of a precise definition, the term geosynclinal has been used in Europe and in America with quite different meanings; this practice has given the impression of a uniformity of definition that does not actually exist.

The essential notion implied by the term geosynclinal suggests a zone within which the thickness of sediments is much greater than in adjacent areas. However, certain basins are characterized by an exceptionally great thickness of sediments that have never been folded. In addition, folded zones exist in which the thickness of the sedimentary series is slight. The other characters of so-called geosynclinal sedimentation vary according to the authors. As an example, we are going to examine the variations in character of the Mesozoic sedimentary series in the Alps, the most classic of the folded mountain chains, and of the surrounding non-folded zones, such as the Paris Basin.

We have already noted that the accumulation of Jurassic beds, which were deposited at a shallow depth throughout the basin, implies that a certain amount of subsidence took place, which varied from place to place. When shallow-water conditions prevail, small overall vertical movements, as well as changes in climate, might either promote the general development of corals or cause their disappearance. Along the periphery of the basin, the old massifs (Armorican, Ardennes, Massif Central, and later Vosges) did not share in the movement of subsidence; thus they were only periodically submerged, and in their vicinity, conditions were favorable for the development of coral reefs.

When we approach the Alps, either through the Jura, the Dauphiné, or Provence, we observe a general thickening of sediments, owing to an increase in the proportion of shales, which is soon accompanied by a decrease in calcareous sediments. It is essentially the zoogenous formations that disappear, following an increase in the depth of the sea in which they formed. The comparison of the limits of extension of the zoogenous formations throughout the Portlandian, Valanginian, Barremian, and Aptian (Fig. 7) indicates a double variation. On the one hand, there is a variation with time; the advance of the reef facies on the periphery of the Alps (in the lower Cretaceous) corresponds to the partial emergence of the Paris Basin and, therefore, to a general diminution in depth. On the other hand, a regional factor appears constantly through an arrangement in space of the zones of increasing depths. Their limits are not simple and may show quite marked sinuosities, the most important of which indicates what we call, as does Pasquier, the Vocontian Trough (valley of the Drome).

The maximum thickness coincides approximately with the border of the reef lentils. The enormous marly series produces a very monotonous relief,

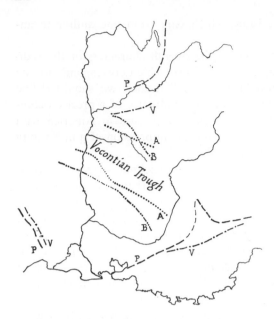

FIGURE 7

Areal distribution of the zoogeneous facies in southeastern France, on both sides of the Vocontian Trough. P = Portlandian; V = Valanginian; B = Barremian; A = lower Aptian.

since the calcareous beds are very thin and evenly spaced. Farther east, the series thins and becomes more and more monotonous; the calcareous beds there are scarcely recognizable. Thus we gradually go on into the ultra-Dauphinois facies (Gignoux). This transition is well exposed between Digne and the Ubaye.

The thinning, on either side of the maximum, evidently does not have the same significance. They may be interpreted by remembering how sediments are distributed in present-day seas; the terrigenous elements scarcely go beyond the edge of the continental shelf, which represents the zone of maximum sedimentation. Toward the shore, accumulation is limited by the currents and the agitation of the water, except for reef formation. The maximum deposition corresponds to a zone already deep enough for the water to be perfectly calm, which permits the deposition of clayey muds. Farther on the contributions are insufficient to produce very important sedimentation.

We note that a deep sea does not necessarily correspond to an important subsidence; subsidence involves an important sedimentation and simultaneous sinking, which, in general, does not surpass the sedimentation enough so that the depth becomes noteworthy. This is a fine distinction introduced by Gignoux, a distinction that the geosynclinal notion does not take into account.

Certain difficulties are encountered in the stratigraphic study of the more internal zones of the Alps, owing to the existence of abundant displacements. However, the Grenoble school has distinguished a series of zones for which the original order of succession has been reconstructed and for which quite detailed stratigraphic scales are known.

These scales may differ considerably from one zone to the next. We often find a quite complete series of stages, which include more or less marly facies or even a "comprehensive series," in which a great number of stages are confused under a uniform facies of clay shales; certain stages alone are represented under quite peculiar facies; in the Briançonnais, on the contrary, the Dogger is represented in part by breccia. In the Kimmeridgian, it is represented by 20 m of nodular limestone, in which pure calcareous nodules are held together by a clayey cement colored red or green. The other stages of the Jurassic and the middle and lower Cretaceous are missing; in places, the Dogger, or the upper Jurassic, may also be missing, in which case the upper Cretaceous is then directly transgressive on the Trias.

It is difficult to say whether the lacunas in such a series correspond to emergences or whether they simply result from nondeposition. Certain breccias do not seem to indicate a real emergence (the particles are not rounded) but, instead, suggest the occurrence of submarine collapses, which often affected deposits that had just been formed. The origin of nodular limestones is probably due to the agitation of calcareous muds. Ferruginous crusts, which indicate nondeposition, have been preserved.

All in all, such sedimentation is characteristic of zones that exhibited a tendency toward emergence (often quite rapid), producing shallow-water conditions in which sedimentation did not take place or in which the previously deposited sediments were reworked. This is characterized by the term "cordillera."

The internal zones of the Alps seem, then, to have been characterized in the Jurassic and Cretaceous by the alternation of cordilleras, which were uplifted in a more or less irregular manner, and by intermediate troughs, the depth of which permitted continuous deposition of clay shale. The absence of extensive terrigenous sediments seems to indicate that the positive movement of the cordilleras was rarely expressed in terms of the emergence of small land areas.

Perhaps such periods of emergence were too brief to produce a profound alteration of the rocks. The alteration that did occur was sufficient only to provide material for the formation of a trivial amount of clayey sand; as a result, the disintegrated rock fragments accumulated in polygenic breccia.

In general, we do not have proof that the uplift of cordilleras was expressed by genuine displacements of their substrata, such as folds or faults. It may be that the later origin of very sharp displacements at the former locations of cordilleras merely indicates the persistence of a certain tendency toward instability of the corresponding portion of the crust. But it is uncertain as to whether subsequent deformations are not merely the amplifications of (which follow the same pattern as) the movements recorded in the sediments. The composition, and hence the mechanical properties, of the sedimentary series differ greatly from one unit to another and from one cordillera to its accompanying trough. This is perhaps sufficient to explain how, during the course of a displacement, perhaps quite different at its outset, these units have separated from each other and have undergone independent mechanical evolutions. Be that as it may, the stratigraphic history of a mountain chain such as the Alps shows that very special conditions of sedimentation existed long before real tectonic deformations took place.

The same is true, *a fortiori,* during deformation. The postdepositional deposits in the region also exhibit characteristic properties. We shall designate the sediments formed during deformation as flysch and those formed subsequently as molasse, thus broadening somewhat the meaning of two terms that have each been applied to masses of Alpine or peri-Alpine rocks that embrace quite different types. In this sense, we may state, as does Marcel Bertrand,[7] that each mountain chain possesses its flysch and its molasse. In the Hercynian range, the coal-bearing sediments would to a certain extent be classed as a flysch, although they are of continental origin, whereas the Alpine flysch is of marine origin. We have previously noted that these coal-bearing sediments were deposited during the course of deformation.

The name flysch[8] is applied, in the Alps, to marine sediments which often occur as a very thick series of alternating beds of shale (often micaceous) and sandstone (often calcareous). The proportions of these two essential constituents may vary within very wide limits, from masses almost exclusively shale to series consisting dominantly of sandstone. These masses may include lentils of zoogenous limestone or fine limestones of pelagic type, as well as conglomerates, or breccias. Breccia fragments are often of enormous dimensions; in particular, we may find isolated blocks of eruptive rocks in the midst of unrelated sediments; these are called "exotic blocks" (for example at Les Gets, in Haute-Savoie). Lugeon has shown[9] that a plate of granite 600 m long and several dozen meters thick, exposed in the substratum of the "Dent de Morcles," is nothing but an immense exotic block. The presence of this block in the middle of the Tertiary sediments could only be due to a landslip.

Flysch was evidently deposited in relatively deep trenches; the absence of any sign of littoral sedimentation (such as ripple mark or cross stratification) corroborates the bathymetric indications furnished by rare fossils. The fact that such large detrital elements have been deposited at quite considerable depths rather than in the shore zone is not without analogy today. Similar features have been observed, although to a lesser degree, in certain archipelagic zones of the East Indies and to the south of California. We can deduce from this that the troughs were directly bordered by lands that must have been subject to very intense erosion. The presence of breccias, which can only be the result of landslips, suggests that erosion was not even sufficient to reduce the profiles. In order for granites to have attained such profiles that slips of huge blocks occurred, the cordilleras must have undergone a very marked uplift. Lugeon was able to show that the Dent de Morcles lentil must have slipped into the flysch sea from a land corresponding to the prolongation of the Aiguilles Rouges, which is situated northwest of the basin and which must have presented a very steep southern slope. The exact point at which the slip occurred has not been determined, but the lentil must have dropped during subsequent movements beneath the level of the Rhone. This plate is not isolated but is accompanied by a whole procession of crystalline breccia fragments; there is also a similar slab of Triassic limestone associated with it.

Judging from the character of the materials that originated in the cordilleras, we can assume that uplift took place so rapidly that sufficient time was not allowed for a regular hydrographic network to be established.

In the Alps, we can distinguish a great number of flysch zones that differ from one another in age and certain secondary details, suggesting that they correspond to distinct troughs, which were separated by the cordilleras, and that the zones emerged successively. The deformation responsible for the emergence of the flysch zones must have differed markedly in character from that of a simple uplift, but stratigraphic data alone will not enable us to determine the nature of these movements.

In the southern part of the Alps, sediments very similar to flysch (essentially sandstone) spread out before the last cordilleras in a region which practically had not been deformed. The sandstones of Annot, in Basses-Alpes and Alpes-Maritimes, show that the characters of this particular sedimentation are due rather to the elevation of the adjacent cordilleras than to a special subsidence of the sedimentary basins. However, the cordilleras that must have bordered the Annot sandstone on the east do not exist today; they must have been hidden by subsequent overthrusts.

Flysch is essentially the product of the initial stages of formation of a mountain chain, during which time the site of accumulation is still in great part covered by the sea. On the other hand, Alpine molasse deposits are formed subsequent to the formation of a mountain chain, or at least subsequent to the principal paroxysm, since they often show evidence of having been reworked during later movements. They are consequently confined to the sedimentary basins situated on the periphery of the mountain chain.

In the western Alps, that is to say in France (exclusive of Haute-Savoie), the peri-Alpine depression, which was invaded by the Miocene sea, is very clearly separated from the principal mountain chain where the flysch is confined. Only in the Upper Miocene (Pontian) do we find traces of tectonic movements. These were evidently the last phases of deformation. Although they were less marked than preceding ones, they were felt much farther to the west. The more or less sandy or clayey deposits of the Rhodanian sea, which persisted until the Vindobonian, were suddenly replaced by torrential sediments that are characterized by their content of enormous volumes of conglomerates consisting of rounded pebbles, forming almost continuous layers. Within these deposits, a number of deltaic deposits are still recognizable, which mark the former outlets of important streams (to the north of Digne and at Grenoble). Evidently a well-established drainage system existed, through which the materials eroded from recently uplifted areas were carried. Thus the uplifted areas acquired forms extremely different from those of a morphologic profile of equilibrium. We are only able to observe the action of erosion on relief forms that are already worn away, in which the *thalwegs* of the gullies have acquired, at least approximately, the concave profile according to which the erosion is minimum. If a stream changes its equilibrium profile through some accidental cause (for example the artificial cutting of a meander loop, as at the time of the shifting of the Kander toward Lake Thoune in 1714),[10] it will return to it with astonishing rapidity. It is difficult for us to imagine what the intensity of erosion could have been that acted upon relief forms that departed at each instant from the profile that erosion tended to impose upon them. We can form some idea of what it must have been by observing the accumulations of Upper Miocene conglomerates, as at Digne-Valensole, where they surpass 1000 m in thickness and exceed 1000 km² in area.

FIGURE 8

Western limits of the conglomerates of Alpine origin, between the Isere and the Durance. G = Oligocene (continental); B = Burdigalian marine); P = Pontian (continental).

In the Basses-Alpes, the materials extracted by erosion from the mountain chain formed by the principal Alpine movements accumulated as conglomerates in a series of small continental basins during the Oligocene. These conglomerates reached the Lower Miocene sea at only one point (Tanaron, north of Digne), inasmuch as the distance from the source was great and, in addition, the intensity of the torrential drift must, by this time, have greatly diminished (Fig. 8).

In Switzerland, the peri-Alpine depression pressed too closely upon the mountain chain, and the Miocene sea took possession of the very location in which the Aquitanian conglomerates had accumulated. At times it is difficult to establish a clearly defined limit between the most recent flysch, which was deposited in the most external trenches, and the first molasse, also marine (Stampian), which was deposited in a basin then exterior to the mountain chain but which may have been incorporated into it during the most recent movements.

In general, however, the stratigraphic character of molasse differs from that of flysch. Molasse may be either a fresh water or marine deposit; its littoral character suggests that deposition took place in moving or agitated waters. Ripple marks and cross stratification are common in these rocks. On the whole, they consist of more or less calcareous or clayey sandstones that occur in thick, uniform masses (the inverse of the alternations of different beds of flysch). Adjacent to the mountain chain, and especially at the site of the outlet of ancient valleys, well-rounded, well-sorted conglomerates accumulated to an enormous thickness. Their escarpments, upon which the pebbles stand out in relief, have earned them (in Switzerland) the name "Nagelfluh." * The thickness of these sediments (several thousand meters) is such that there can be no doubt that subsidence took place. The essential character of molassic formations is to mark the accumulation adjacent to the mountain chain of the materials extracted by erosion, which had already shaped the relief and, in particular, established an organized drainage net.

In view of the post-tectonic character of these deposits, we might expect them to be flat-lying. However, they have not only been tilted but have often been involved in overthrusts of considerable importance. These movements date from a closing phase of activity that, in the Alps, lasted until the Upper Miocene (perhaps to Pliocene in some cases). They were active along the edges of (or even beyond) the mountain chain, that is, within the domain of the molassic sedimentation in which traces of them are preserved.

A typical flysch implies the formation of a mountain chain within a marine domain. However, when a mountain chain originates outside the sea, the products of erosion will also accumulate in neighboring depressions. For example, the coal-bearing beds on the edge of the Ardennes mountain chain were formed in this way. In like manner, post-tectonic sediments of the molasse type may form under either marine, lacustrine, or continental conditions. In the latter case, the deposits will take the form of torrential conglomerates or piedmont gravels, which are the necessary satellites of every mountain chain formed during an uplift that is followed by a period of violent erosion, wearing down the newly formed relief. The age determination of the conglomerates surrounding such a mountain chain constitutes one of the surest ways of dating the deformation (or deformations). In the Aquitanian basin, which extends to the foot of the Pyrenees, the Tertiary comprises a series of conglomerate beds that extend varying distances toward the north and whose presence at every instant is a measure of the erosion activity responsible for the development of the features of the uplifted area. Generally speaking, the tilting of the piedmont gravels emphasizes the progressive and continuous character of the movements. It seems even possible to state definitely that the deformation tends to affect a broader and broader zone reckoning from the rough outline in which it first appeared.

Piedmont gravels are normally deposited on the nondeformed foreland, just in front of the mountain chain. As the zone affected by the deformation progressively broadened, the gravels were again tilted. This later tilting does not necessarily indicate a distinct tectonic phase (as is the case in the Alps where

* Terms for which there is no English equivalent have been placed in parentheses or in quotes [Translator].

the end of the Oligocene and beginning of the Burdigalian are separated by a period of regression), but simply expresses an extension in time of the tectonic deformation through a period during which erosion may act in a very important manner.

We might be tempted to interpret the immense detrital formations of the Siwalik Hills (Miocene and Pliocene) at the foot of the Himalayas in this manner. Teilhard de Chardin has demonstrated [11] how the study of the conglomerate series (old piedmont gravels that were eventually incorporated into the subsequently formed mountain chains) has enabled us to accurately depict the chronology of the movements responsible for the continental flexures in China and Central Asia. However, these flexures show that the succession of facies that we find in the Alps throughout their tectonic evolution cannot be applied to all mountain chains: this succession of essentially marine facies characterizes a "sea-born" mountain chain, which, in its most general sense, is what the term "geosynclinal chain" refers to. The continental mountain chains in China, whose importance was demonstrated by Teilhard de Chardin, evidently have a completely different stratigraphic history.

Even within a marine domain, a long period of evolution, such as is recorded in the Alpine sediments, is not a necessary condition for subsequent deformation. There is little doubt that the evolution of the cordilleras and trenches in the Jurassic indicates an instability of the crust and that the Tertiary deformations merely constitute another manifestation of this instability. But deformations may also have taken place that were not "foretold" so long in advance. The Alpine domain offers us quite a striking example: If the first deformations, in the Oligocene, seem to have been confined in a long unstable domain, later the deformation made itself felt much farther, even into the Jura, that is, into a domain which presented in the Jurassic a clearly epicontinental character, very comparable to the Paris Basin, for example. In the Pyrenees (or in Provence, a prolongation of the Pyrenees), such examples are even more striking, although it is not possible to find in them the classic scheme of Alpine stratigraphy. Until the Middle Cretaceous, no evidence indicates the occurrence of trench subsidence. On the other hand, it may have been that some of these regions tended to gradually emerge. Such is the case for the axial zone of the Pyrenees, the Mouthoumet Massif (which seems to have been joined to the Montagne Noire) and perhaps for the center of the Provence crystalline mass. It is difficult to determine when these zones emerged, because erosion may have removed certain deposits. Epicontinental facies are distributed around these centers, numerous stages of which are completely missing.

It is only in the Albian, beyond the centers of emergence, that we find thick accumulations of clayey sediments, indicating a certain deepening. From the Cenomanian on, an important phase of deformation resulted in the development of basins that were separated by emerged zones in which a thick accumulation of detrital sediments, comparable to Alpine flysch, were deposited. Subsequent movements alternately opened and closed a series of basins in which more or less detrital sediments accumulated. Thus the Middle Cretaceous in Provence corresponds to the emergence of the Durancian Isthmus (characterized by continental bauxites). A persistent, shallow arm of the sea was transformed into a lake (or rather into a series of lakes) in the Senonian. These lakes were bordered by high land due to an early phase of deformation; the sediments, detrital, because of their position, which resulted from the destruction of these highlands, were in turn deformed at the time of a new tectonic phase, in middle Eocene.

The character of sediments deposited in or upon the immediate periphery of a mountain chain like the Alps, at the time of the tectonic deformations, resulted from vertical displacements (through which these deformations were expressed) and frequently caused emergences.

These movements at times triggered the gravity flow of plastic masses, some of which were transported into neighboring seas, where the mode of sedimentation was otherwise entirely normal. We thus find overlapping flow masses, with possible inclusion of older rocks of many ages, intercalated in the midst of the stratigraphic series. Since these flows (or slides) are relatively rapid in relation to the duration of sedimentation, the deposits that immediately follow upon the flow or slide (which may be very thick) are immediately younger than the sediments upon which they rest, and at times cannot be paleontologically distinguished from them. The Apennines provide us with an example of such an arrangement. In the frontal parts of the pre-Riffian nappes of Morocco, a marly mass occurs in which the study of the foraminifera enables us to recognize Cretaceous or Tertiary remnants mingled capriciously. In the Rharb, borings for oil have penetrated this nappe, which is several hundred meters thick, in the middle of a Miocene section that is 2000 m thick. This same arrangement can be observed in outcrop beyond Fez.[12]

In his classic work,[13] Haug stated a general law: To each phase of folding affecting geosynclines there would correspond a regression in the latter, and a transgression upon the continental areas. If this were actually so, the stratigraphic analysis of any sedimentary series would indicate the general rhythm of the deformations of the earth; but things seem more complex. This law cannot be used safely; instead, we must seek everything that may test it; this may lead, in time, to distinguishing and clarifying its limits of application. It does not present a final solution, but it does pose a question concerning the general rhythms that may govern all the deformations of the earth's crust, which in turn control sedimentation. This question is still open to discussion and is one of the most captivating to which we might apply ourselves.

We have tried to show how the formation of a mountain chain could, depending on the case, be revealed in the sedimentary succession. The sediments may also record other types of tectonic deformations. Thus a major fault may separate adjacent sections, some of which sink, thus permitting accumulation of a very thick sedimentary series, whereas others sink less and are covered by much thinner beds, perhaps presenting lacunas; still others are uplifted with the result that all traces of deposition may be swept away by erosion. The comparison of the sedimentary series of these different sections of course teaches us something about the action of faults. Thus the stratigraphy of the Alsatian Tertiary, found only within its limiting faults, involves the study of fault action.

A curious example of the very profound differences between the sedimentary series of adjacent faulted sections exists in the California Coast Range.[14] In a given block, the Cretaceous is absent, whereas the Tertiary (Oligocene and Miocene) attains a thickness of 600 m; in adjacent blocks, the Cretaceous is well-developed, and the Oligocene and Miocene are absent beneath the transgressive Pliocene. Evidently the movement along these faults must have changed directions from one period to another.

Many other events that are more or less connected with the deformation of the earth's crust may leave traces in the stratigraphic series. Among these are volcanic eruptions. Discharges of volcanic ash may become mingled with ordinary sediments far beyond the area within which volcanic flows accumulate. In the stratigraphy of recent deposits in the North Atlantic, studied in the long cores obtained from the bottom of the sea by such apparatuses as the Piggot Gun, such beds of volcanic ash furnish very reliable data. Even in this quite recent epoch, the chronology of these eruptions will doubtless be easier to establish through the study of marine sediments rather than through the study of the volcanic assemblages.

We are much less certain as to what criteria can be used to recognize the action of an earthquake on contemporaneous or slightly older sediments. We need only mention certain peculiarities of stratification that have been attributed to earthquakes, sometimes through a lack of any other explanation rather than for intrinsic reasons. Breccias have been found formed of angular elements, some very voluminous, of an earlier formation, interstratified in a possibly quite fine sediment.

In northern Scotland, at Dun Glas, there is a Kimmeridgian bed of coarse, shell-bearing limestone in which blocks of Old Red Sandstone are packed to a thickness of 60 m. Some of the blocks are immense and angular; others are small and rounded. Beneath this bed, the entire Jurassic Series is normal and continuous. All the evidence suggests that a fault caused the sudden elevation of the Old Red Sandstone above the sediments that were being deposited. Bailey and Weir[15] think that the blocks were wrenched from the tilted edge of the fault by seismic sea waves, that is, by tidal waves caused by an earthquake.

During earthquakes beds of water-saturated sand are sometimes forced into fissures in the overlying strata, causing temporary spouting of sand or of debris-laden mud (California, 1906; Cachar, India, 1869). After the earthquake, sand remains in these fissures, forming "clastic dikes." By analogy, Diller[16] interpreted the presence of sandstone dikes[17] (formed by injection of sand from below) in the middle of Cretaceous beds as being the result of ancient earthquakes. But clastic dikes may have a different origin; some result from the filling of fissures from the top down.[18]

The very different breccia that occurs in the Tithonian throughout the department of the Drôme[19] seems to have been formed as a result of seismic shocks. The Tithonian is composed of thin layers of very fine-grained limestone (probably of pelagic origin) among which thick, massive layers (2–10 m thick) of breccia are intercalated. The breccia particles, which are subangular, hardly differ in color from that of the cement. These beds of breccia were formed as a result of the reworking of freshly deposited, unconsolidated muds. During reworking, these muds were formed into more or less voluminous lumps that were subsequently redeposited. The cause of such a reworking, affecting close to 100 km, in a basin wherein the conditions of deposition were very homogeneous, can hardly have been other than a seismic shock.

Shirley attributes the existence of a greatly disturbed zone, several meters thick, that occurs between two intact beds of coal [20] to an earthquake contemporaneous with sedimentation. The fact that these displacements are visible at exactly the same level throughout nearly 80 km and that the surrounding coal beds are unbroken seem to him to exclude the hypothesis of a spontaneous slip on the bottom. At one point the sandstone forms clastic dikes, whereas elsewhere the masses of sand have behaved as if rigid in the midst of fluid muds.

The transgression responsible for deposition of the beds that overlie the displaced mass establishes the age of the movement. The fact that a thick bed of coal remained intact at several decimeters beneath the displaced beds proves that this coal had already attained a certain mechanical cohesion.

In a part of the region occupied by the Drôme breccias, we observe, in the Sequanian and especially in the Neocomian, bed contortions[21] that appear in the following manner: In the midst of a series in which the stratification of the marly limestones is perfectly regular for about 2 m, we find irregularly twisted and folded beds between two perfectly flat beds (Fig. 9). This phenomenon is repeated at different levels in the series.

FIGURE 9

Example of "slumping" in marly bedoulian limestones, near Rosans (Hautes-Alpes). Thickness of the zone affected = 2 m. (From a photograph).

Contortions of similar beds are frequently observed in very varied formations. They are due to *slumping* of still imperfectly consolidated muds along a slightly inclined bottom; even if the inclination of the bottom was very slight, it does not seem that an earthquake would have been required to trigger their movement. These contortions thus constitute a mere stratigraphic curiosity, but they can be misleading if they are confused with folds of tectonic origin. Such contortions of nontectonic origin will be recognized essentially by the regularity of the encasing beds. The absence of any trace of crushing, such as slickensiding (since the mud was deformed when still soft), distinguishes them from similar contortions due to displacement parallel to the bedding.

Macar and Autun have described such folds in sandstone beds of the Ardennes Devonian that sank into the clayey muds and caused the formation of hardened pseudo-nodules that show a characteristic folded structure in the midst of shales.[22] In Chap. 8, we shall discuss other structures to which a tectonic origin might be erroneously attributed.

Notes and References

1. *Explication de la Carte géologique de la France,* vol. 2, pp. 605–612, Paris, 1848.

2. Pruvost, Pierre, *Sédimentation et subsidence,* Soc. géol. France (Livre Jubilaire), vol. 2, pp. 545–564, 1930.

3. Barrois, Ch., Bertrand, P., and Pruvost, P., *Le conglomérat houiller de Roucourt,* Congr. Internat., Mines, Metallurgie, et Géol. Appliquée, Comptes-rendus, pp. 147–158, 1930.

4. See the papers presented at the Eighteenth Internat. Geol. Congr., London, 1948, Section C, Rhythm in Sedimentation, Proceedings, part 4, London, 1950, and in particular:

Moore, R. C., Late Paleozoic Cyclic Sedimentation in the Central United States, op. cit., pp. 5–16.

Bersier, A., *Les sédimentations rythmiques synorogéniques dans l'avant-fossé molassique alpin,* op. cit., pp. 83–92. See also:

Rutten, M. G., Rhythm in sedimentation and in erosion, 3ᵉ Cong. Strat. et Geol. Carbonifre, Heerlen, pp. 529–537, 1951.

Lombard, A., *Les rythmes sédimentaires et la sédimentation générale,* Essai de synthèse, Revue Inst. Franç. Pétrole, vol. 8, pp. 9–57, 1953.

5. Roman, F. and Goguel, J., *Les failles des environs de Privas,* Soc. géol. France, Comptes-rendus, no. 2, pp. 14–16, 1936.

6. Brouwer, H., *The Geology of the Netherlands East Indies,* Macmillan, New York, 1925. (See p. 31.)

7. Bertrand, M., *Structure des Alpes françaises et récurrence de certains faciès sédimentaires,* Cong. géol. Internat., 1894, Comptes-rendus, pp. 161–177, Lausanne, 1887.

——, *Oeuvres Complètes,* vol. 2, pp. 925–939, Paris, 1928.

8. Tercier, Jean, *Le Flysch dans la sédimentation alpine,* Eclogae geol. Helv., vol. 40, no. 2, pp. 163–198, 1947 (overall study and extensive bibliography).

9. Lugeon, Maurice, *Hommage à Aug. Buxtorf et digression sur la nappe de Morcles,* Naturforsch. Gesellsch. Basel, Verhandl., vol. 58, pp. 108–131, 1947.

10. Bachmann, H., *Die Kander im Berner Oberland,* Bern, 1870.

Noë, Géneral G. de la, and Margerie, Em. de, *Les formes du terrain,* Paris, 1888. (See p. 63.)

11. Teilhard de Chardin, P., *Les graviers plissés de Chine,* Bull. Soc. géol. France, 5 sér., vol. 2, pp. 527–531, 1932.

——, *Remarques sur les flexures continentales de Chine,* Bull. Soc. géol. France, 5 sér., vol. 16, pp. 497–502, 1946.

12. Levy, R. C., and Tilloy, R., *Livret-guide des excursions A-31 et C-31, Maroc septentrional, Chaîne du Rif, partie B,* Nineteenth Internat. Geol. Congr., Algiers, 1952.

13. Haug, Emile, *Les géosynclinaux et les aires continentales: Contribution à l'étude des transgressions et des regressions marines,* Bull. Soc. géol. France, 3 sér., vol. 28, pp. 617–711, 1900.

14. Clark, Bruce L., Tectonics of the Coast Ranges of Middle California, Bull. Geol. Soc. America, vol. 41, pp. 747–828, 1930.

15. Bailey, E. B., and Weir, J., Submarine Faulting in Kimmeridgian Times, East Sutherland, Trans. Roy. Soc. Edinburgh, vol. 57, pp. 429–467, 1933.

16. Diller, G. S., Sandstone Dikes, Bull. Geol. Soc. America, vol. 1, pp. 411–442, 1890.

17. See Fig. 18 in R. A. Daley, *Our Mobile Earth,* New York, 1926.

18. Pruvost, Pierre, *Filons clastiques,* Bull. Soc. géol. France, 5 sér., vol. 13, pp. 91–104, 1943.

19. Goguel, J., *Contribution à l'étude paléogéographique du Crétacé inférieur dans le SE de la France,* Bull. Carte géol. France, vol. 44, no. 215, pp. 40–44, 1944.

20. Shirley, J., The Disturbed Strata on the Fox Earth Coal and their Equivalents in the East Pennine Coal Field, Quart. Jour. Geol. Soc. London, vol. 111, pp. 265 ff., 1955. Goguel, J., Bull Carte géol. France, vol. 44, no. 215, pp. 459–518, 1944.

21. Goguel, J., *Glissements sousmarins dans le Crétacé inferieur,* Bull. Soc. géol. France, 5 sér., vol. 8, pp. 251–256, 1938.

22. Macar, P., and Autun, P., *Les pseudo-nodules et glissement sous-aquatiques dans l'Emsien inférieur de l'Oesling* (Grand Duché de Luxembourg), Ann. Soc. géol. Belgique, vol. 53, pp. B 121–150, 1950.

———, *Les pseudo-nodules du Faménien et leur origine,* Ann. Soc. géol. Belgique, vol. 52, pp. 3–74, 1948.

CHAPTER FOUR

Study of Rock Deformation: Continuous Deformations

Continuous and discontinuous deformation—Deformation of fossils; role of the compaction of sediments—Deformation of colored beds—Similar folds—Modification of structure—Schistosity and its interpretation—Recent methods of statistic analysis of structure—Intimate mechanism of deformation—Petrographic distinction of successive phases—Deformation of an eruptive rock before and after consolidation—Mylonites—Quartz or calcite veins—Joints—Influence of heterogeneous beds or veins; boudinage and ptygmatic folds.

IN THE PRECEDING chapters, we have seen how it is possible to gather information regarding deformations of the earth's crust by indirect methods. Such information is often very valuable, especially for determining the age of movements. But by far the commonest method in tectonics is the direct observation of the result of these deformations. This can be achieved in two ways: (1) by proving that the rock element under observation has been displaced (for example, that a bed that was formed horizontally is now tilted); (2) by proving that this rock element has been deformed (when a bed is folded, the elements at the inside of the fold must have been compressed; similarly, those at the outside of the fold must have been stretched). Reserving the study of displacements for a later chapter, we shall discuss how to describe and interpret the changes in form of rocks.

If equal pressure from all directions is applied to an isotropic element of matter (hydrostatic pressure) there is no change of form. Any deformed rock element must then have been subjected to an oriented pressure. However, the inverse is not true; a rock element may have been subjected to an

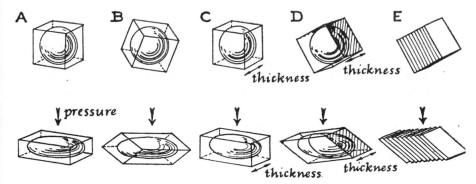

FIGURE 10. *Diagram of an elementary deformation.* [*From* Bull. Soc. Géol. France, *5ᵉ série, XV, p. 511, 1945.*] *(A) In the general case, a small sphere is transformed into an ellipsoid; a cube circumscribed around the sphere is transformed into a right-angled parallelepiped the edges of which are parallel to the axes of the ellipsoid. All cubes with different orientation (B) are transformed into oblique parallelepipeds in which the form and dimensions of all surfaces are distorted. Deformation in which thickness remains constant (C) is a special case. This is the only mode of deformation in (D), in which the deformation is zero in two plane directions (one of which is indicated by shading). After deformation, a parallel face has the same form and the same dimensions as in the initial state; this does not necessarily imply that it has maintained its form and dimensions throughout deformation. Such a deformation could result from the slipping of parallel laminae over one another, as shown in (E).*

oriented pressure without being deformed. This distinction must be kept in mind.

We must first distinguish between what are called continuous and discontinuous deformations. During continuous deformation, two points that are initially adjacent will remain adjacent. During discontinuous deformation, two points that are initially adjacent will be displaced along slip surfaces. Between two such slip surfaces, the materials have undergone continuous deformation.

If we subject a small sphere of matter to continuous deformation, it will be transformed into an ellipsoid (Fig. 10). The three axes of this ellipsoid correspond to three perpendicular diameters of the sphere (which originally occupied different directions). These are the *principal directions* of the deformation. Along one of these directions, the compression is maximum, and along another, the extension is maximum; that is, the change in the distance between two points will be respectively greatest or least along these two axes. The third direction is the "principal median direction" of the deformation. In this direction, the magnitude of the elongation or compression will lie between the two extremes.[1]

Deformation produces a change in volume that is associated with the changes of length in the principal directions. The ratio of the volume after deformation to the initial volume is equal to the product of the ratios of the lengths after deformation to the initial lengths, along these principal directions. Only Lavoisier's principle of the conservation of mass gives us information on the change of volume. If there has been no removal or addition of matter (by solution or crystallization), the change of volume is the inverse of the change of density. Since density changes are always slight (deformation generally involves a diminution of porosity), the change of volume is generally slight. Volume variation, which almost always is a decrease, may sometimes be disregarded in a first approximation.

If the deformation is the same at all points within a certain volume, that is, if all the elementary spheres have been transformed into similar ellipsoids and are similarly oriented, the deformation is then called homogeneous. If this is not the case, the deformation varies from one point to another. The fact that the matter remains continuous implies a relation between the deformations at the different points, which permits quite a wide uncertainty. A sphere of finite dimensions will be transformed into any sort of form. In homogeneous deformation, points that initially lie in a straight line, remain in a straight line. Homogeneous deformation is an approximation which permits the representation of any sort of deformation within a very small volume.

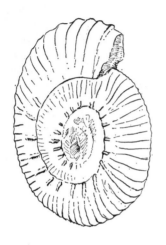

FIGURE 11

Example of an ammonite deformed during deformation of the containing rock.

How is it possible to record through observation the continuous deformation undergone by a rock? This may be quite difficult if there is no guiding structure within the rock mass. If guiding structures do exist, they may be of a different petrographic nature from the surrounding rock and thus deform in a different manner. Farther on we shall examine this phenomenon, which corresponds, for example, to a Belemnite included within a marly limestone. On the other hand, ammonites are generally preserved as a mold; as such, they constitute a structure that does not disturb the homogeneity of the rock.

Quite often, ammonites (Fig. 11) or trilobites are found preserved as deformed impressions.[2] The successive whorls no longer make a circular spiral, but an elliptic spiral. The line joining two initially symmetrical points (two homologous tubercles, for example) is no longer perpendicular to the plane of the volutions. The relation of the thickness to the diameter is modified; by comparing a deformed specimen with a nondeformed specimen of a given species, we can determine this modification. We then possess all the elements needed to define the homogeneous deformation undergone by the rock. If we wish to calculate its elements, the simplest approach is to imagine a sphere initially circumscribed within the ammonite and to trace the ellipsoid into which it has been transformed and which will be defined by three conjugate diameters (two in the plane of the volutions, and a third diameter corresponding to the transformation of the normal to the plane of the volutions). The axes of the ellipsoid are then determined, but the steps involved in calculation would take too long to indicate here.[3] If we do not have a nondeformed specimen, but do have several specimens of the same species, which need not have come from the same plane, but which have undergone the same deformation, we can still carry out the complete calculation. But the deformation thus indicated extends from the burial of the dead animal's shell on down to the present. It may be due not only to the definitely tectonic deformation of a rock, but also to the transformation into sedimentary rock. Marls and limestones (at least fine-grained pelagic limestones) seem to have been deposited in the form of mud originally having considerable porosity. This mud has progressively become more compact through vertical compression; as a result, the fossils that it contained may have undergone considerable deformation. In the case of organic fragments which have produced coal, a comparison of the organic debris contained in the coal with that contained in the silicified nodules that constitute "coal balls" shows that the thickness of the sediments has been reduced to one-twentieth of its initial value. That is an extreme figure, but equally great compression has been observed in certain clays in which the fossils have been crushed. In limestones, the shrinkage is quite variable, but it may be notable. We do not know to what extent the form of fossils is altered during the first period of shrinking of the mud. In a sandstone, the shrinking is generally very slight.

As an aid in tectonic studies, it is, on the whole, quite a delicate matter to utilize the deformation of fossils. In any event we should exclude the effects of compaction, which may have preceded tectonic deformation.

A conglomerate may supply data for the study of deformation, provided the deformation is uniform in its cement and in its pebbles. This requires either excellent cementation or deformation in a "climate" of metamorphism such that the difference between the pebbles and the cement is not significant. Owing to the uncertainty that exists concerning the initial flattening of pebbles, we can recognize only a very great deformation, sometimes up to 20:1, as in the example of the conglomerates of the Rehamna, described by Gigout, who was able to prove that the extension plane of the pebbles is a schistosity plane, or the elongation direction the lineation.[5] (See also the Purgatory conglomerate, near Newport, Rhode Island.)

Attempts have been made to determine the deformation of a rock from the shape of colored spots that are supposed to have been circular originally, which is evidently difficult to prove.

Other marks that may exist in a rock, such as colored beds parallel to the stratification, are in general planes and consequently cannot serve to show a homogeneous deformation since they remain planes after deformation. But if the deformation is not homogeneous, they indicate these inequalities and enable us to see if a bed has been bent or twisted.

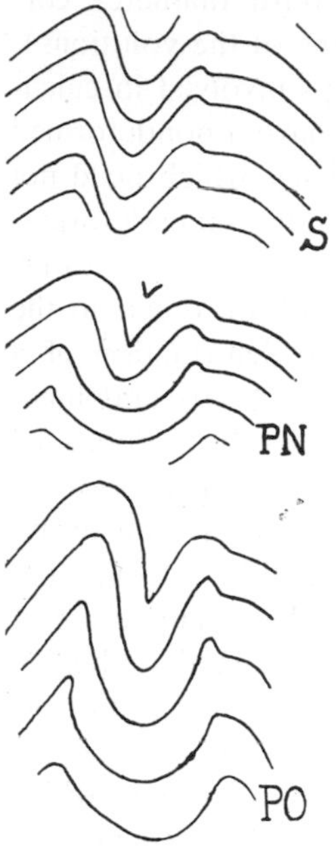

FIGURE 12

(S) Similar folds, or shear folds; (PN) Parallel folds, or flexure folds, as seen in a section normal to the fold axis; (PO) Parallel folds as seen in a section oblique to the fold axis. Note that only in the normal section can we see that the thickness of each bed remains constant.

We shall merely point out here a particular case of such a deformation. When the plastic deformation of a homogeneous rock can be reduced to the relative slip of parallel beds in the same direction (from the kinematic point of view only, since we must not give any physical significance to this image), it is shown[6] that the work done is the same whatever may be the manner in which the deformation is spread among the successive beds. A colored bed may thus assume any form, but any other parallel colored bed will assume the same form. If these marker beds are numerous, the surface of the rock will present the aspect of a fold, but this fold, from the point of view of its origin, is very different from those to be studied later on (shear fold, as opposed to flexure fold). The folded beds are simple colored horizons whose mechanical properties are indistinguishable from those of the rock and which have played no role in the genesis of the folds. The form of such folds is called "similar." The sinuosities of all successive beds are exactly superposable; consequently, the distance between two consecutive beds, that is, the thickness, varies according to their dip (Fig. 12). It is necessary to distinguish carefully between these folds and "parallel" folds into which the beds have slipped relative to each other, the slips following the layers that separate them, which preserves approximately their original thickness.

The appearance of the "similar" folds that we are discussing remains the same no matter along what directions they are cut by the outcrop surface that exposes them. However, in "parallel" folds, the apparent thickness of the beds may vary considerably if they are cut by an oblique surface rather than one normal to the trend of the folds. The examination of sections oriented in different directions should enable us to recognize the trend of the folds. We must make observations parallel to this direction in order to study an approximately normal section; thus we can avoid mistaking parallel folds, observed on an oblique section, for similar folds (Fig. 12).

Rocks seldom contain marks whose original form we know, whether they are fossils, colored beds or pebbles. In general, however, we are not completely helpless, since deformations undergone by a rock must necessarily have modified its structure. If structural analysis enabled us to recognize the deformations undergone, the solution of tectonic problems would be greatly facilitated. Unfortunately, it is a very complex problem, which is still far from being solved. Historically, structural analysis has involved two successive phases, which should be discussed separately, in order to distinguish properly what is accepted and what remains doubtful.

For more than a century, geologists (principally those of the English school) have been seeking to determine the origin of schistosity, that is, the tendency of rocks to break into more or less thin leaves, parallel to a fixed plane. (In English, the expression *slaty cleavage* tends to be replaced by the term *flow cleavage,* which implies a hypothesis of genesis, or by the term *foliation,* which is used to avoid confusion with the term cleavage, applied to crystals.) They soon realized that this schistosity could be due only to deformation undergone by the rock after its consolidation. Of course, we must distinguish between schistosity that results from deformation and that which is due to the original texture. For example, in a sedimentary rock, mica flakes (or at times certain fossils) are deposited horizontally; therefore, the rocks tend to split parallel to the stratification, which utilizes in part the cleavages of the micas or the surfaces of the fossils. Schistosity of mechanical origin is therefore significant only when it is oblique to the stratification. This is rather common, but it is sometimes difficult to distinguish schistosity from stratification in such a case. If the two are confused, grave errors may result, both through the failure to recognize the deformation undergone and through masking the general structure of the region. To distinguish between stratification and schistosity demands the most attentive observation in the field. Inasmuch as schistosity is, in general, very prominent, we should endeavor to recognize the direction of stratification, marked by beds of different composition, calcareous or sandy. Ripple marks may also enable us to recognize the true stratification. It frequently happens that, in passing from one bed to another of slightly different composition, the schistosity changes slightly in direction, as if it were refracted (*step of the slate*). This phenomenon, to which we shall return later, enables us to recognize stratification easily.

The first English authors, Sorby, Sharpe, Haughton, Phillips, King, and others, quite quickly recognized that schistosity follows one of the principal planes of the deformation ellipsoid, the one perpendicular to the direction of maximum compression. The direction of maximum elongation and the median principal directions are thus in the plane of schistosity. We can even state precisely, following Albert Heim, that the lineation or "side of the slate" (*longrain, Linearstreckung*), the secondary direction of cleavage, parallel to which the schistosity is more pronounced than transversely, should correspond to the principal direction of elongation.

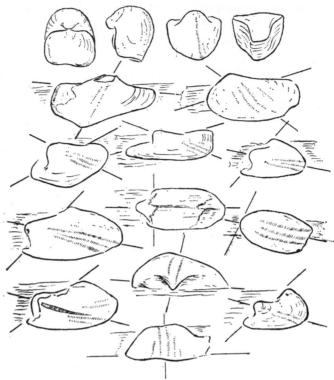

FIGURE 13. Pentamerus (Gypidula) galateus, *Rancennes schist (Eifélian). Samples collected by M. Ricour at Mont d'Hams, near Givet (Ardennes). Top, an undeformed specimen. Below, a series of deformed samples included in a rock that was made schistose by local deformation. In all examples, the deformation indicates a flattening parallel to the schistocity.*

This rule, which is indicated by simple considerations of symmetry, has been verified [7] by experiments upon the most varied substances, from wax and clay to steel; the artificial schistosity determined by their deformation is indeed perpendicular at each point to the direction of maximum crushing. If the experimental conditions are complex, as is true in many cases, it may be necessary, for a full understanding, to analyze the elementary deformation; the deformation of steel sheets passing through a rolling-mill consists of a reduction in thickness by crushing rather than a slipping of flakes. Numerous observations in the field have confirmed this rule whenever it has been possible to identify directly the deformation undergone by the rock. It is not possible to enumerate here all the published observations; however, the following is a very characteristic one, still unpublished. Figure 13 shows, alongside an undeformed specimen of *Pentamerus (Gypidula) galeata,* a whole series of specimens found a few meters from the first, in a zone where the Devonian limestone (somewhat marly) has become schistose near a fault. The samples are depicted such that the schistosity is horizontal and is seen in section. For each sample, two originally rectangular planes have been indicated (symmetry and commissure planes); it is easy to see that in all cases the deformation corresponds to a flattening perpendicular to the schistosity, with a stretching in the plane of the latter.

It is particularly striking to read descriptions of authors who profess other theories and yet confirm the rule indicated above. For example, Oftedahl (quoted by Fairbairn[8]), who has studied 128 pebbles from an arkose in Central Norway, states that "the two greatest axes are in the plane of foliation with the greater of these two parallel to the direction of the thrust and parallel to the lineation."

We find a confirmation of the above rule in the study of masses containing rocks of different natures. We shall see later the evidence furnished by inclusions harder than the surrounding rock (which break or deform in a peculiar manner), such as veinlets forming ptygmatic folds, pebbles that are sometimes broken, or truncated belemnites. The total deformation that they indicate is always in harmony with the schistosity of the surrounding rock.

When the deformed rock is a single bed, included between rigid beds, the deformation is reduced to relative slip of the rigid beds. The principal directions of deformation are at 45° to the attitude of the beds. The same holds true for the direction of schistosity (numerous observations in the Ardennes have been cited, particularly by Kaisin).

Numerous observations on the relation between schistosity and folding have been made by Fourmarier[9] in various regions, and his conclusions confirm the statements made above. According to Fourmarier, "schistosity is in close relation to a stretching of the material, or rather to a spreading of this material in a privileged direction." Thus, he specifies that the force is usually directed upon the plane of schistosity, elongating the material in the direction of the schistosity and diminishing its thickness in a perpendicular direction. Inasmuch as the folds are related to the direction of the forces, a relation exists between their behavior and the direction of schistosity. This has been verified by Fourmarier in numerous cases. On the whole, the schistosity is parallel to the axial plane of the folds, and the lineation is directed along the line of maximum dip. But if this is the general rule, a careful study of the divergences that may appear, based on a mechanical interpretation, may furnish interesting information. The refraction of schistosity across different beds is an example.

Fourmarier insists that schistosity (at least flow schistosity) appears only if the material has been deformed. As we shall see later on, this is possible only when the pressures are sufficiently great and therefore below a certain depth. Fourmarier thought he could establish this depth at a minimum of 6000 m, but in reality, things are not so simple. According to the types of rock and the intensity of the oriented pressures, the depths at which schistosity may appear vary considerably and are sometimes far less than this figure.

If a mass containing different beds (more or less calcareous or sandy shales) presents an oblique schistosity, it will be noted that the direction of schistosity varies from one bed to the next (step of the cleavage).

Analysis of the distribution of mechanical forces furnishes a quantitative explanation of this phenomenon (see Chap. 12, p. 185), in the hypothesis of schistosity normal to the maximum compression, though it is not possible to reconcile it with the theory that we shall consider now.

If we have insisted somewhat on the multiplicity of arguments that bear out the point of view indicated above, it is because an inexact analysis of the deformation (see note 1, end of chap.) has led Becker and a certain number of authors who have followed him to assume that the schistosity would appear along one of the so-called "slip planes," that is, at 45° to the direction that we have accepted. Certain authors thought they could reconcile the contradiction between the two theories by recognizing two sorts of schistosity (flow cleavage and fracture cleavage). Flow cleavage, which is recognized by the fact that the division planes may appear at almost any point, is probably due to a deformation of the mass of the rock, whereas fracture cleavage, which is revealed only by a limited number of parallel division planes, probably originated without mass deformation. This distinction has but very limited application, as is shown by the transitions observed from one to the other of the two types of schistosity, particularly in the refraction of schistosity, in which schistosity often passes from the "flow" type in the shales to the "fracture" type in the resistant beds, the relations remaining exactly the same, however, as when the schistosity is of the flow type in both kinds of beds.

If one type of schistosity is perpendicular to the maximum pressure and if the other is oriented at 45°, as has been suggested, they should both occasionally be found in the same rock, but this has never been observed. And again, if the theory concerning the schistosity at 45° of the maximum pressure were valid, we should sometimes observe two schistosities in a single rock; however, this is never the case.

It is our belief, then, that whatever the form may be under which the schistosity appears, whether flow or fracture, we must adhere to the mechanical interpretation indicated above. In the article cited above,[1] we have investigated the origin and discussed the argument in favor of this theory of schistosity at 45° to the principal directions, and we have shown that it is based on erroneous reasoning and should be formally rejected.

The preceding considerations apply to the first deformation of an originally isotropic rock. But if the rock becomes schistose as a result of deformation, it may subsequently be subjected to a force of different orientation whose principal directions are oblique to its schistosity. The anisotropic rock may react quite differently to this new compression than an isotropic rock would, and for certain forms of schistosity, the schistose beds may slide over each other. An analogous phenomenon is produced in strata whose normal mode of overall deformation is a fold that has resulted from relative slip of the beds over each other. This secondary slipping of schistose beds may either leave characteristic traces (such as striations) on their surface, deform the surfaces of fissures or small transverse veins, or, finally, cause folds whose dimensions (a few millimeters to a few centimeters) are proportional to the thickness of the schistose beds, which are individualized in the relative slipping.

In the first two cases (if we disregard the roles of the two successive phases), the structure may apparently confirm the appearance, accepted by various authors following Becker, of a schistosity appearing obliquely in relation to the principal directions of the force. But in the latter, it is evident that the folding, which only in places implies the relative slipping of schistose beds, is posterior to their genesis and should be attributed to a subsequent phase.

Schistosity is only the megascopic aspect of a modification of the structure of the rock. A century ago, geologists such as Sorby had already concerned themselves with what this modification consisted of. Had the flattened grains been oriented parallel to the schistosity? What was the role of recrystallization? The question had not been answered; moreover, it presented only a speculative interest, and the results indicated above are absolutely independent of the modification of structure that is illustrated by schistosity.

The relation between the structure of rocks and the deformations undergone was studied by quite different methods in Austria in about 1920, principally under the direction of Bruno Sander and Walter Schmidt. Since about 1935, the methods applied by these authors have been employed on a broad scale in various countries, notably in the U.S.A. These methods, which tend to set up a veritable *"corps de doctrine,"* aim at a detailed statistical analysis of the structure of rocks, designated in English by the term *fabric* or *petrofabric,* and in German, by the term *Gefüge.* Unfortunately, the descriptive part and the theoretical interpretation, often quite open to criticism, have been mingled in an inextricable manner by the above authors, who developed the methods of Gefügeanalyse. H. W. Fairbairn endeavored, without being completely successful, to separate them in order to present the points that are still doubtful and the observational data acquired.[10] The Austrian authors have of necessity studied especially the crystalline schists upon whose deformation no other evidence was available, which has made controls impossible. Such controls would have been indispensable at the beginning of the development of this method, which has developed in a very independent and often very theoretical manner.

The structural petrographic analysis involves not only the study of the mineralogic nature and dimensions of the grains, but also of their form and, above all, their crystallographic orientation. Of course, this study can only be statistical; it requires the measurement of a great number of grains, from about 100 to 500. As in every statistical study, it is necessary to know how to decide whether characteristics of a given distribution are significant or are due simply to chance; for this purpose, a series of criteria has been formulated and discussed by Chayes in Fairbairn's book.[10]

The considerable work involved in the calculations has led most authors to make an *a priori* choice among the data they would take into consideration; thus, the external form of grains has been very little utilized. Most often, determination has been made of the directions of the optical axes of the crystals, a procedure that can be made relatively rapidly if Federov's universal microscope stage is used. But it should be noted that for uniaxial crystals, such as quartz or calcite, optical measurements do not completely define the orientation of the crystal.

For calcite, the study of the cleavage planes and twin crystals may result in a complete determination of the orientation of the crystals and the deformations that they have undergone individually along either of the possible directions of mechanical twinning, by a petrographic method much more complicated than the mere determination of the optical axes. In the hands of Francis J. Turner and his co-workers, this method has given very promising results when applied to the analysis of deformations whose nature is otherwise known, especially deformations experimentally produced in the laboratory.[11] The movement of the microscope stage limits the scope of the possible measurements and may seriously distort the statistics, even preventing measurements in certain directions. The authors do not always discipline themselves to making separate measurements for three thin sections at right angles.

The directions measured, such as the optical axis of quartz and calcite, the normal to the twin plane of the calcite lamellae, or the normal to the cleavage plane of the micas, are transferred to an equivalent projection of the sphere, and the limits of zones are drawn for which the density of the points is a chosen multiple of the mean density. If the rock is isotropic, the statistical analysis will show that the fluctuations of the density of the points marked on the sphere around the mean density are a matter of chance and hence of no significance. If this is not the case, the rock is anisotropic. The diagram presents in zones of great density one or several preferential orientations, either parallel to a determined direction (concentration around a point) or along a more or less complete girdle which indicates the distribution of the axes in a plane, or at least within an angle to this plane. This occurs especially if a crystallographic element (other than that taken as a guide) is parallel to a determined direction (for example, for parallel amphibole crystals the normals to the cleavages evidently lie in a plane). It is not possible by the use of optical measurements to distinguish this case from that in which the crystals are oriented at random around their axis, which is in a plane. Measurements of diffraction by X-rays which could allow this distinction are not yet in current practice.

If we admit—and this is a point which seems to have not yet been sufficiently discussed—that the initial rock was isotropic, the anisotropism revealed in the diagram should be due to the deformation. It is often possible to recognize the existence of symmetry planes on the diagram. The total symmetry may be roughly triclinic, monoclinic, orthorhombic, or may revolve about an axis. We have seen that an elementary deformation has the symmetry of an ellipsoid, that is, orthorhombic or revolutionary; but the structure of the rock depends upon prolonged deformation, the principal directions of which have not necessarily remained fixed in relation to the material, and the influence of all the successive elementary deformations may be superposed.

In its relation to the geographic directions, the anisotropism thus revealed would represent objective information on the deformation undergone by the rock. But it has become established practice to use three mutually perpendicular axes, a, b, c as reference directions. These are determined by macroscopic examination; however, their determination lends itself to certain ambiguities, and their very definition rests upon an inexact mechanical analysis. W. Schmidt and B. Sander in effect accept Becker's interpretation, according to which the schistosity would produce a "slip plane," taken as plane ab, the movement having taken place along direction a; b would be marked by the axis of the folds, the undulations of the schistosity, and so forth. The American authors, although they admit, at least in certain cases, that the schistosity is perpendicular to the maximum pressure, consider that slips take place at the same time on two symmetrical oblique planes whose intersection is represented by b. They still define direction a as the direction of the plane of schistosity, which would be directed along the bisectrix of the two slip planes. According to their interpretation, the directions of the reference axes chosen could either coincide with those of the deformation ellipsoid or (for a and c) form an angle of $45°$ with them, without there being anything in the indications furnished that would aid in making a choice between the two cases.

We should add, too, that direction b is considered as that of the elongations of elements in the schistosity plane, whereas, according to the descriptions of Albert Heim, his "Linear Streckung" (equivalent of the lineation) would be directed instead at right angles to the folds. Is there not a confusion of very different things under the same name? The fact that three directions have been chosen as reference axes whose definition leaves room for so much ambiguity involves a risk of rendering useless an immense mass of patiently accumulated observations and of arriving at doubtful tectonic conclusions. The ways in which these definitions are applied, and consequently the meaning attached to the axes designated as a, b, and c, is liable to vary from one author to the next, and this could lead to serious misunderstandings.

However, let us put this difficulty to one side. Having determined the preferred orientations of the constituent minerals, or at least one of their axes, we are faced with the problem of relating the preferred orientation to the deformation undergone. Among the intimate mechanisms of deformation, such as the mutual displacement of grains, solution, and crystallization (Riecke's principle), there is one that has attracted almost exclusive attention; that is, the deformation of crystals by slipping on reticular planes. This may or may not be by twinning, depending on whether or not the symmetries of the crystal have been altered as a result of reorientation of the lattice. For a considerable number of minerals, the possible slip planes and the directions of movement are now known. It has been accepted that the orientation of these crystals in the rock is what has made possible the deformation by reticular slip. If we assume the rock to have been originally isotropic, how did the crystals rotate and come to occupy this position? What is the role of recrystallization? These are two questions, among many others, to which most expositions bring only dogmatic affirmations in the way of answers. Only the works of Turner and his collaborators, cited above, constitute an objective analysis of the modifications undergone by crystals following deformation.

But quartz poses a much more serious question. For this mineral, although one of the most abundant constituents of rocks and certainly one of the most studied by the practitioners of the *Gefügekunde,* we have observed no slip direction or mechanical twin direction. All the evidence leads us to believe that none exist and that quartz can only be deformed by other mechanisms. However, in order to explain the preferred direction of the axes of quartz grains, certain authors have not hesitated to imagine, in an entirely gratuitous manner, slips following such and such a crystallographic direction, such that these directions are placed in accordance with the assumed slip directions of the rock for the observed orientation of the axes. This amounts to saying that in the present state of our knowledge the distribution of the grains of quartz in a rock can teach us nothing definite regarding the deformation that it has undergone.[12] However negative this conclusion may be, it is still very important in that it enables us to attach only the proper value to the statements of certain structural geologists who base their findings upon petrofabric analysis alone and yet do not hesitate to challenge all the conclusions obtained earlier by other methods. T. C. Phemister has presented the negative results that he obtained in his study of the orientation of quartz grains in the Dalradian rocks in Scotland, in which the deformation was otherwise well known, but in which he was unable to find any correlation between these deformations and the statistical orientations, which are generally unsignificant. He concludes that quartz recrystallizes much too easily to retain any trace of the deformations undergone.[13]

We have already alluded to the mechanical interpretation of deformations based essentially on the notion of relative slipping of successive flakes, according to Becker's conception. The mathematical reasoning of this author involves serious errors that completely vitiate the conclusions. Without going into detail, we simply point out that, according to Becker, the crushing of a testcylinder between the jaws of a press (a phenomenon that evidently implies a symmetry of revolution) would result from the superposition of two deformations at constant thickness in rectangular planes; these deformations being produced by oblique slips, the schistosities should outline a quadrangular pyramid, doubtless parallel to the chosen axes of reference.

This initial error invalidates all the subsequent work, the mechanical basis of which remains inaccurate and very debatable. Despite the effort toward objectivity, accomplished at other points, an author like Fairbairn speaks of *tectonic transport,* when it is quite evident that one specimen can indicate only the deformation and not the displacement that it has undergone. Moreover it is difficult to determine to what extent this *tectonic transport* is gliding and to what extent it constitutes displacement.

To sum up, the necessity for a critical revision of the mass of data on *petrofabrics* becomes very keenly felt. It is probable that a certain number of observations will be useless through inability to recognize the significance of the reference axes used. All the data relative to quartz are still to be screened. The mechanical interpretation must be completely worked over. It is to be feared that after this work of revision, the conclusions that may be retained will represent but a small part of those that are now advanced.

But this work of revision must be carried out, because there can scarcely be any doubt that, considering the anisotropism of certain rocks, the structural analyses of the rocks will in the end furnish valuable, definite evidence concerning the deformations undergone. Independent of any interpretation, the mere fact that all the rocks of the same nature in a given area present the same orientations of crystals indicates that they have undergone the same tectonic history; thus, it should be possible to relate deformation with crystal orientation in rocks of different nature. When the orientation of the crystals changes that should indicate that we are penetrating an area that has undergone different deformations and that may belong to another tectonic unit.

If it is kept in mind that, mechanically, the force, and consequently the deformation that results from it, for an isotropic rock present three trirectangular planes of symmetry (orthorhombic symmetry), it may be concluded, when the symmetry presented by the orientation of the crystals is of a different type, that there is either interference between the original anisotropism of the rock and the effect of the deformation or superposition of the effects of several successive deformations. If we can recognize points at which the same rock has not been deformed, it is then easy to determine whether or not it was originally anisotropic (however, this is a precaution that has been taken but too rarely). Before seeking to disentangle the effect of several superposed deformations, which unfortunately must be very frequent, it is necessary to study with great care the effect of the most simple deformations.

Certain applications of petrofabrics to tectonics have clearly been premature. But it must be hoped that a revision of the methods will place in the hands of structural geologists an instrument capable of furnishing them positive indications.

Let us return to the mechanics of intimate deformation of rocks. We have already pointed out that the internal slip within crystals was not the only possible phenomenon. The grains that constitute the rock may become displaced in relation to each other; any direction except that parallel to the axis

FIGURE 14. *Example of deformation by crystallization around grains (natural size).*
In thoroughly crushed Werfenian rocks, at the base of one of the northern
Alpine limestone nappes (Tyrol). During an early phase of deformation,
a breccia was produced, which consists of marly fragments in gypsum
cement.

During a later phase, which corresponds to a compression in the vertical
direction and an elongation in the horizontal direction, secondary gypsum,
white and slightly fibrous (shaded in figure), crystallized on the surface
of the marly fragments and in the fractures of the largest. The secondary
gypsum contributes to the transverse elongation. Its crystallization was
evidently directed by the existent forces. This specimen demonstrates the
analogous phenomenon that could be produced around the grains of a
rock undergoing deformation.

of greatest compression then tends to approach the principal direction of
maximum elongation. This direction may be indicated by a frequency diagram.

But the grains may change form. For example, in a limestone, there may be
solution in the interstitial water on faces under pressure, and deposition on
the stretched faces, according to Riecke's principle that the solubility increases
with the pressure undergone by the crystal. When more resistant grains are
present, which remain unaltered in the rock during the course of deformation, the force is modified in their vicinity, and there appear on their edges, in
the expansion direction, zones of less pressure, which are favored places for
recrystallization. Figure 14 shows a macroscopic example of such a phenomenon, in which fibrous gypsum has recrystallized (this can be done under
ordinary laboratory conditions). Fairbairn has published [14] photomicrographs
showing the recrystallization of quartz ("pressure shadows") around a crystal
of pyrite, which was left unaltered. Such extension aureoles have also been
observed around the quartz grains in a deformed limestone (Nappe de Morcles, unpublished). There would doubtless be interest in systematically seeking such indices of deformation by studying them in space and not only in the
plane of a thin section.

The same recrystallization may take place by molecular diffusion, although it may be difficult to establish a limit to the action of the solvent which exists in every rock, if only as a trace. It is not certain that such a deformation changes the orientation of the optical axes of the crystals, but it modifies their form, and a general elongation of the grains along one direction is recorded.

Crystalline grains may also change their form through the action of twinning and by slipping on reticular planes. The second case differs from the first only in that the deformed portion of the crystal, owing to the symmetries, resumes an orientation equivalent to its original orientation. The twins can be seen only under the microscope; it is moreover quite difficult to recognize the direction of the movement and to analyze the deformation through their study.

Finally, the deformation may have been accompanied by a more or less complete recrystallization, which may, owing to suitable thermal and chemical conditions, have taken place at a moment when the rock was undergoing an oriented pressure. Many petrographers consider that this state of oriented pressure, of *stress,* favors the appearance of certain minerals rather than others, although the thermodynamic theory of the phenomenon has never been even roughly outlined. In any event, the conditions of stress favor certain orientations of minerals rather than others. In particular, the phyllitic minerals

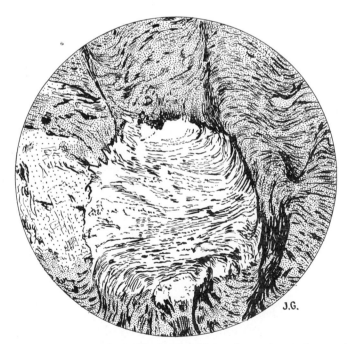

FIGURE 15. *An intact crystal of albite (shown in white) from the crushed schists of Mont d'Ambin (Franco-Italian Alps). Note the twisted inclusion lines. Light stippling: chlorite; heavy stippling: muscovite. Magnification 85×. [From Soc. Géol. France, Bull., 6ᵉ série, t. II, 1952.]*

seem to crystallize by preference perpendicularly to the strongest pressure. It is only in this way that the very common schistosity of banded metamorphic rocks can be explained.

It should be emphasized that in the case of recrystallization, it is the state of stress that determines the orientation of the crystals whatever the deformation may be that has actually taken place. In other cases, deformation, displacement, or twinning of crystals show the deformation. The deformation was evidently produced under the action of the stress, but if the latter had acted without producing deformation it would certainly not have changed the structure of the rock.

The history of a rock, in which several phases of recrystallization and deformation may have succeeded each other, may become an extremely complex thing. In certain cases, it is possible to recognize certain phases of this history by petrographic examination; deformations that took place following recrystallization are recognized by the presence of broken crystals, or by twisted twins or cleavages. A certain degree of recrystallization may perhaps not have completely obliterated the traces of earlier deformation. Quite often, there have been found large porphyroblasts of garnet or feldspar bearing S-shaped twisted inclusion lines, which seem to indicate a rotation of the crystal during the course of its growth (Fig. 15).

With regard to crystalline schists in the Massif Central, A. Demay[15] has shown how it was possible to recognize several alternating phases of deformation and recrystallization; but since the same observations are sometimes subject to different interpretations, we should retain only those successions that are very constant and which have been verified on the basis of a great number of specimens.

Although it is a very particular case, we should mention here the deformation of an eruptive rock before total consolidation; it can be shown by the stretching, or even the orientation, of the inclusions, or by the orientation of tabular or acicular crystals (which tend to be aligned in the direction of maximum elongation in the plane formed by the maximum principal direction and the median principal direction).

Eruptive rocks that have been deformed after crystallization may be recognized by the presence of broken crystals (feldspar, for instance) or by the presence of quartz with undulatory extinction, that is, broken, twisted and recemented; a classic example is the protogine granite of Mont Blanc. There does not seem to have been any attempt to use these characteristics to evaluate the deformation undergone by the rock.

In mylonites, this deformation has gone very far, even to the pulverization of all the crystals; but such a deformation rarely affects a large volume. Very often it is confined to narrow strips that have permitted a striking relative slip of the masses that they separate. These mylonitic strips are a transition toward discontinuous deformations, to which it will be fitting to connect them. Here, too, there has been no effort to evaluate numerically the deformation and to indicate whether the elongation has been ten or a hundred times. The important thing is the total displacement of the mylonitic strip.

We have seen that a limestone, for example, may undergo a homogeneous deformation by solution and growth of crystals along different directions. The same phenomenon may be shown in the appearance of veins of calcite, which appear white against the more or less colored background of the rock. (In a similar manner, veins of quartz or gypsum may be produced in a siliceous rock.) These veins often appear in the form of isolated lentils, and it is evident that the solution that deposited them did not come from far away through a fissure, but simply oozed out of the walls (lateral secretion). The origin of the calcite was certainly quite near the fissures in which it was deposited; this circulation is understandable, because the grains of calcite that dissolved supported a greater pressure than those that were deposited. In certain cases, the calcite (or the quartz) deposits may contain geodes, and we have proof that the fissure was wide open; at that moment its walls supported only the pressure of the impregnating liquid. When we observe wide-open fissures on the convex side of a twisted bed without calcite, we may wonder whether or not they were widened by solution. But in many cases, it may be assumed that the fissures were only virtual and that their walls still supported a certain pressure, but less than the crystallization pressure of the nascent crystals, which might thus push back the walls and widen the fissure.

It is easy to see where the calcite has

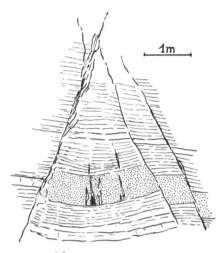

FIGURE 16

Example of open tectonic fissure. Section exposed in the cliff near St. Cyr, on the border of the Var and Bouches du Rhone departments. A small local fault cuts across the marly sandstone series of the Upper Cretaceous, the beds of which are bent back at their contact. In a relatively thick bed of sandstone (stippled), this curvature has produced a stretching of the convex side (proportional to the thickness, other things being equal) in which fractures were formed and subsequently filled with calcite. These calcite-filled fractures are lacking in the thin beds. One of these fractures, 4 cm thick, is open, its walls simply being carpeted with crystals of calcite.

been deposited, but not where it was dissolved; the network of veins does not enable us to make a complete analysis of the deformation, which must have been greater than is indicated by the separation of the vein walls. Sometimes, the dissolution of calcite occurs along stylolithic surfaces whose attitude gives an important clue as to the deformation of the rock.

FIGURE 17

A network of quartz veins in a Triassic quartzite, Rognon d'Etache, Ambin Massif, Savoy, France. (Sketched from a photograph.)

1m

Very often these fissures are grouped in systems that almost always show an echeloning that is quite easy to interpret (Fig. 18). Evidently there was a relative displacement in the direction of the arrow. The fissures opened perpendicular to the direction of least pressure (relative traction). We must not apply the classic rupture theory to such fissures (applicable, for example, to compression tests in the open air), but we must seek among all the possible fissure directions those for which the pressure supported by the walls will become in the first place inferior to the pressure (hydrostatic) of the impregnation liquid or to the crystallization pressure of the calcite.

The network of quartz veins in a mass of quartzite, represented in Fig. 17, enables us to reconstruct two successive times of deformation. In the first (Fig. 18), a network of *en echelon* fissures appears, indicating a deformation that was due to shearing. In the course of a second phase, this type of deformation has continued, but this time by plastic deformation of the quartzite, in which the veins of quartz have been twisted.[16]

The impression of rotation given by the twisted veins of Fig. 17 are thus due

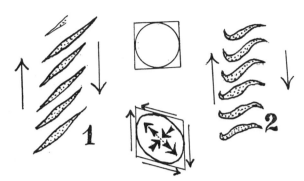

FIGURE 18. *Diagram of the stages (1 and 2) leading to the results shown in Fig. 17. Center, a kinematic diagram of the corresponding deformation; the arrows arranged in the center indicate the principal directions of the deformation. The arrows indicate the shearing that resulted from deformation of the square.*

to the succession of deformation phases, which remained fixed in space while the material itself was deformed. An analogous interpretation would doubtless be valid for the twisted inclusion lines found, for example, in certain garnets.

Numerous analogous systems of veinlets are often superposed in a rock and yet are quite recognizable. They correspond then to modifications that are echeloned in time (Fig. 19). In other cases, the fractures are multiplied

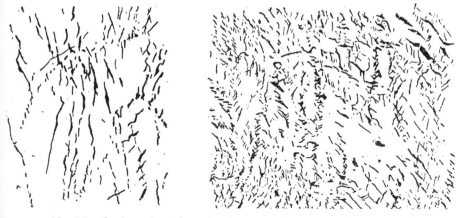

FIGURE 19. *Distribution of veinlets of calcite (veinlets shown in black) in a marble of unknown origin (left) and in a Triassic Briancon limestone (right). In the limestone, several deformations seem to have succeeded one another. (Scale, 1:10.) [Goguel, J., Introduction à l'étude mecanique des deformations de l'Écorce Terrestre, Mém. Carte géol. France, 2nd. ed., Paris, Fig. 20, 1948.]*

and their relations show that they appeared together. Thus the rock may appear much fractured, even converted into a veritable breccia in which it is no longer possible to recognize the initial mutual positions of the fragments. All the intermediate stages exist between such breccias and simple networks of veinlets. But in the breccias, it is probable that the cementation by the calcite is often later than the crushing.

It is possible to compare with veins, the structures described in the Moine series of Scotland under the term *rodding*.[17] Veins of quartz, originally in the form of lentils, were caught in the later deformation and were finally reduced to rods parallel to the direction of the folding which they indicate. *Mullions* are similar cylindrical masses, but were formed by the surrounding rock and were isolated and, to some extent, rolled by the deformation. These structures do not seem to have been described in other regions.

Except in the special case where such veins of lateral secretion have appeared, homogeneous deformation of a rock may be difficult to identify. Schistosity seems to appear only in a quite strong relative deformation; we do not always have deformed fossils at hand, and the analysis of the structure is a long and painful operation that will give no clear result for a slight deformation.

There is thus almost no possibility of identifying a homogeneous deformation of a rock by only ten or twenty percent (definite percentages given only to make the estimate meaningful). We shall see later what indirect methods are being used, but in their application and, in general, in any tectonic interpretation, we should never lose sight of the possibility that a homogeneous deformation might pass unobserved.

However, there are structures that exist in all rocks and which seem, *a priori,* susceptible of bringing us information on their mechanical history, namely, joints.

A rock mass is never continuous; we observe it divided by numerous fissures or joints. In general, we distinguish between joints, which are open, and cleavages that appear along well-determined directions under the action of a blow, for example; but this distinction is perhaps somewhat artificial. In addition, the directions of cleavages and joints often coincide.

Joints, properly so called, possess no throw; the two parts of the rock that they separate are not normally displaced in relation to one another. But we sometimes find systems of repeated fissures, very analogous to joints, that show traces of friction as if they had undergone slight relative movements.

When the joints are well developed and regular, a thing more often observed in granites than in basic rocks, they are generally parallel to three directions, and outline blocks in the form of parallelepipeds. Moreover, they are very unevenly spaced along these various directions. In sedimentary rocks, one of these directions coincides most often with the stratification.

The orientation of joints proves the existence (at the moment of their formation) of anisotropic physical conditions, and among these conditions we can scarcely recognize anything else than the pressure that can be anisotropic.

It would seem then that the observation of joints should provide us with some accurate data, if not on the deformations undergone by the rocks (joints exist in rocks that do not appear at all deformed), at least on the pressures that they have been subjected to. But at what moment were they subjected to these pressures, and how were the pressures oriented in relation to the joints? We are far from knowing the answers to these questions.

In his studies, Cloos has shown that, in granite, the joints have a systematic direction[18] that seems to be related to forces similar to those present during emplacement of the body (and which have left their trace in the structure of the rock). This leads us to assign them a quite ancient age, confirmed by the relations between joints and veins of pegmatite or of lamprophyre (Fig. 20).

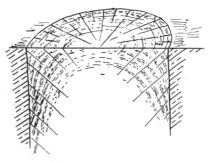

FIGURE 20

The directions of fissures in a mass of intrusive granite (such as that of Eygurande), showing domal foliation, radial vertical fissures, and oblique fissures toward the interior of the mass. [Inspired by Cloos.]

We are much less well informed on the matter of sedimentary rocks, and the observation data themselves are still very meager. In an important study, H. de Cizancourt[19] has shown how statistics bearing in principle on 200 joints observed in each single outcrop, whose directions are represented in spherical projection, enable us to define the directions of greatest frequency and sometimes enable us to distinguish two closely adjacent but not confused systems. Cizancourt concludes that the direction of the joints provides us with information on the forces acting at the time of maximum orogenic activity. But for the strongest pressure undergone by the rock to have determined the direction of the joints, the anterior fissures would have had to be effaced at this moment, but there is nothing to warrant this assumption.

Let us consider another hypothesis. The joints could have originated only at the moment when the rock was sufficiently close to the surface and under the action of the pressures that were in force at that moment. The difference in the case of granite is explained by the fact that when the sedimentary rocks were deposited, they were soft and without tension. This question calls for further research. It is the same with the orientation of joints in relation to the pressures in operation. Two hypotheses are suggested. According to one of them, which is essentially Becker's,[20] the directions of the joints were probably at an angle of 45° to the principal pressures, following the "glide planes" of the ellipsoid of deformation. But when such a rupture appears in a rock, it is immediately followed by a displacement of its margins. However, there are joints in undeformed rocks, and, in general, no slip takes place along the joints; moreover, in any deformation, there are no slip planes in which the deformation is zero.

The other hypothesis would consist of correlating at least one of the sets of joints with the schistosity, which we know appears perpendicular to the strongest pressure. The joints would appear along the principal directions of the force; thus we could explain the fact that often one of the systems is wide open and the other closed. Evidently if a direction of least resistance already exists, such as the stratification, the other directions may be deflected and can no longer be orthogonal.

In the study cited above, Cizancourt presented, on a map of the Pyrenees, the directions of the pressures, deduced from those of the joints. This attempt may be premature, since this relation is not even definitely established, but he indicates what may be expected from the study of joints once they are better known. The necessity for employing a statistical method and making very numerous measurements may have repelled certain observers. But there is no doubt that systematic studies of joints may produce very interesting information, although they may sometimes require interpretations. From studies already made along this line, no simple law has yet evolved that would enable us to readily determine the directions of forces exerted or of the deformations that have been produced. To begin with, we must operate in regions that were moderately and regularly folded; we must not be satisfied with accumulating figures, but we must look very closely at the nature of joints (open or closed, mineralized or not, with or without traces of friction, more or less spaced and continuous). Measurements should be closely spaced in order to be sure of the continuity of the directions and to clarify their relation to the chief disturbers (faults and folds). Only later can a regional interpretation be attempted. But special care must be taken neither to fall into the excesses that marked the last studies of Elie de Beaumont nor to limit oneself to finding, systematically and repeatedly, a certain number of preferred directions.

The existence in a rock of recognizable elements—veins or heterogeneous beds of different resistance—enables us to demonstrate its deformation. Generally, the bed that holds the evidence is more resistant than the rest of the rock; it will not simply participate in its deformation, but may, for example, break without its fragments changing much in form. The relative position of fragments will give us information on the deformation of the rock in which they are enclosed. In like manner, if compression is exerted along the direction of the resistant bed, it may fold without changing its length (ptygmatic folds); this folding reveals the contraction.

The presence of the resistant bed modifies the distribution of the pressures, owing to both its thickness and its vicinity, and so we shall postpone the complete analysis of the phenomenon to Chap. 12. It is only as a first approximation that we may consider the elements of the resistant bed as simple markers buried in the plastic mass.

We can thus understand that, if fragments of the resistant bed are found separated from one another (it is said to have undergone a *boudinage*),[21] the plastic rock has stretched along its direction as result of compression at a right angle. the amount of the stretch in the different directions of the plane is easily determined by observation of the stretch of the bed in its plane (Figs. 21 and 25). Often the spaces between the fragments are not occupied by the

FIGURE 21

The boudinage of a rigid bed included in a plastic mass.

plastic rock itself but by recrystallized material, such as calcite. In its movement to occupy the intervals between the fragments, the plastic rock may also twist the angles of the latter.

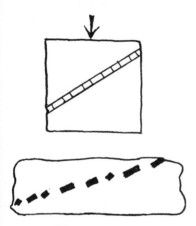

FIGURE 22

Separation and rotation of fragments of wood included in a deformed block of plastiline.

The fragments of the same bed may not have remained in alignment, but may have more or less pivoted. This evidently indicates a certain obliquity of the compression, which may be realized simply by crushing a block of plastiline in which the sections of a wooden slab have been placed along a line; an oblique compression, in addition to their separation, causes their pivoting in the direction indicated in Fig. 22. But a complete mechanical analysis enables us to state more exactly the effect of the forces.

If the bed was rigid in the direction of the compression, it usually folded; the little irregularities that it presented inevitably increased and its undulations were amplified, the bed offering much less resistance to the torsion than to a longitudinal crushing. The various fragments included between the bends may even have been pushed one against the other perpendicularly to their initial direction. This arrangement is that of the *ptygmatic folds* that we often observe in metamorphic rocks, formed for example by an aplitic vein. As would be expected, they are transverse in relation to the schistosity (Fig. 23).

The phenomena of boudinage, on all scales, are not rare in metamorphic rocks, but they are also to be observed in sedimentary rocks, which sometimes present almost no other index of deformation. Thus, A. Lambert has shown me undulations of beds in the calcareous marls of the Upper Jurassic and in

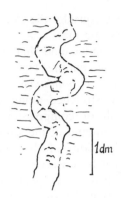

FIGURE 23. *Ptygmatic folds. Left, a schematic representation. Right, a quartz vein in a Brianconnais limestone. (Sketched from a photograph.)*

the Neocomian of the Kabylie des Babors that greatly resemble ripple marks, but which seem to be the result of the boudinage of calcareous beds that were a little more rigid than those surrounding them (Fig. 24). The fragmentation of these calcareous beds is marked by veins of calcite and also by a decrease

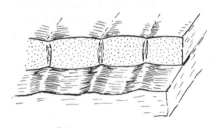

FIGURE 24

Boudinage of a limestone bed in a somewhat more marly mass, simulating ripple-marks (Kabylie des Babors, Algeria).

in thickness accompanied by a wrinkling of the surface of the adjacent beds. In addition to the presence of calcite veins, these wrinkles are distinguished from real ripple marks by the presence of flat panels between the wrinkles.

In the coal measures on the road from Modane to Fréjus (French Alps), veinlets of siderite have been observed that have undergone a typical boudinage, the interval between the fragments being occupied by calcite; the siderite behaves as if less plastic than the shale (Fig. 25).

Shattered belemnites, which have long been known, can be explained in a similar manner.[22] When they are oblique to the principal directions, their fragments may undergo a slight pivoting (Fig. 26). Fissured pebbles, the pieces of which are separated, have been observed within a more plastic cement (Fig. 27).

Around a crystal or a rigid nodule that was not affected by the deformation, zones of decreased pressure appear on the margins, whereas zones of excess pressure appear along the direction of the maximum pressure. The zones of decreased pressure may be the site of certain crystallization: of quartz on the edge of a magnetic crystal in the "knots" of the schists of the Ardenne;[23] of sodium chloride on the periphery of a crystal of like nature;[24] of quartz or

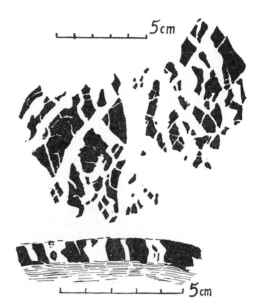

FIGURE 25

Stretching of a vein of siderite (in black) in a coal-measure shale, as seen in plan and in section. (Sketched from a photograph.)

FIGURE 26. *Broken and stretched belemnite.*

FIGURE 27. *Pebble, stretched and truncated, in a schistose rock.* [*After Diller, J. S., Bull. U.S. Geol. Surv., vol. 353, 1908, p. 21; quoted by G. F. Becker, Am. Jour. Sci., vol. 24, p. 1, July 1907, and reproduced in Bull. Soc. Géol. France, 5ᵉ série, no. 15, p. 517, 1945.*]

feldspar on the edge of the "eyes" of augen-gneisses. The principal interest of these diverse peculiarities is to confirm the relations indicated above between the deformation of a homogeneous rock and the schistosity that results therefrom.

Notes and References

1. The reader should be on guard against an inexact manner of presentation that is to be found in numerous publications that reproduce more or less indirectly the ideas of Becker (Becker, G. F., Experiment on Schistosity and Slaty Cleavage, Bull. U. S. Geol. Surv., vol. 241, 1904).

When we try to find out whether there exist in the material under study planes along which there would not be any deformation, such that the deformation there may be reduced to the slipping of such planes upon each other, we discover that *such planes do not exist*. This applies except for a special case in which the deformation along the median principal direction is zero. In that case, two planes, symmetrical to each other and passing through this median principal direction, are not deformed at any given time. These planes are at right angles if there is no change of volume involved. For a completed deformation, these planes do not, in general, remain fixed in the material; that is, there are no flakes in the material that do not become deformed; the distance between two points situated in such a plane had previously diminished; it is simply stationary before beginning to expand again.

This particular case has often been confused with the general case, and the deformation has often erroneously been represented as the slipping of parallel planes upon one another like a pack of cards. Such a pack of cards, when laid on a table and given a push, will be transformed from a right prism into an oblique prism. This representation in no way corresponds to reality, and all deductions drawn from it are inexact.

See also Goguel, J., *Sur l'origine mécanique de la schistosité,* Bull. Soc. géol. France, 5 sér., vol. 15, pp. 509–522, 1945.

2. See figures in Haug, E., *Traité de Géologie,* Vol. I, pp. 230–231, A. Colin, Paris, 1907.

3. Goguel, J., *Introduction à l'étude mécanique des déformations de l'Écorce Terrestre,* Mém. Carte géol. France, 2nd ed., Paris, 1948.

4. Duffet, H., *Notes sur les déformations des fossiles contenus dans les roches schisteuses et sur la détermination de quelques espèces du genre Ogygia,* Ann. Scient., Ecole Normale Superiéure, Paris, 2 sér., pp. 183–190, 1875.

5. Gigout, Marcel, *Sur les déformations plastiques dans les conditions du métamorphisme régional des conglomérats du Nord des Rehamna (Maroc occidental),* Acad. Sci. Paris, Comptes-rendus, vol. 242, p. 390, 1950.

6. See reference 1 in Chapter 1, Goguel, J., *Introduction . . . ,* p. 276.

7. Goguel, Jean, *Sur l'origine mécanique de la schistosité,* Bull. Soc. géol. France, 5 sér., vol. 15, pp. 509–522, 1945.

8. Oftedahl, C., Deformation of Quartz Conglomerates in Central Norway, Jour. Geol., vol. 56, pp. 476–487, 1948. (Quoted by Fairbairn, *Structural Petrology of Deformed Rocks,* 2nd ed., 1949.)

9. Fourmarier, Paul, *Essai sur la distribution, l'allure et la genèse du clivage schisteux dans les Appalaches,* Ann. Soc. géol. Belgique, vol. 60, pp. M 69–131, 1936.

———, *L'étirement des roches et la schistosité,* Bull. Soc. géol. France, 5 sér., vol. 19, pp. 569–575, 1949.

———, *Schistosité et grande tectonique,* Ann. Soc. géol. Belgique, vol. 76, pp. B 275–301, 1953 (and many other publications).

10. Sander, Bruno, *Gefügekunde der Gesteine,* Springer, Wien, 1950.

Schmidt, W., *Tektonik und Verformungslehre,* Borntraeger, Berlin, 1932.

Knopf, A. E., and Ingerson, E., Structural Petrology, Mem. Geol. Soc. America, no. 6, 1938.

Turner, F. J., Mineralogical and Structural Evolution of Metamorphic Rocks, Mem. Geol. Soc. America, no. 30, 1948. (See chapters 9 to 14.)

Fairbairn, H. W., *Structural Petrology of Deformed Rocks* 2nd ed., Addison Wesley, 1949.

11. Turner, F. J., Griggs, D., Miller, W. B., Handlin, J. W., Chih, C. S., Borg, Iris and Sosoka, J., Deformation of Yule Marble. Part I: Compression and extension experiments at 10,000 atm., room temperature; Part II: Predicted Fabric Changes; Part III: Observed Fabric Changes; Part IV: Effects at 150°.

Turner, F. J., Preferred Orientation of Calcite in Yule Marble, Amer. Jour. Sci., vol. 247, pp. 593–621, 1949.

12. In the treatise cited, Fairbairn concludes the chapter devoted to the deformation of quartz (p. 133) as follows: "From the foregoing discussion of quartz, the reader will doubtless have concluded that there is as yet no accepted theory of a general nature that will explain all the known facts of its orientation."

13. Phemister, Th. C., The Use of Quartz as an Index of Movement in Tectonites of Metamorphic Origin, Nineteenth Internat. Geol. Congr., Algiers, 1952, fasc. 3, pp. 113–116, 1953.

14. Fairbairn, H. W., Pressure Shadows and Relative Movements in a Shear Zone, Trans. Amer. Geophys. Union, vol. 31, pp. 914–916, 1950.

15. Demay, A., *Microtectonique et tectonique profonde,* Mém. Carte géol. France, Paris, 1942.

16. An analogous disposition has been described by Shainin, V. E., Conjugate Sets of Enéchelon Tension Fractures in the Athens Limestone at Riverton, Virginia, Bull. Geol. Soc. America, vol. 61, p. 509, 1950.

17. Wilson, G., Mullion and Rodding Structures in the Moine Series of Scotland, Proc. Geologists' Assoc. London, vol. 64, part II, pp. 118–151, 1953.

18. Cloos, H., *Zur Mechanik der Randzonen von Gletschern, Schollen und Plutonen,* Geol. Rundschau, vol. 20, pp. 66–75, 1929.

————, *Plutone und ihre Stellung im Rahmen der Krustenbewegungen,* Sixteenth Internat. Geol. Congr., Washington, 1933, vol. 1, pp. 235–253, 1936.

19. Cizancourt, H. de, in: Inst. Franç. Pétrole et Ann. Combust. Liquides, Revue, vol. 2, no. 1, pp. 3–24; no. 2, pp. 81–98; no. 3, pp. 141–154; no. 5, pp. 252–254, 1947.

20. Becker, G. F., see work cited in reference 1 of this Chapter, especially p. 36.

21. Wegmann, C. E., *Note sur le boudinage,* Bull. Soc. géol. France, 5° sér., vol. 2, pp. 477–491, 1932.

Corin, F., *A propos du boudinage en Ardennes,* Bull. Soc. Belge de Géol., Paléont. et Hydrol., vol. 42, pp. 101–117, 1932.

See also reference 1 in Chapter I, p. 281.

22. See, for example, E. Haug, *Traité de Géologie,* vol. 1, p. 232, Paris, 1907; Albert Heim, *Geologie der Schweiz,* vol. 1, p. 81, Leipzig (Tauchnitz), 1922.

23. Gosselet, *L'Ardenne,* Mém. Carte géol. France, p. 62, 1888.

24. Friedel, G., *Observations sur les cristaux de sel gemme difforme,* Bull. Soc. Franç. Minéral., vol. 53 (Livre jubilaire), pp. 122–156, 1930.

CHAPTER FIVE

Study of Rock Deformation: Discontinuous Deformations

Definition—Faults, throw, slickensides, breccia—Mylonites—Deformation of the margins of a fault—Morphologic role of a fault—Age—Nature of the movement—Limitation of sedimentary basins by faults.

THE DEFORMATIONS that we have just studied are continuous; that is, initially adjacent points within a mass of rock remain so throughout deformation. However, discontinuous deformations also play a great role among tectonic phenomena. Faults, surfaces of overthrust, and stretching are examples of discontinuous deformation. Discontinuous deformation takes place along a surface. Two initially adjacent points, situated on opposite sides of such a surface, will be displaced during deformation. On the other hand, the material on either side of this surface undergoes continuous deformation. There may be other surfaces of discontinuous deformation (they may even be quite close to each other), but deformation cannot be discontinuous throughout an entire mass. No matter how numerous the discontinuity surfaces may be, they separate blocks within which the deformation is continuous.

After deformation, the two masses on opposite sides of the surface of discontinuity may either be separated from each other or may be in contact, but naturally they can not penetrate one another, at least without solution (stylolites). The case in which the two walls are in contact is by far the most important in tectonics. For practical purposes, we may describe discontinuous deformations as the result of the slipping against each other of the two walls, which remain in contact during movement. However, the form of the surface generally deviates from a plane, in which case the two walls cannot remain in complete contact with each other. Although secondary deformations may

64

widen the zones of contact, cavities may exist locally after the movement. During movement, projections from the walls, upon which the maximum pressure bears, may be broken into fragments, which constitute a fault breccia.

We often find that numerous discontinuity surfaces succeed one another within a thin zone situated between two almost intact masses. Such a zone is called a crush zone.

Inversely, if a slight thickness of rock between two intact walls undergoes a very intense continuous deformation, the overall result is as if there existed a single surface of discontinuity or a crush zone. Relative movements along discontinuity surfaces may also accompany intense continuous deformation. The point of view for such an intense crush zone or stretch zone depends somewhat upon the scale adopted. In detail we may attempt to unravel the slips and the plastic crushing although things are often so complex that it is difficult to do so. On a regional scale, however, the thickness of a crushed zone is negligible; the movement takes place almost as if there existed a single surface of discontinuity.

Vertical or steeply inclined surfaces of discontinuous deformation are called faults. In popular language, this term is used in a different sense to mean a simple fissure or a more or less open breach. Beginners are sometimes confused for this reason. However, the geologic definition of the word fault is perfectly clear; it implies the relative movement of two rock-masses along a surface. It also implies that, in general, the walls have remained in contact and may even be perfectly cemented together. Closely connected with the definition of fault is the notion of displacement—the distance that the two walls have moved relative to each other. According to this definition, the displacement has an orientation and a direction which in general we specify by referring to the upthrown wall and the downthrown wall, both terms being used in only a relative sense, as it is impossible to define the absolute movement of either wall. To define the direction of the relative movement, we also use the French word *regard*. A fault with a north *regard* is a fault whose north wall is downthrown.

The displacement in the fault plane may be oriented at any angle, from horizontal to the line of greatest dip. A fault with a horizontal displacement is often called a strike-slip fault or a transverse fault (French: *faille de décrochement*), although this French term may assume another meaning in folded regions, as we shall point out in Chap. 10. When the only reference planes we have available for determining the relative displacement of the two walls are horizontal (the general case in sedimentary terrains), a horizontal displacement is very difficult to recognize, and we must often be satisfied with measuring the vertical component of the displacement, or the "vertical displacement," or, more accurately, the projection of the displacement on the normal to the beds if they are inclined (the stratigraphic throw). If the surface of the fault is inclined, we immediately derive from the vertical displacement the component of the displacement along the line of the greatest dip. But we should always keep in mind the possibility that a horizontal component of displacement may pass completely unnoticed.

It is important to establish the direction of fault surfaces since they are often nearly planar and may extend regularly for a considerable distance (whether in a free, simple fault or a more or less complex crush zone). The *strike* is the compass direction of a horizontal line in the fault plane (for example: N30°E, or NNE); strike is also given as an azimuth, counting from the north and going toward the east. Two opposite directions or two azimuths differing by 180° are equivalents. Miners formerly used a division of the semi-circumference into 12 hours, measuring clockwise from the north (6 hrs. = EW, 3 hrs. = SW, and so on). This practice is no longer in use.

If the dip of the fault plane is also known, the angle that it makes with the horizontal is indicated; a complete dip notation includes the direction toward which the surface is inclined (for example, strike: N30°E; dip: 70°SE). There is no uniformly established usage for indicating the direction of movement, but it seems natural to define it as the angle that it makes with a horizontal line in the plane of the fault (Fig. 28), also indicating the sense of movement.

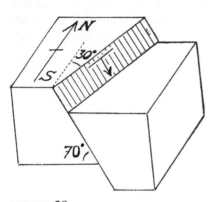

FIGURE 28

Definition of the strike and dip of a fault (N30°E, dip 70°SE).

Displacement is not constant throughout the whole length of a fault; it may vary progressively to the point of disappearance. A change in the direction of displacement may be due to the existence of two faults close together with displacements in contrary directions, or due to the fact that a fault moved first in one direction and then in the opposite direction. But very often there is a constant horizontal component of displacement, in which case the apparently variable direction of the vertical throw (or of the displacement perpendicular to the beds, if they are not horizontal) is due only to slight variations in the direction of displacement, which may fluctuate around the horizontal, or due to undulations of the beds prior to faulting (Fig. 29).

FIGURE 29

The horizontal component of the displacement explains how the apparent vertical throw can change direction (the arrows indicate the true displacement).

A surface of discontinuity that is nearly horizontal may be termed a "flat fault," a "surface of overthrust," a "surface of stretch," or simply an "abnormal contact," a term which implies no interpretation. The notion of overthrust assumes the superposition of two masses, initially separated from one another, by motion along a surface of discontinuity. On the other hand, the term "surface of stretch" is used for a surface approximately parallel to the stratification in a sedimentary series, if the movement along it causes the disappearance of one or several beds or reduces their visible thickness. We shall return to these later.

The presence of a fault is commonly deduced from observations on the position of the different formations. It appears then as an hypothesis—often so probable that it is almost certain—for systematizing the observations. We shall postpone discussion of this case to the next chapter in order to consider here the case in which the fault, or more generally, the abnormal contact, is directly observable.

A fault is evidently much more easily recognized if it brings into contact different formations than if it is wholly in the same formation.

We shall interpret as a fault (an "abnormal contact" or a "mechanical contact") any contact between two different rocks that is not a result of their genesis or of the genesis of the younger of them. This negative definition obliges us, for completeness, to review all the ways in which a rock may form in contact with another. These are (1) by sedimentary deposition in continuity, owing to a change in the nature of sedimentation, (2) in concordance, following a cessation of sedimentation or even an emergence, or (3) in discordance. In these cases, the stratification of the more recent formation is parallel to the contact; if there is discordance, we sometimes find fragments of the older formation reworked into the more recent, or we may find that the latter penetrates into the hollows or clefts of the substratum. Such characteristics exclude the existence of an abnormal contact.

An eruptive rock may form veinlets or varied injections in the midst of other terranes, in which case the normal contact again presents characteristics that enable its sure recognition. Abnormal contact certainly exists between two sedimentary rocks if they are separated by a surface transverse to the two stratifications.

The positive characteristics that enable us to recognize displacement along a surface of discontinuity are the same whether the rocks in contact are the same kind or not. However, these characteristics may not be perceptible; for instance, a fault is normally invisible in the midst of a homogeneous clay. It is in especially hard rocks, such as limestones, that traces of slips are recognizable.

Normally the surface of the fault has remained a surface of discontinuity; its distinction from joints, which have no displacement, may be a very fine one. Faults are generally more marked and especially more continuous and may or may not be related to one of the fissure directions that are periodically

FIGURE 30. *Horizontal fault mirror in a core of the Fitou boring. [Cf. Destombes, J. P., Les sondages de Fitou (Aude). Public. Bureau Rech. Géol. et Géophy., no. 7, Paris, 1949.] On the surface, polished by the movement, the striations produced by hard particles of the two walls (in relief or hollow) show that the movement of the missing part took place from right to left. The gray spot with irregular contour is a film of calcite, later deposited on the fault plane. The displacement is unknown, but may be very slight. [Photo by Bachelet].*

repeated. But above all, fault surfaces always show traces of slipping; some, in particular, show a polish and are thus called "fault mirrors" or slickensides (Fig. 30). Such surfaces are often fluted or striated, indicating the direction of movement and, at times, even its sense. By passing our fingers along the flutings in alternate directions, it is very easy to decide in which direction slip is less impeded by surface roughness. Perfectly smooth fault mirrors have been observed for displacements as small as 50 cm (for example, in the Permian of the Dôme de Barrot, near Léouvé, Alpes Maritimes). A fault surface is rarely entirely simple. In places several surfaces very close together cause little scales ending in a very sharp dihedral angle on certain of their edges. Often the striations of these surfaces are not parallel; this we can explain by assuming a series of successive movements in slightly different directions.

Locally a fault may be, or may have been, open. The space is often filled with fragments torn from the walls and later crushed by the movement. In general, they have been subsequently cemented, producing a fault breccia distinguished by the following characteristics: angular, unsorted fragments, generally all of the same nature; the cementation is sometimes later than the movement and may result from the deposition of calcite by circulating water.

However, it is not unusual to find slickensides cutting the breccia; all transitions between a true fault breccia and a crush zone may be found. These direct traces of crushing are very valuable in distinguishing fault breccia from slope breccias, which often preserve cavities and form superficial deposits on slopes. Faults often facilitate the circulation of underground waters. The intersection of a fault with the surface is often marked by large springs (which may indicate but by no means prove the existence of a fault). Old circulations have often been the cause of a clay, calcite, or more complex deposit. Certain metalliferous veins mark faults (but not all, since many occupy fissures). Sometimes the vein filling the fault is harder than the surrounding rocks and remains in relief when exposed, but more often the products of crushing, more or less mixed with clay, constitute a zone of less resistance. It has often been found, without being understood, that in the immediate vicinity of a fault, massive limestones have acquired a greater resistance to erosion and solution, which enables them to remain in relief on the slopes.

The term mylonite, although it has at times been extended to include all rocks that present traces of tectonic crushing, essentially designates a pulverized eruptive rock in which it is not possible to recognize the constituent minerals (quartz, feldspar, and so on) except under the microscope.[1] A mylonite of granular rock may present a deceptive appearance of very fine grained rock, but in general we observe transitions in the field; in any event, microscopic examination enables us to make a sure diagnosis.

Mylonites form thin bands (a few meters or tens of meters thick) that can sometimes be traced for long distances (more than 100 km in the Limousin) but which are not very continuous. Besides easily recognizable mylonites, rocks of approximately normal appearance may have undergone a homogeneous deformation which must also be considered. The same overall deformation may have been produced either by the thorough crushing of a thin layer of mylonite or by a slight homogeneous deformation of a great mass of rock.

Mylonites were evidently produced by faulting at depth and, consequently, under such pressure that they could at no moment remain open. Thus they are characteristic of deformation in a zone somewhat deeper than the zones in which breccia and slickensides are produced.

In even deeper zones, where eruptive rocks are incompletely consolidated, faults or other abnormal contacts provide the channels through which injections of eruptive rocks are forced. Such channels are, of course, completely obliterated by the injections. In Chapter 18, we shall return to the conditions under which it is possible to study the deep tectonics wherein mechanical deformation and magmatic phenomena play a part. We must keep in mind that the zone in which mylonites may be produced lies between two depth limits whose values it would be premature to evaluate.

Let us return to the case of a true fault, which originated much nearer the surface. We have seen that instead of being reduced to a simple surface, a fault may occupy a belt of considerable thickness, formed of fault breccia and crush zones. Beyond this fault zone, the rocks that constitute the margins of the fault may present interesting traces of deformation. One of the most striking is the drag that is often observed in a well bedded rock. Drag is of great interest, since it indicates the sense of movement, at least in the direction transverse to the stratification (without regard to the component of displacement parallel to the stratification). Depending on the mechanical properties of the rocks, the thickness of the alternate beds, the distance of the rigid formations, and so on, the drag may extend a greater or lesser distance from the fault; the length of these distortions is not at all proportional to the displacement.

Certain plastic beds have been stretched out along the plane of the fault instead of having broken freely. Thus when tracing such faulted beds, we can observe all stages of transition between fault and flexure, that is, a deformation for which the same overall throw results from a double folding and often from a stretching of the beds. On the Carry coast, near Marseille, a small fault exists in beds of the marine Aquitanian series. A stretched bed of conglomerate with perfectly rounded pebbles occupies the space between the walls of the fault where a fault breccia would ordinarily be expected. However, conglomerates do not always behave like plastics. In those of the Upper Miocene, at Volonne (Basses-Alpes), certain flat faults can be recognized where pebbles were sheared during movement.

Where beds have been dragged and truncated by a fault surface, the stratification is often greatly accentuated, and joints are much more frequent than they are farther away from the fault, separating thinner beds which may even take on a schistose aspect. Similarly, tectonic deformations often exaggerate the stratification where the beds have slipped along bedding planes (Fig. 31). This schistosity, which is only an exaggeration of the stratification, must not be confused with the schistosity that may be caused by the localized mechanical deformation that is sometimes observed in the immediate vicinity of a fault. In a slip parallel to the plane of a fault the directions of maximum elongation and maximum compression are inclined at 45° to the plane of the fault and are located in a plane determined by the direction of movement. The schis-

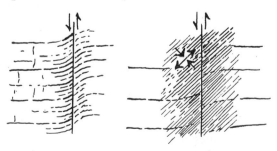

FIGURE 31. *Left. Drag at the margins of a fault, showing exaggeration of the stratification. Right. Development of schistosity in the walls. The arrows indicate the principal directions and the force determined by the friction.*

tosity parallels the direction of maximum extension, which is perpendicular to the direction of maximum compression, that is, at 45° to the plane of the fault, thus indicating direction of displacement. This schistosity which affects the whole mass to a certain thickness is unrelated to the secondary faults that parallel the principal fault and which may extend for a certain distance.

Although the direction of schistosity may be in accordance with a more or less exaggerated drag, the two features should not be confused. They may be distinguished by noting that with distance from the fault, the schistosity thins without changing direction, whereas the stratification bends to resume its normal direction.

So far, we have assumed that we were able to observe the fault and its margins in a transverse section; however, natural or artificial exposures are not always available.

If we are limited to the study of erosion surfaces, the question immediately arises regarding the role of faults in shaping the topography. We have discussed, above, the case of fault scarps formed by the action of a movement posterior to the fashioning of the surface and which made a relief form not yet destroyed by erosion. But such recent faults are to be found only in certain regions; they seem to be entirely lacking in Europe. The only morphologic role of faults is, then, to separate two rock-types that differ in their resistance to erosion. The softer rock may be on the downthrown side if it is the more recent, or it may be on the upthrown side if it is older than the resistant rock that constitutes the other wall. In the second case, an inversion of the relief is produced, and the downthrown side stands out in relief. Both cases may appear alternately along the same fault.

Where a fault separates a hard rock, such as a limestone, from loose formations, such as marls or sands or simply a crushed limestone, their removal by erosion may expose the fault face for a considerable distance. No matter how hard the rock may be, atmospheric corrosion will, in the long run, destroy the polish of the face and obliterate the flutings, but the face may remain quite recognizable. In the Monts de Vaucluse, such fault mirrors bordering masses of Urgonian limestone stripped off the Aptian marls and Albian sands that surmounted them, which can be followed for a length of several kilometers and which, in places, are several tens of meters in height. In certain locations these mirrors appear very rectilinear, whereas in others they may be quite sinuous, with angles (which correspond perhaps to bifurcations of faults) and changes of direction of several tens of degrees.

The age of a fault, like that of any other tectonic movement, can be determined if it can be traced in the stratigraphic series, which serves as a reference for the geologic time scale. A fault is evidently younger than the formations that it affects and older than those that may eventually rest in transgression on an erosion surface that has not been affected by the fault. If a fault is believed to be related genetically with other structures of known age, it is possible to estimate its age indirectly.

When it is possible to determine the age of a fault precisely, it is often found that it has been active several times; the magnitude of the displacement may differ from bed to bed in a single section. Thus the throw of the Baux fault, in Bouches-du-Rhône, is 800 meters in the Cretaceous and 10 meters in the Miocene. An old fault generally constitutes the line of least resistance along which later movements are naturally localized.

Age determinations are particularly accurate if faulting took place while sedimentation was in progress in the region, or if sediments were being deposited on at least one of the fault blocks. Examples of the first case are found in certain parts of the Franco-Belgian coal basin, where faults exist whose displacement diminishes regularly toward the surface, suggesting progressive movement; thus we have proof that the movement extended over quite a long period. However, study of the deposits has shown that subsidence of the basin was not continuous but took place in a series of jolts.

Certain sedimentary basins, especially those that existed in France during the Oligocene, are bordered by faults that were active during sedimentation. This case must not be confused with that of faults younger than the deposits eroded from the upthrown side. Bordering faults that were active during deposition often left traces in the succession of deposits. One of the most striking cases is found in the Oligocene basin of Alès (Gard), where each of the movements of the fault is indicated by a bed of very coarse breccia in the midst of fine lacustrine sediments.[2] The repeated occurrence of these breccias at different levels indicates at last eight principal phases of movement. It is uncertain, however, whether all phases of movement were sufficiently strong for the breccia to extend as far as the zone of outcrops at a distance of several kilometers. We have already noted the violence of movement that the nature of these breccias indicates. These observations enable us to consider the movement of a fault as continuing during a long period but with numerous displacement episodes, some of which are very sharp.

During certain earthquakes, the almost instantaneous movement of certain faults has been accurately recorded, and amplitudes of one or several meters have been measured. For example, at the time of the San Francisco earthquake, in 1906, the horizontal displacement along the San Andreas fault was several meters, which seems to have been the case during earlier quakes. Certain mechanical considerations[3] suggest that faulting normally occurs as a series of successive movements, which are very sharp but of low amplitude and which may be repeated throughout a very long period. The polish of fault mirrors seems to result from such rapid movements; in cases where a fault has moved slowly, a polished surface is not produced. Each fault mirror probably resulted from a movement of quite low amplitude (a meter or even less).

This concept of fault action explains, among other peculiarities, why traces of different movements are almost always observed, such as non-parallel striations and the existence of several adjacent fault mirrors that cut each other at very acute angles. Since fault mirrors originate and acquire their polish during the course of a single phase of movement of very low amplitude, it follows that some fault mirrors must correspond to secondary movements that can be neglected in the overall interpretation. Such is the case for mirrors in the heart of argillaceous rocks which disappear perhaps in the long run and are often characteristic of secondary movements near the surface, such as land slips, though the passage of important old faults may not be marked by anything. The intensity of crush phenomena, marked by the thickness of the breccias, furnishes no better index of the amount of fault displacement than does the formation of fault mirrors.

Faults vary in importance, this importance being evaluated by the visible length of outcrop, or by the displacement. In certain deformed rocks it is possible to recognize, on the scale of the thin section or hand specimen, little surfaces of discontinuity that indicate the mode of deformation of the rock. However, except for jumbled zones of very limited thickness, there is no transition between such surfaces and true faults; we sometimes find faults that have throws less than a meter and which are quite visible at the contact between two very different formations. We can see there, or in mining operations where a bed is being followed, that the interval between these faults has remained perfectly continuous. Then we find all sizes of displacement, though the most important faults are rarely simple but are made up rather of sheaves of secondary fractures. The most important faults separate regions whose evolution has been different, particularly with regard to the accumulation of sediments in depressed regions having no equivalents in the uplifted areas. Such faults then appear as major features of the regional geography. In France, faults of this sort bound the Rhenish trench and the Limagne; in East Africa, the great fractures of the Rift extend from Mozambique through the Great Lakes, Abyssinia, and the Red Sea, even to Syria, a distance of over 6000 km. Certain relationships exist between certain faults and volcanic phenomena; however, we shall return to these later.

Notes and References

1. Raguin, E., *Géologie du granite,* Paris (Masson), 1946. (See especially p. 83.)

2. Goguel, J., *Les brèches urgoniennes d'Alès* (Gard), Bull. Soc. géol. France, 5ᵉ sér., vol. 6, pp. 219–236, 1936.

3. Goguel, J., *Introduction à l'étude mécanique des déformations de l'Écorce Terrestre,* Mém. Carte géol. France, 2nd ed., Chap. 18, Paris, 1948.

CHAPTER SIX

Observation of Displacements of Rocks

Inclination of beds—Dip and its measurement—Causes of error—Direction of beds—Usable criteria—Order of succession of beds, reference horizons—Horizontal variations of facies, recognition of paleogeographic zones—Recording of results on topographic map—Observation of axes; perspective deformations—Structural surface—Results of subsurface work and well logs—Study of a metamorphic region; statistical method; interpretation of complications of detail.

IN THE FOREGOING chapters, we have discussed how we can recognize whether or not the rock being studied, either in the field or in the laboratory, has undergone a change of form. Such studies, at least theoretically, can be made on all kinds of rocks, including eruptive rocks, but they are significant only for rocks that have undergone a relatively severe deformation.

Within a sedimentary series, it usually is possible to reconstruct the initial arrangement of the beds and, in particular, the relative positions of the different horizons. By comparing this reconstruction with the present arrangement, we deduce the displacement undergone by each part of a given rock under study. In order to understand the range of such observations (which supply most of the data used in the study of the tectonic deformations of a sedimentary series) it suffices to review what we can determine regarding the initial arrangement of such formations. For all the data on the initial state, there is corresponding information on the displacements undergone.

We know that strata are originally horizontal. Where strata are inclined, we may conclude that they have been tilted. The attitude of the plane of stratification is defined by the magnitude of its dip (inclination) in the downslope direction and by the dip azimuth (Fig. 32). On a map, the projection of this line of steepest slope is generally accompanied by that of a horizontal line in the plane (strike). Sometimes, more or less strong dips are indicated by the relative lengths of the dip arrow and the base line. For vertical beds, the sign —·— may be adopted; a cross + is used to indicate horizontality. Dip is expressed by indicating first the inclination and then the direction (or azimuth); example: dip (of) 30° (toward) S20°W. For vertical beds we should give the direction of the horizontal line in the plane, which introduces a discontinuity: from the dip 80° toward the NE we pass to vertical beds striking NW-SE which is not very rational.

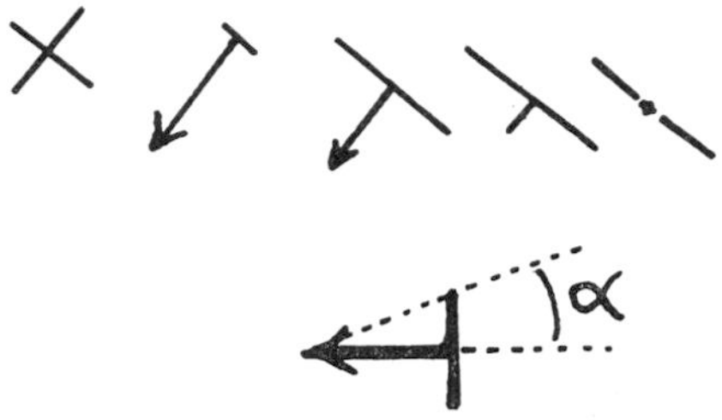

The measurement of dip depends on the manner in which the stratification appears (the same conditions prevail for a plane of schistosity, a joint, or a fault). If the surface of a bed is acces-

FIGURE 32

Graphic representation of dip (left to right, dips increase from horizontal to vertical). To indicate the value of the dip, the dip symbol is drawn such that the angle α, shown in the lower part of the figure, graphically represents the dip angle.

sible and is sufficiently smooth, a compass with a straight edge may be placed on it, its azimuth read, and a measurement made of the maximum angle between the horizontal plane of the compass and the surface of the bed (Fig. 33).

FIGURE 33

Measurement of dip on cleared surface of a bed.

For making this measurement, a number of instruments have been devised, but they are of little practical value, since the surface to be measured is usually inaccessible. In general, the stratification of a series of beds is best recognized in section. If the surface of the outcrop is not flat, it is easy to determine whether the eye is or is not in the projection of a stratification plane; if it is, the plane appears as a straight line, and if not, it reproduces, more or less attenuated by perspective, the irregularities of the surface along which the outcrop is cut (Fig. 34). The observer moves into a position such that the bedding plane being measured appears as a straight line. The direction of the plane is defined by the eye, then the line is determined. Several cases may arise depending on whether the horizontal and the line of greatest slope meet or do not meet in the visible part of the plane. If the horizontal lies in the

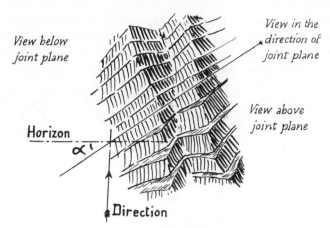

FIGURE 34. *Measurement of dip on truncated beds.*

visible part of the plane, its position can easily be checked with a leveling instrument (clinometer, lyre level, etc.) and its direction determined with a compass. The slope is then measured in an azimuth perpendicular to this, giving the dip of the bed. A direct reading may be taken using a clinometer held perpendicular to and in the line of sight of the plane, oriented parallel to its visible part. The direction is not so well determined if the maximum slope is sought, in order to determine the direction of dip.

The handiest, most accurate instrument for making dip measurements is the Peigné compass. Dips can be easily measured even if neither the horizontal nor the line of greatest slope lies in the observed plane. A plumb-line at-

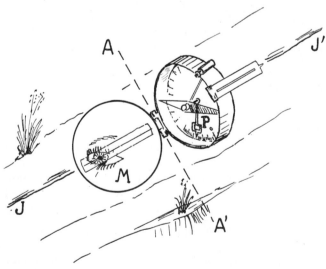

FIGURE 35. *Use of Peigné compass for measurement of dip.*

tached to its axis makes it easy to align the limb vertically (the plumb-line swings freely without moving away from the limb), and a mirror, M, in the cover, pivots around an axis A-A', parallel to the limb. When the image of the eye can be seen in the mirror as the observer sights on the stratification plane, the mirror is then perpendicular to the line of sight. Moreover, if the limb is vertical, and if the axis of the instrument covers the stratification line under study, the plumb-line then indicates the true dip. The direction of the limb is the direction of the dip. It may be checked and measured in a second operation (Fig. 35).

Other instruments and other methods could be employed: as soon as the apparent dips α_1 and α_2 and the azimuths A_1 and A_2 of two lines situated in the plane of the faces have been measured, the value of the dip and its direction are determined, both of which can be calculated by a very simple working-drawing (Fig. 36).

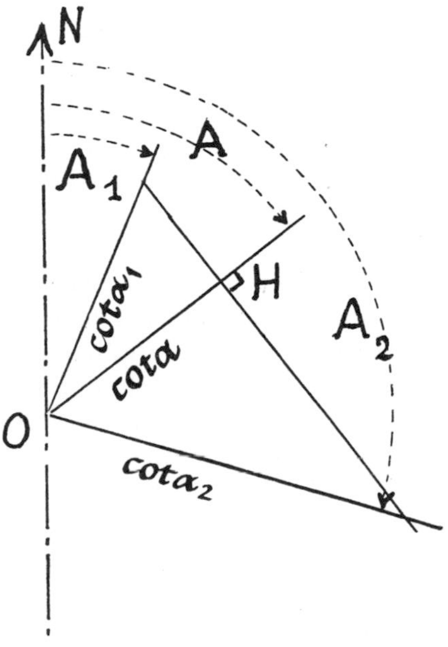

In certain precision surveys, the geologist merely checks and marks three points, which do not fall in a straight line, but which lie in the same plane, and leaves to a topographer the task of surveying them with a transit and calculating the dip of the bed. By choosing points sufficiently far apart (some tens of meters), it is possible to greatly reduce the error introduced by small local undulations and to establish a median figure for the dip. It must be remembered that when the amount of the dip is very small, its direction cannot be determined very accurately.

It is often necessary to determine the direction of a line, such as a fold axis, which is defined by its plunge (the angle between the axis and the horizontal) and its direction (the azimuth of the axis). (See Fig. 37.)

FIGURE 36

Graphic calculation of the dip of a bed when the apparent dips, α_1 and α_2, and the azimuths, A_1 and A_2, are known for two lines situated in the plane of the bed.

Frequently the direction to be defined is traced in a determined plane whose dip is known (for example, striations in the plane of a fault or of ripplemarks on a stratification plane, etc.). Then in this plane we then measure the angle between the horizontal and the direction considered (in descending sense), which is designated in English by the term *pitch*,[1] for which we propose the French equivalent *inclinaison*. The formulas of spherical trigonometry, a simple working drawing, or better still, Wulff's stereographic net, well

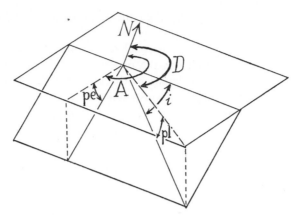

FIGURE 37. *Definition of the direction (D) and plunge (pl) of a line. In the dip plane (pe), and in the azimuth plane (A), this direction may be defined by its pitch (i).*

known to crystallographers, can be used to convert dip and pitch measurements to measurements of plunge with its direction.

The measurement of dip requires only a little practice, but it is sometimes difficult to recognize the stratification. Schistosity of mechanical origin is commonly mistaken for stratification, since schistosity is often more pronounced than stratification. When in doubt, a careful search should be made for beds that differ in either composition or in color from the surrounding beds. Such beds by themselves indicate the stratification in a sure manner. In crush zones it is possible to mistake the direction of slickensiding for stratification.

In certain cases, the stratification may not have originally been perfectly horizontal. We know, for instance, that the coarse, suspended materials carried into a lacustrine delta sink the moment they reach the calm water of the lake and are sometimes deposited in beds that are inclined at quite a large angle, as much as 30° (Fig. 38). For an old formation the nature of the deposits and especially their lateral passage to free lacustrine sediments should make us suspect the initial horizontality of the deposit.[2] Inversely, in Quaternary formations (sands or gravels), inclined strata furnish the best evidence for lacustrine deposition. For example, at Fraissinouse, 10 km west of Gap, conglomerates that are inclined at about 15° can be seen alongside the highway. However, the inclination of these beds by no means indicates deformation of the Quaternary. It is the opinion of J. Tricart that through the detailed

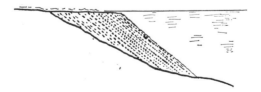

FIGURE 38

Diagram of the formation of a lacustrine delta deposited as dipping beds.

study of lacustrine deposits (noting the dip of flattened pebbles, and other features) it is possible to determine their initial dip with sufficient accuracy to deduce, by comparison with their present dip, the angular displacement that the beds have undergone. Tricart has applied this method to the Pliocene delta of the Var.[3]

Running water may deposit sediments on slopes, but such deposits exhibit cross-bedding. It is often difficult to obtain accurate dip measurements in such a formation, inasmuch as it varies considerably with distance.

After deposition, and in the absence of any tectonic deformation of the beds, stratification may be disturbed by different causes, such as the solution of underlying beds, the differential sinking of clayey-sandy sediments, or submarine slipping of newly deposited beds. Certain near-surface disturbances that are related to the development of relief may also enter the picture, such as slides and solifluction. The geologist must be familiar with these various phenomena, since serious errors of interpretation might be made if they are ignored. For this reason, these phenomena will be the subject of a special chapter (Chap. 8).

In folded regions, sedimentary beds are sometimes overturned. Certain sedimentary peculiarities may enable us to determine the order of deposition. For example, the footwall and hanging wall of a coal bed often have characteristic features; the former are often coarse and perforated by roots, whereas the latter are fine and well bedded (Fig. 6).

In cross-bedding, in principle, it is the younger beds that cut the earlier beds.

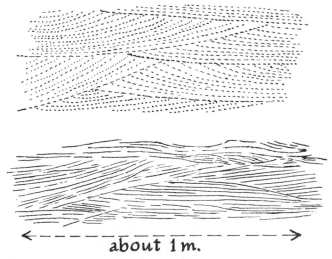

←— — — — — — — — — — — — — —→
about 1 m.

FIGURE 39. *Cross-bedding. Above, Normal case. Below, Exceptional case in which certain beds wedge out against earlier deposits. (Middle Jurassic of Yorkshire, sketched from photograph.)*

But sometimes, if more rarely, we see beds end suddenly against an older bed (for example, in certain sands of the Estuarian series of the Middle Jurassic in Yorkshire, England). In general, no hesitation is possible. The order of deposition is recognized even in isolated blocks of Vosgian sandstone (Fig. 39).

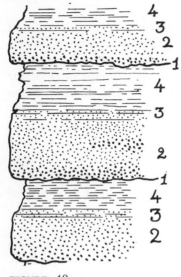

FIGURE 40

Example of graded bedding in the Macigno of the Apennines: (1) surface of discontinuity, often with concave curvature toward the top; (2) coarse sandstone, sometimes with larger grains (2 to 3 mm) at the base; (3) the sandstones are divided into very flat plates and pass progressively to marls; (4) shaly marls. The thickness of each of the complex beds may vary from a decimeter to a meter. (Do not confuse with the cyclothems represented in Fig. 6, page 19, which result from a different phenomenon and are to be observed in littoral or very shallow sediments.)

Certain shaly-sandstone or marly-arenaceous formations exhibit *graded bedding,* in which sandstone bands that rest on an irregular surface grade progressively upward to shales (Fig. 40). The coarsest elements of the sandstones are often found at the base, but are also found at other levels within a given sandstone bed. Signorini has successfully used this criterion to determine the succession of the macigno beds in the Apennines.

Recent discoveries in oceanography enable us to explain the origin of graded bedding as follows: The terrigenous materials (clay and sand) are deposited on the continental slope where the water is normally immobile. But since the slope of these deposits becomes quite steep, they become unstable. For fortuitous reasons, or on the occasion of an earthquake, slides are produced, and their moving mass mixes with the water, forming a suspension. Since the suspension is heavier than water, it tends to descend along the bottom; its speed produces a turbulence which maintains the suspension and which may appreciably erode the bottom, especially in the canyons that cut the continental slope. These *turbidity currents* may travel hundreds of kilometers, stopping only on a flat bottom. The materials carried in suspension are deposited progressively; the coarser quartz grains settle first and the muds last. Where the turbidity currents are formed there may be several successive waves in a given current, producing irregularities in the granulometry of the deposited quartz.

Geologists obtained an indication of the size that turbidity currents may attain when, in 1929, an earthquake set a turbidity current into motion causing several breaks in a number of transatlantic telephone cables. Since the times and locations of the breaks were recorded, it was possible to calculate the velocity and extent of the current. This current swept a breadth of 250 km and travelled a distance of 550 km, from a depth of 3500 m to 5200 m, in 13 hours. Since its remaining speed at that time was 22 km per hour, it was able to propel itself much farther. We know nothing of the tonnage moved by this apparently exceptional phenomenon, which occurred south of Newfoundland.

Turbidity currents, traces of which may be recognized by their graded bedding, appear to be one of the essential mechanisms of sedimentation by which the distribution of terrigenous materials in deep trenches is brought about in a manner such that the surface of the deposits remains nearly horizontal regardless of their thickness. The possibility of recognizing the order of deposition in such deposits, which constitute flysch, is all the more important, since they make up considerable thicknesses with a very monotonous facies and lack the marker beds or the fossiliferous horizons that would be necessary to define successive stratigraphic levels. Even in sandstones that were not deposited by turbidity currents, the marks at the bottom of the layer (load cast) provide a clue to the sense of deposition.

The characteristics that have just been indicated are of constant use in the tectonic analysis of certain regions: foot and hanging walls of coal in folded coal-bearing basins, such as the Franco-Belgian basin; cross-bedding in Scotland; and graded bedding in the Apennines. Other indices are of rather exceptional use and at times of delicate evaluation.[5]

When seen in profile, ripple marks characteristically exhibit sharp crests separated by rounded hollows, which makes it possible to distinguish them from their counterimprints when they are preserved in sandstones. Certain fossils preserved in the position in which they lived may furnish indications: *Stigmaria* in vegetation footwalls of the coal measures, hippurites layers (observation of Marcel Bertrand in Beausset),[6] occasionally oysters. Fossil evidence, such as reptile footprints preserved in Mesozoic sediments or the burrows of worms or borers (pholads), are additional criteria. The latter are connected with characteristics peculiar to transgressive deposits (the presence of pebbles, the reworking of fragments of the substratum, the penetration of sediments into clefts and so on), which make it possible to distinguish transgressive sediments from those upon which they rest.

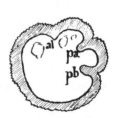

FIGURE 41

Section of a hippurite, seen from above; the two pillars are to the right of the ligamentary ridge. If the hippurite were turned over, the inverse arrangement would be seen.

Occasionally, other indications give clues as to the order of deposition, such as the impressions made by pebbles falling into a soft formation (Fig. 42). However, the most valuable characteristic for the reconstruction of the initial state consists of the superposition (in a determined order) of beds that can be recognized individually on the basis of either their fossils or their facies. The

knowledge of thicknesses or of the vertical distances that separate two determined horizons in normal series makes it possible to arrive at a very
accurate determination of the present form of mineral masses.

FIGURE 42

Deformation of
beds adjacent
to a pebble.

Even under the most favorable conditions, we are unable
to recognize accurately the initial position of a random outcrop in the series. Certain stages may present a very monotonous facies for a considerable thickness, and there is great
danger of not finding exactly where the characteristic fossil
should be that would make possible the recognition of each
subdivision. Thus, particular attention should be given to the
search for reference "horizons" whose place in the stratigraphic series can be precisely established. The contacts between two lithologically different formations might be a good choice for such
horizons, since they would then be easily recognized in the field. However,
the change of facies may not be exactly synchronous everywhere. For example,
the contact between the marls and sandstones in the Nummulitic (Eocene)
series in the departments of Basses-Alpes and Alpes-Maritimes certainly varies
in age from one place to another.

Thin, lithologically characteristic beds are often used. There may also be
a rather thin bed with characteristics within a given series, as "marker beds."
It is necessary to be familiar with the rest of the series in order that other beds
having similar characteristics are not mistaken for the marker bed. For example, the limestone at the base of the Nummulitic series of the Alpes-Maritimes is always easy to recognize (Fig. 141), but is of slightly variable age
according to location. The Tithonian limestone in the same region is always
easy to recognize.   ,

In a thick monotonous formation such as the continental clastic facies of
marls and conglomerates, it may be very difficult to locate an outcrop strati-
graphically. If a marker is found—for example, a bed of breccia with particular characteristics—it may be not very continuous, or the same characteristics may be found elsewhere at a different level. The measurement of dips
cannot substitute for precise stratigraphic data.

Sometimes a level may be defined, not by a single facies, but by a succession
of strata whose individual facies would be commonplace but whose order
of succession is characteristic. Finally, the rhythm of a similar succession of
beds may be characteristic, at least in one region, whose area will have to be
determined by careful examination. This method of identifying the different
parts of a particular stratigraphic series is principally used in the interpretation of well logs for which only the electric resistance measured by the Schlumberger "electric log" is available; experience has shown that the more or less
denticulated character of the curve can be quite characteristic.

All in all, the degree of accuracy of geometric data obtainable from
stratigraphic study varies considerably. The structural geologist should constantly check the accuracy of his stratigraphic data. He should seek markers

or valid subdivisions, even within small areas, as well as the lateral changes that might modify the sequence. These stratigraphic checks furnish reliable data for the geometric analysis of forms and, in addition, indicate changes in strata that might provide evidence regarding contemporary deformation.

If worm tracks among the marks on the underside of sandstone beds run at random in many directions, the "flow casts" indicate the direction and the sense of turbidity currents. Whereas ripple marks, which indicate the direction of current flow, may be very variable and due to quite local eddies, Kuenen has shown (especially in the Oligocene "Macigno" of the Apennines) that the direction of "flow casts" is remarkably constant, both within a given bed and from one bed to another, which testifies to the permanence of the regime of the turbidity currents that caused them. This direction is of great interest from the sedimentological point of view; in particular, it is remarkable that the turbidity currents of the Macigno came from the northwest; that is, they followed longitudinally the furrow in which this formation was deposited.

Ten Haaf [7] has shown, moreover, that this direction was sufficiently constant in the autochthone such that the aberrant "flow casts" could be used to determine, in the masses detached from it and embedded in the allochthonous mass scaly clays (*Argille scagliose*), the rotation undergone, which may reach 90°. This rotation not only confirms the allochthonous character of these blocks, but it furnishes information of prime importance in any attempt to reconstitute their emplacement. This new technique may prove quite useful, since flysch-type formations, similar to the Macigno, occur quite frequently in mountain chains.

In the horizontal sense, sedimentary beds are in general very uniform, and, moreover, the facies changes are due to paleogeographic conditions whose details we do not know. The fact that different outcrops in a region where the rocks have been displaced show different facies (or even stratigraphic successions that differ by the presence or absence of a particular stage) is evidently due to the positions that the corresponding units occupied during deposition. But we are ignorant of the paleogeographic distribution of these peculiarities.

Without forming any hypotheses, analogies, or contrariwise differences of stratigraphic composition, we make it possible to bring together a series of outcrops as belonging to a single unit and to separate other units from it. In certain regions of very complex deformation in the Alps just this possibility of grouping together elements from related sources gives us at once some very important information.

We can go further and attempt to reconstruct the original relative disposition of units characterized by the different stratigraphic series that we shall have learned to distinguish. This requires that we take into account any similarities, transitions that might be sometimes observed in a continuous outcrop, and any clues that kinematic reconstruction of movements might provide regarding the initial position of various units, as we shall see in a later chapter.

The paleogeographic synthesis that we are thus led to construct, by placing the presently jumbled units in their original relative positions, concerns the whole chain; studies relative to different parts of the chain mutually support each other by analogy or by virtue of more or less hypothetical considerations.

In such complex problems, it is often assumed, as a first approximation, that the different paleogeographic zones were arranged in belts parallel to the trend of the mountain chain. The possibility of thereby achieving a coherent synthesis justifies this simplifying hypothesis, but it should be looked upon as only a first approximation. Certain zones may have had only a limited extent. Two zones with certain common characteristics are not necessarily on the same alignment, but may constitute transitions on both sides of another zone.

The simplifying hypothesis regarding longitudinal paleogeographic zones is completed by assuming that each of the zones thus defined has undergone the same tectonic evolution, which we often express by saying that the tectonic lines coincide with the isopic lines (that is, lines of the same facies). Here again, we are dealing with only a first approximation, thus it is not unusual for the isopic lines to be oblique to the tectonic lines. That is, in each of the segments cut by tectonic dislocations a progressive variation of the facies is found. This may greatly facilitate the accordance of the different zones whose mutual relations have been effaced by the dislocations. Nevertheless, even in the most favorable circumstances, the reconstruction of paleogeography remains qualitative; it is possible to determine the order in which the various units succeeded one another, but it is not possible to evaluate the distances that separated them. This method has been applied by Jean Boussac to the Nummulitic of the Alps.[8] In a series of maps made by this author, the various units are shown in their initial relative positions in order to show how the facies were related. Regardless of whether additional details may change this synthesis, the principle involved will remain of interest.

After having made a stratigraphic study of an outcrop, and having determined its initial orientation, its relative initial height, its approximate zone of origin, the present position of the outcrop should then be plotted on a topographic map. This step is of prime importance in the study of tectonic deformations, since the quality of the results obtained will depend on the accuracy of this map. If no topographic map is available, it may be necessary to determine the topographic position of the observation points by survey. This method is used in very detailed tectonic surveys for technical purposes, but it is generally preferable to make separate surveys of the topography and of the geology, because of the difficulties involved in topographic surveying. The topographic work may vary from the simple task of completing an existing map to one of making an entirely new map. Coherence and wealth of detail are often preferred over absolute accuracy in establishing the position of each point. Even a large scale map (1:10,000 or 1:20,000) may be inadequate for mapping certain particularly complicated areas. Instead of remaking a map on a large scale, it is often convenient, especially for the study of very steep slopes, to use sketches or photographs to define the position observed. It is always possible to transfer observations from perspective drawings to a regular map. Especially when a map is surveyed by photogrammetry, every geologic notation on photographs may be entered on the map in the course of its completion,[9] but is is also possible to operate at sight, being guided by the details shown on the map. The use of a barometric altimeter, or a surveying instrument, often permits the altitude of observation points to be obtained with greater accuracy than does the use of the map alone; indirectly this may aid in the determination of the planimetric position.

Geologic observations are limited to only a part of the surface under study, inasmuch as Quaternary deposits (moraines, talus, alluvium, and glaciers) conceal certain portions. Despite the abundance of ravines in mountains, vegetation may also hinder observations. Natural outcrops, as well as underground workings, may make observations possible at isolated points or on continuous cleared surfaces. In such cases, it may be possible to determine the continuity of the sedimentary succession. Even in the absence of an established stratigraphy, in the midst of a series impossible to subdivide, regularity of stratification may supply a strong presumption of continuity if the outcrops are well exposed. In other cases, outcrops show a continuous series only over a limited area. Moreover, disturbance may bring any member of a series into contact with some other series. When usable outcrops are discontinuous, we might either assume that they belong to a single series within a certain area or assume the existence of a disturbance. Farther on we shall see how the application of observations may lead to either of these hypotheses.

In a single outcrop we can often observe the manner in which the dip of a bed varies; it may be curved and form what is called a fold. Thus we may directly record the deformation of a certain rock mass. The great scarps of mountainous regions sometimes show several folds, and it is possible to trace the capricious form that an originally horizontal bed has taken. A photograph or a sketch of such a scarp supplies information of great value, but we must keep in mind that we are observing the intersection of the particular bed with the topographic surface and that the complications of this line may result from the irregularities of the topography as well as from the form of the bed. We should always complete such a study by determining the true dip of the beds. This can be approximated, even from a distance, by examining the effect of the irregularities of the surface on the line of the outcrop as has already been explained (p. 76). Binoculars are often necessary for this purpose. The comparison of the directions of intersection of the outcrops on the two sides of a ravine enables us to determine the direction and amount of the dip.

In the absence of outcrops, or where outcrops are sparse, topographic expression may supply valuable indications. A hard bed included between softer layers is generally indicated by an escarpment, and by following this, it is possible to obtain the approximate attitude of the bed. The trace of an outcrop from one side of a valley to the other, or on the two sides of a ridge, supply a first approximation of the dip. Bedding planes are sometimes exposed as a result of the erosion of loose overlying material; the topographic surface then coincides with the surface of the bed and constitutes what is called a *structural surface*. However, the coincidence may be only approximate, since a certain thickness of the hard bed may have been carried away, or parts of the overlying material may remain exposed in the structural hollows.

One of the criteria that enables us to relate a projection or a break in the slope to the presence of a hard bed is the continuity of these projections in the direction of stratification. If the interpretation of an isolated relief form is especially difficult, a look at the whole picture leaves no room for doubt, because of the continuity and the parallelism of the relief forms that mark the successive hard beds. In the absence of a point from which such an overall view may be had, the examination of air photographs may supply the information. There is an advantage to using air photographs, in that they can be viewed stereoscopically. The observation of two photographs, taken from the air at a distance of several hundred meters, furnishes the sensation of an exaggerated relief, as if the terrain had been reduced to a scale close to that of the observer. The same device may be employed with two photographs taken on the ground and on which details may appear that direct examination from the same viewing points could not have brought out.

It often happens that, even in an area of quite limited outcrops, there are to be observed folds in hard beds that consequently present a very small radius of curvature. Naturally such observations should be noted, but we shall have occasion to return later to their interpretation. If at times such folds are important elements of the regional structure that just happen to be at the point observed, they may also be only mere details, resulting from irregular deformation of a relatively small mass with particular characteristics. Along the highway from Saint-Claude to Sept-Moncel, in the Jura, the attention of tourists is called to the sharp fold of a Tithonian bed, called "Chapeau de Gendarme," (Policeman's Hat) that is completely unrelated to the overall form of the fold, which is perfectly discernible at a distance but which has a much greater radius of curvature. When outcrops are sufficiently numerous, a succession of folds of small radius, separated by short distances, may often be seen. Thus, we must not attempt to conclude too much from an isolated observation.

When the distance separating two outcrops that correspond to two members of a stratigraphic series is observed to be less than the normal separation, there is reason to suspect a fault, an abnormal contact, or, more rarely, a mechanical thinning of the series, even if no outcrop exists to expose these distortions, as has been indicated in the foregoing chapter.

In old mountain chains (Precambrian or Paleozoic) or in deeply eroded

Tertiary mountains, such as the Alps, underground workings (tunnels or bore-holes) broaden the domain of possible observations but without radically changing their nature. On the other hand, in basins or tectonic assemblages that have not yet been uplifted and which have been only superficially affected by erosion, boreholes furnish information that is unobtainable at the surface. We are only beginning to understand the importance of structural features, such as overthrusts and shearing, which, originating at great depth, have never reached the surface. The Pre-Riffian nappes (Morocco) and the overthrusts on the border of the Jura would, of course, have remained unknown or scarcely suspected if well logs had not thrown light upon them. The signifi-cance of salt domes could hardly have been understood if observation had been limited to the very small number of them that are exposed in outcrop.

Subsurface studies must be carried out but without neglecting surface observations, which remain essential whenever they are possible. They may be part of a reconnaissance to precisely evaluate a structure of economic interest (mining or public works), for which as accurate a study as possible is neces-sary. This kind of study, whenever possible, should be made by successive approximations; the location of boreholes should be determined at each stage as a function of knowledge already acquired, and of the unanswered questions and of their significance for the projected works. Considering the cost of such reconnaissance work, we can hardly expect it to be carried out just for the solution of a scientific problem.

Theoretically, the exploration of underground caves could supply useful information, but most of these are confined to well-determined calcareous masses, and data from them are of but little importance. On the other hand, certain tunnels have supplied information that has contributed to the solution of problems that the mere study of outcrops would have left unsolved. The Simplon Tunnel has played a fundamental role in the synthesis of the Pennine nappes. The sewer constructed by the city of Toulon toward Cap Sicié brought about the solution of a problem regarding the structure of that cape, proving the overthrusting of the phyllites upon the Permian.[10] The principal practical difficulty is that such work is never done at an opportune time. For example, the Simplon Tunnel contributed to posing a problem; on the other hand, the Cap Sicié sewer was not put through until half a century after the problem had been studied in outcrops. Generally a covering of masonry will prevent any further study along the tunnel once it is completed. So the data from such projects must be gathered during excavation, even if they are not of immediate interest. Numerous underground galleries could be cited for which we do not know the exact section of the covered parts. This renders any tectonic interpretation unreliable, yet one may be needed in planning of other works. Similarly, sections of numerous boreholes are inaccessible when needed.

In order to avoid future difficulties of this sort and the monetary waste in-volved, the *Bureau des Recherches Géologiques et Géophysiques* has been assigned the task, in France, of gathering and preserving the sections of all underground works. Official geologic surveys are fulfilling an analogous mission in most other countries.

In an underground gallery, some difficulty is encountered in the identification of rocks under inadequate lighting; experience has shown that many grave errors may be committed. For this reason, a great many samples should be brought up to be studied in daylight. But the certainty of having an absolutely continuous section available is an inestimable advantage. In practice, since the geologist cannot always be at the spot where work is going on, an agreement should be made between him, the crew foreman, and the surveyor to have a detailed sketch of the walls made as the work progresses (shoring is sometimes finished very rapidly) and to have the necessary samples put aside. We always have large scale maps on which it is easy to record data; however, in the case of certain old mines the orientation of these maps, which may have been related to magnetic north, is doubtful. The situation may be the same for certain wells for which we have a geologic survey of the walls but no indication as to their orientation.

In boreholes, observations are more delicate. When cores are available, they can be studied from the petrographic and stratigraphic point of view and can often be used for plotting dips; but, in general, they are used without knowing their orientation, except through the use of certain quite delicate devices. But certain parts of a well core are always missing, and it is difficult to say whether the rock was simply worn away by friction in the hole, whether certain soft beds were systematically crushed, or finally, whether a highly fissured fault zone was pulverized by the drill.

When equipment is used that destroys the rock, such as rotary drills, observation is a much more delicate problem. Except for the cores obtained, which are sometimes systematically sampled and studied in an attempt to establish the stratigraphic horizon and the dip, observations are very incomplete, since they are based only on the "cuttings" (pulverized rock) brought up, after some delay, by injected water. We are thus led to characterize the rocks traversed by properties that can be measured on the spot, such as resistivity, porosity recorded by the polarization that results from electrofiltration, spontaneous radioactivity, and radioactivity induced by neutron bombardment. This poses the problem of correlating between these parameters and other characteristics by which we customarily define these rocks.

These electric measurements may be made in such a way as to indicate the dip and its orientation, which the examination of cores could not give. In rotary-bored wells, it is necessary to allow for the deviation of boreholes from the vertical.

A new drilling technique (Calyx), now gradually coming into wider use, provides an exploration borehole up to several feet in diameter. This makes it possible for the geologist to go down into the hole in a special gondola and

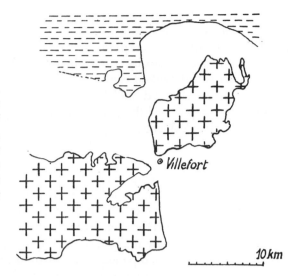

FIGURE 43

The transverse fault of Villefort. Simplified geologic map of the granitic masses (crosses) of Mont Lozere (W) and Borne, intrusive in mica schists. The edge of the gneisses (dashes, to the north) undergoes the same lateral displacement as the granitic masses.

directly plot observations of the walls; in order to be sure of the orientation of the plotting, one or more plumb lines must be set up.

In a region of crystalline or metamorphic rocks, it is much more difficult to find reference points whose initial position is known and which can serve to identify actual displacements. Faults exist whose offset can be estimated by the horizontal or vertical distance that two portions of a granitic mass have been separated. An example of this is the Villefort fault in the Cévennes (Fig. 43), which has displaced the granitic masses of Mont Lozère and Borne some 10 km (G. Fabre).

But in most cases, such easily identifiable reference points are not available. For purely descriptive purposes, we may attempt to plot the directions of schistosity and, eventually, the direction of linear stretch of the schists, and determine the present arrangement of the zones of metamorphism. However, the interpretation of these observations is in part hypothetical. It is often accepted that the schistosity was originally horizontal and that the zones of equal metamorphism normally succeeded one another from the bottom up. The very language employed in the descriptions of overturns, overthrusts, anticlines and synclines implies these assumptions. We shall return later (in Chap. 14) to a discussion of the value to be attached to these hypotheses and the interpretations resulting from them.

Just from the descriptive and cartographic point of view, the plotting of the directions of schistosity and the distribution of facies does not pose any problem at first sight. However, we must keep in mind that metamorphic facies are not defined in such a way as to make it possible to separate them by clear-cut boundaries; so we can only map large overall groups without being able to go into much detail. Moreover, we cannot assume that schistosity is parallel to the contacts, as in the case in sedimentary terranes; there is no reason why schistosity should have this property.

In regions where outcrops are sparse, it is impossible to plot completely the character of the schistosity, especially if complications of detail are numerous. Then a statistical method can be employed, which involves plotting the directions of schistosity and studying their distribution in space, for example, by projecting the poles of the planes of schistosity onto a sphere represented in projection. It is evident that if the complications are composed of folds parallel to a given direction, these poles will then fall along a great circle. By studying limited areas one at a time, it is possible to recognize structures that would not be evident from map study or as a result of direct examination. But it seems evident that the statistical approach contributes no information that would not be gained by the direct examination of folds in a region where outcrops are extensive. However, even under these conditions, a statistical approach may be of some interest, for example, in determining the direction and plunge of an axis from dip measurements by using the method of stereographic projection, which is the most convenient way of solving all problems of directions in space.[11]

Either by direct survey or by statistical analysis, it is possible to recognize the major characteristics of the structure as well as minor folds. We are often faced with the problem of determining the relations that exist between them, in order to know to what extent knowledge of minor folds, which are by far the easiest to see, gives us information regarding the structure as a whole.

It is evident that complications of detail are related to the overall deformation of a given region and that they indicate the degree of compression along a given direction. The localization of compressed regions along any given direction depends on the major structure; in an anticline, the compression is greatest in the lower beds, whereas the reverse is true for a syncline. Such a relation can only be worked out by a relatively complex analysis that would indicate the distribution of the forces at different points. It is sometimes found that this distribution of forces was uniform enough to produce similar complications that are apparent on all scales (in thin section, hand specimen, outcrop, and major structure), but this can by no means be considered the general case. On the contrary, we should expect to find a variety of structural detail within the different parts of a major structure each variation indicating the existence of different stresses.

Notes and References

   1. Clark, R. H., and McIntyre, D. B., The Use of the Terms Pitch and Plunge, Amer. Jour. Sci., vol. 249, pp. 591–599, 1951.
   2. It is interesting to note that when H. B. de Saussure established that certain beds in the Alps had been tilted after their deposition, the proof seemed to him particularly convincing for the Carboniferous conglomerate of Vallorcine, which we now know might

have been deposited on a slope, but he retained some doubt concerning the marly beds in that he thought the mud might have adhered to a sloping surface.

3. Tricart, J., *L'étude tectonique des formations détritiques grossières,* Revue de Géomorph. Dynamique, vol. 4, no. 6, pp. 282–295, 1953.

4. Heezen, Bruce C., and Ewing, Maurice, Turbidity Currents and Submarine Slumps, and the 1929 Grand Banks Earthquake, Amer. Jour. Sci., vol. 250, pp. 849–873, 1952.

5. A great number of these indices have been assembled by R. Shrock, *Sequence in Layered Rocks,* New York (McGraw-Hill), 1948.

6. In determining the position of a hippurite, it is not necessary to observe its apex or little valve; a simple section is enough. In effect, it shows an angular ligamentary ridge and two rounded pillars which, as seen from above, follow each other clockwise, and in an inverse sense if the section is seen from the apical side (Fig. 41).

7. Haaf, E. ten, Tectonic Utility of Oriented Resedimentation Structures, Geologie en Mijnbouw, new ser., vol. 19, pp. 33–35, 1947.

8. Boussac, Jean, *Etudes stratigraphiques sur le Nummulitique alpin,* Mém. Carte géol. France, Paris, 1912.

9. This method has been applied in the Tödi mountain chain, where vertical projections were traced directly by the use of a projection apparatus, Helbling, R., *Studies in Photogeology,* Zürich (Orell-Füssli), 1949. (Four maps and 3 plates of vertical projections.) The same work appeared also in a German edition.

10. Destombes, J. P., *Une coupe géologique du Cap Sicié (Var),* Acad. Sci. Paris, Comptes-rendus, vol. 230, p. 458, 1950.

———, *La nappe du Cap Sicié,* Bull. Soc. géol. France, 6ᵉ ser., vol. 1, pp. 133–138, 1951.

11. The description of methods for this purpose can be found in treatises on crystallography (G. Friedel, *Leçons de Cristallographie,* Paris, 1926) and in modern works on the analysis of structures.

The principle consists of using simultaneously a grid representing the projection on a meridian of the sphere, with parallels and meridians regularly spaced and a sheet of tracing paper that is superposable on the grid but which can revolve on its center. If desired, either a stereographic projection may be used or an equal-area projection, which preserves the significance of the density of the points. A line is represented by one point, a plane by a great circle (superposable on a meridian of the grid for suitable orientation). A plane is best represented by its pole; that is, the line perpendicular to it. Considering the projection plane as horizontal, the division of the corresponding meridian supplies the azimuths from which it is easy to indicate a direction, such as a dip. Owing to the graduation determined by the parallels, it is sufficient to turn the grid until a given meridian passes through two points to obtain the angle of these two directions. The pole of the plane may be located in the same way.

CHAPTER SEVEN

Data of Geophysical Exploration

Range of geophysics—Gravimetry—Telluric currents—Magnetism—Electric well-logging and seismic refraction—Seismic reflection—Significance of seismic refraction for the structure of the earth's crust and for the overall structure of the earth; application to oceanic zones.

THE VARIOUS techniques of geophysical exploration[1] play an increasingly important role among the methods of gaining information for the geologist. The cost of these methods unfortunately limits their use to problems posed by applied geology. Among the different applications, the search for oil is most directly connected with structural problems; as a result, the methods of geophysical exploration used by oil men have a direct bearing on tectonics. On the other hand, investigations carried out for most public works involve only shallow depths and only rarely furnish useful tectonic data. Thus, we must review here how the results of these methods of exploration can be interpreted and what information they can furnish, as well as what must not be expected from them.

It is quite a widespread illusion, perhaps because of the sensitivity of the apparatus employed and the accuracy of certain calculations, that geophysics can provide us with accurate information that would enable us to solve the problems of deep structures, or, in a word, enable us to see right through the rocks. However, we cannot disguise the fact that the data furnished by geophysics, assuming that all instrumental and operational corrections have been properly made, depend only rather indirectly upon the structure being investigated and that these data introduce many other factors. Interpreting a geophysical survey involves visualizing a geologic structure consistent with measurements made at the surface, but in some cases more than one interpretation may fit the data. Geophysics enables us to test a particular hypothesis and show whether or not it is compatible with the measurements. It can only very rarely establish that a given hypothesis is the only possible one.

In establishing an interpretation, constant care should be taken to introduce as few arbitrary hypotheses as possible; the ideal would be to present that which all the possible geologic hypotheses compatible with the measurements obtained must necessarily have in common. It is not always possible to do this, however, and, in most cases, an interpretation is really a synthesis involving geologic considerations or theoretical hypotheses as well as the results of measurements. Elementary honesty toward a reader who often cannot check the geophysical work requires that the geologic hypotheses used be clearly expressed. Especially in the study of scientific questions, in which problems much more complex than those presented by the search for oil are attacked with insufficient means, there are too many examples of papers by authors who seek to justify a hypothesis on the basis of measurements that could just as well lead to another explanation.

In the search for oil, a constant check on the efficacy of geophysics has resulted in the improvement of several methods; they are approximately the same methods as are applied in a general study of geology. In the first place, the generally applied methods of broad reconnaissance are susceptible of covering a fairly large area, if necessary, with a coarse grid (2 or 3 km between data points). Essentially, these methods are expected to give evidence of anomalies that might suggest the location of hidden structural complications. At the same time, these methods give some information regarding the nature of these complications but generally not enough to define them precisely. The simultaneous use of two independent methods helps to reduce the uncertainty. In any event, the reconnaissance results thus obtained call for additional research.

The methods of broad reconnaissance depend on measurements of gravity, telluric currents, and magnetic properties.

Gravity intensity, which is measured with the aid of very sensitive gravimeters,[2] depends solely on the density of the rocks. It is impossible to reconstruct completely the distribution of densities in depth from measurements made at the surface. In particular, the effect of a continuous horizontal layer cannot be found. But with a given anomaly, that is, a deviation from uniformity, it is possible to specify the tonnage and the maximum depth of the anomalous mass. Of course this disturbing mass is only a fluctuation of density added to the density which is assumed constant in each horizontal layer. By trial and error it is possible to seek a probable form for the disturbing mass and thus account for the measurements. Physically, there are an infinite number of solutions; it is not possible, for instance, to distinguish between several parallel faults, one less inclined fault, or a progressive variation of density. But if the geology suggests a hypothesis we can try to test it (Fig. 44).

Density almost always increases with depth, and gravity anomalies are directly connected with structural complications; thus, anticlines give positive (heavy) anomalies and synclines give negative anomalies. But gravimetry is sensitive to all depths, and deep irregularities may have such a marked effect that they almost conceal the effect of more superficial structures. In the Paris Basin, a deep Hercynian granite may manifest itself in the same way as a syncline in the chalk.

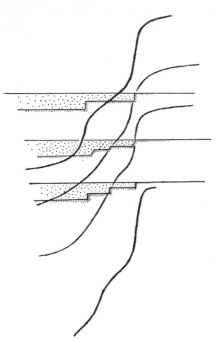

FIGURE 44

Gravimetric interpretation of a fault (east border of Bresse.) Below, Observed gravimetric profile. Above, Three profiles calculated for the arrangements indicated.

The telluric method[3] is based on the study of the distribution of continually varying spontaneous currents that circulate within the earth's crust, in systems that extend over large areas. Sedimentary terranes are much better conductors than crystalline basement rocks; their current distribution thus depends almost entirely on the thickness and nature of the sedimentary terranes. All irregularities of basin filling, especially hidden anticlines, are marked by anomalies. Sometimes it is possible to obtain some indications from the different effects that a given structural complication might have on currents of different directions, but it is difficult to make a quantitative interpretation.

The problems to which magnetic methods apply best are those posed by certain metal mines. Here the exploration may give quite precise evidence regarding the form and inclination of a mineralized mass, provided it contains a small proportion of magnetite or pyrrhotite. It is also possible to locate masses of basic eruptive rocks, such as basalts. When employed along with other methods, in particular gravimetry, magnetic measurements can facilitate the interpretation of certain anomalies. For example, we may consider an anomaly that is due to heavy nonmagnetic rocks as indicating the presence of an anticline, whereas if both magnetic and gravimetric anomalies were obtained, the presence of eruptive rocks may be considered more probable.

Magnetic measurements made at the surface have often been used for the detailed study of structures, with stations very close together. The development of airborne magnetometers, which are more sensitive than apparatus used on the ground and less subject to the influence of accidental disturbances, has appreciably broadened the scope of magnetic methods. It will soon be possible to study vast sedimentary basins very rapidly. It may be admitted that magnetic anomalies depend essentially on the position of the crystalline basement, whose depth can be calculated and whose irregularities are to be recorded. Dikes and other eruptive rocks have a very marked effect, but it is evident that important detailed structural complications may pass entirely unobserved.

Essentially these three methods have as their object the localization of complications in detail. They furnish hardly any evidence concerning the distribution of beds in depth. In order to study the latter to a first approximation assuming horizontal stratification, but with the possibility, with some complications, of recording the dip or even other irregularities, essentially two methods are available: electric sounding[4] (resistivity surveys) and seismic refraction.[5] The first method consists of studying the distribution in the ground of a continuous current for varying lengths of the sounding line; seismic refraction involves measuring the travel time of a seismic wave for different distances

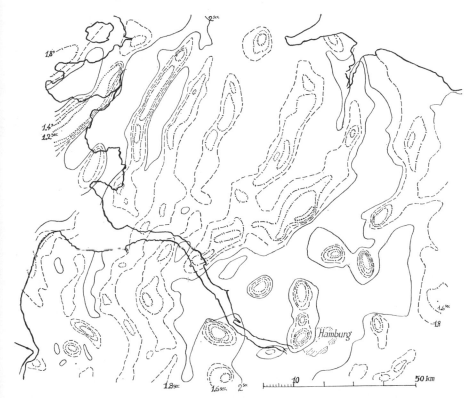

FIGURE 45. *Survey by seismic refraction of a part of Hanover (after the 1/500,000 scale map published by the Reichsamt für Bodenforschung); measurements by K. Röpke and W. Haubold, Gesellschaft Seismos. The map gives the travel times of sound waves over a course of 4 km. In the north, anticlinal wrinkles in which the high speed beds approach the surface and give shorter travel times. In the south, salt domes appear.*

between the point of explosion and the receiver. In both cases, the depth of investigation increases with the spread. The calculations are very simple for the seismic method, but they are so difficult for electric sounding (resistivity surveys) that we should limit ourselves to comparing curves calculated *a priori* (for a succession of layers) with the measured curves. These establish the changes with depth of the characteristic property; either electric resistivity or seismic velocity. In both cases, a bed having properties intermediate to those of its neighbors may easily escape attention if it is not very thick in relation to its depth, even then the exact position of the transitions cannot be determined, but only the general arrangement of the variations.

However, the information obtained is very valuable and, through quantitative estimates of depth, completes the methods of general exploration cited earlier. In particular, telluric exploration campaigns are always completed by electric sounding, which utilizes some of the same apparatus. These methods of investigation in depth are very easily converted into reconnaissance methods; we need only determine the best spread and move from place to place. Electric sounding results in a "resistivity map," which gives us information to a depth that is a function of the length of the spread employed. Seismic refraction uses the fan-method in which, for the sake of economy, each explosion is recorded by a series of receivers placed in a circle at a determined distance from the shot point. By properly choosing this distance (with the aid of preliminary profiles), it is possible to express all the variations in depth of a horizon characterized by relatively rapid wave speed. The plains of Hanover and those of neighboring regions have been completely explored by fan shooting, employing a spread of about 4 km. This technique revealed a great number of tectonic complications, anticlinal wrinkles, and salt domes, which have since been studied by other methods (Fig. 45).

When an anomaly has been recognized, the best method for studying it is seismic reflection, which can also be used for discovering structural complications if cost is no consideration. With this method, "mirrors" (reflecting horizons) have been recognized that are capable of reflecting sound and producing an echo. This phenomenon is currently made use of in determining ocean depths (ultrasonic soundings, asdic, and so forth); it makes possible the measurement of the thickness of glaciers[6] without great difficulty. (See the profiles determined by the French expedition to Greenland.) But in geophysics its use is somewhat more delicate, since multiple reflectors may exist that correspond to hard beds or to sequences of beds, and it is necessary to distinguish the corresponding echos. On the other hand, seismic velocity varies with the depth, thus it is necessary to determine the depth separately, either by shooting a refraction profile or by making measurements in a well, if one is available.

A seismic reflection echo is received by a series of neighboring geophones, and the offset on the tracings of the time registration makes possible the precise determination of the direction of the sound wave. To reconstruct its path and to locate the point of reflection and the attitude of the reflector is then only a problem in optics. (In certain cases there may be multiple reflections.)

Unlike other methods whose precision decreases with depth, such that only mean properties of quite large volumes are indicated, seismic reflection gives information that is localized precisely and even oriented. On the other hand, the reflection is not a characteristic property and does not enable us to recognize a rock. Rarely can we follow continually a reflecting horizon for a series of nearby explosions so that it can be identified with a particular stratigraphic horizon. Usually we can only trace a "phantom horizon" parallel to the reflectors, without being able to say to what bed it corresponds; hence the information obtained is only of a structural nature.

The application of seismic reflection is especially easy when the dips are low, although quite strongly inclined reflectors may be located if the law of velocities is well known. Often the reflections from synclines are stronger than those from anticlines. Faults may go undetected, yet sometimes they cause multiple reflections. Despite these difficulties, seismic reflection may, when

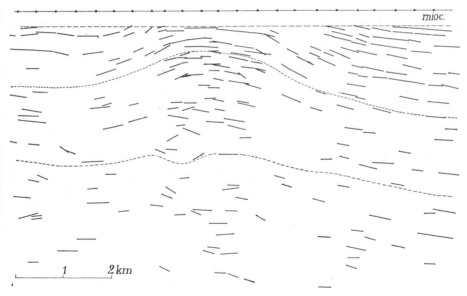

FIGURE 46. *Example of a section determined by seismic reflection, prepared by the Compagnie générale de Géophysique in Aquitaine. The section indicates the position and orientation of the surfaces on which were reflected the sound waves produced by explosions at the positions indicated. The values used for the propagation velocities as a function of the depth were determined in a nearby well. Under the discordant Miocene, an anticline can be seen very clearly outlined; at about 3000 to 4000 meters depth, its structure becomes more complex. The two dotted lines, parallel to the reflectors or "phantom horizons," are to aid in the interpretation of the structure.*

all the reflections from a given section are recorded, give remarkable profiles, which clearly show all the undulations of the reflecting beds. Profiles in different directions indicate domes and basins and the detail of their forms. Numerous studies carried out in all petroliferous regions, most of which unfortunately remain unpublished, have made possible the determination of structures that were later verified by drilling (Fig. 46).

Except for seismic reflection, which alone enables us to determine structures, the other methods, such as gravimetry, can only be used to obtain data that would support or refute a given theoretical interpretation; more often, they serve to remove uncertainties, to locate precisely the positions of wrinkles buried under a sedimentary cover, and so on. They may occasionally provide some quantitative data upon a visible complication in surface geology, such as the throw of a fault bordering a basin of recent sedimentation.

The methods indicated above are those actually in use in deep geophysical exploration (in contrast to investigations of shallow depths required by public works); that is, essentially for the study of sedimentary basins in the search for petroleum.

The study of ancient metamorphosed, or strongly folded, massifs is much less advanced and geophysics provides us with little more than information regarding such details of their structure as injections of basic rocks that are magnetic, sufficiently abundant mineralizations that may produce electric currents as they are oxidized, and crush zones.

The data furnished by certain geophysical methods are strictly limited in depth; electric procedures, for instance, give us hardly any information except on the sedimentary cover. On the other hand, gravimetry and seismic refraction are not limited in depth. Through the latter method, by placing the receiver far enough away from the shot point and using large quantities of explosive, it is possible to determine the distribution of seismic velocities over several tens of kilometers. This results in distinguishing, in the crystalline crust, a series of beds designated in a somewhat conventional manner as "granitic," "intermediate" and "basaltic," even "ultrabasic," whose thicknesses vary in different regions.[7] The evidence so obtained agrees with that obtained during earthquakes, which in the same manner, gives us the distribution of seismic velocities as a function of depth, even to the center of the earth.[8]

Seismic refraction has been applied to oceanic zones, and up to now, principally in the North Atlantic, by Maurice Ewing.[9] With profiles reaching a length of about one to two hundred kilometers, it has been possible to determine the constitution of the ocean bottom to a thickness of some ten kilometers, as well as the structure of the continental shelf along the United States. The most accurate data regarding the constitution of ocean bottoms have been obtained using this method. Results of the highest importance may be expected from this method in coming years.

Gravimetry measures the combined effects of rocks situated at all depths.

The law of diminishing attraction in inverse ratio to the square of the distance is by no means sufficient to weaken the effect of deep layers and may be compensated by a greater volume. This constitutes a serious obstacle from the point of view of applied geology in that anomalies due to masses located at shallow depth can be recognized only by their small area and by the rapidity of their variation in the horizontal direction, although they must often be distinguished among anomalies that are much greater, but diffuse and slowly varying, which may come from deep layers. The information furnished by gravimetry for these deep layers is of such importance that we shall return to the matter in Chap. 16.

The development of geophysics has been so rapid that it is certainly imprudent to attempt to predict its future. It can, however, be stated that if the study of relatively simple sedimentary basins by petroleum geologists, has, at times, produced accurate results, they have been obtained only at the expense of very considerable work. An attempt to unravel, for example, the structure of the Alps in depth would require much more exacting labor; it is thus imprudent to try to draw conclusions from a few isolated measurements or even from a campaign of minor importance. In any event, it should be remembered that a hypothesis, even when supported and suggested by such measurements, remains a hypothesis, in spite of the accuracy and precision of the measurements.

Notes and References

1. Heiland, C. A., *Geophysical Exploration,* New York (Prentice-Hall), 1946.

Nettleton, L. L., *Geophysical Prospecting for Oil,* New York (McGraw-Hill), 1940.

Cagniard, L., *La prospection géophysique,* La Science Vivante, Paris (Presses Universitaires), 1950.

2. Lejay, P., *Développements modernes de la gravimétrie,* Paris (Gauthier-Villars), 1947.

3. Migaux, L., *Une méthode nouvelle de géophysique appliquée: la prospection par courants telluriques,* Ann. de Géophys., vol. 2, pp. 131–146, 1946.

4. Schlumberger, C. and M., *La méthode de la carte de résistivités du sol,* Ann. des Mines, Sept. 1930.

Maillet, R., and Migaux L., *Conrad Schlumberger et la prospection électrique,* Ann. des Mines, no. 1 and 2, 1942.

5. Rothé, Ed., and Rothé, J. P., *Prospection Géophysique,* Tome I, Paris (Gauthier-Villars), 1950; vol. 2, 1952.

Poldini, E., *La prospection électrique du sous-sol,* Lausanne (Rouge), 1947.

6. Süsstrunk, A., *Sondage du glacier par la méthode sismique,* La Houille Blanche, Special number A, pp. 309–318, May 1951.

7. See, for example (and for bibliography), Rothé, J. P., and Peterschmitt, E., *Etude séismique des explorations d'Haslach,* Ann. Inst. Phys. du Globe, Strasbourg, vol. 5, part 3, Géophysique, pp. 77–90, 1950.

8. The best overall exposition is the one by J. Coulomb, *La Constitution Physique de la Terre,* Collect. "Sciences d'Aujourd'hui" (Albin Michel), Paris, 1952.

9. Ewing, M. *et al.*, Geophysical Investigations in the Emerged and Submerged Atlantic Coastal Plain, Bull. Geol. Soc. America, Part 1, vol. 48, pp. 753–801, 1937; Part 3, vol. 50, pp. 257–296, 1939; Part 4, vol. 51, pp. 1821–1840, 1940; Part 5, vol. 61, pp. 877–892, 1950.

Ewing, M. *et al.*, Recent Results in Submarine Geophysics, Bull. Geol. Soc. America, vol. 57, pp. 909–934, 1946.

Gutenberg, B., Crustal Layers of the Continents and Oceans, Bull. Geol. Soc. America, vol. 62, pp. 427–440, 1951.

CHAPTER EIGHT

Some Deformations of Nontectonic Origin

Slumping of sediments on the bottom—Differential subsidence—Melting of dead ice—Pressure of glaciers—Effects of freezing—Solifluction—Balancing—Slides—Flowage of argillaceous beds—Solution of salt and gypsum—Hydration of anhydrite—Concretions.

THE PHENOMENA to be reviewed in the present chapter may have very different origins. The only thing they have in common is that they could be easily mistaken for tectonic phenomena. To avoid such errors, which have often been made, the geologist must be familiar with these phenomena so that their occurrence may be recognized. Even with great care, it is difficult to discriminate between the results of tectonic deformation and the phenomena here described.

Nontectonic displacements of beds may be produced either at the time of deposition or shortly thereafter but still close to the surface; we shall first examine the former. Slips on the bottom of recently deposited sediments may produce folding and crumpling of beds that resemble tectonic folds (Fig. 9). Such slips (in English, "slumps") have been recorded on bottoms sloping only 2 to 3 degrees, in lakes as well as in the ocean. The Zug (Switzerland) catastrophe, during which several houses built on the shore of the lake were dragged under water, was attributed to such a phenomenon. Similar effects were observed in recent muds when the artificial lake of Sautet (France) was emptied. Such slumps are frequent in the Black Sea. Certain changes in depth following earthquakes along the shores of Japan also seem to be due to slips. Many such slumps probably go unnoticed, which may explain why their traces in sediments seem to have been long unrecognized. But they have now been pointed out in many regions in sediments of all ages. Most typically, they

101

consist of a series of strongly folded and contorted beds, which are generally relatively thin (two meters or less), located between undisturbed beds of the same composition. In some cases, the stratification of the contorted beds is sometimes well defined, in which case it is possible to ascertain whether the later beds are resting on contorted beds with a slight discordance or whether the folded mass has piled up so that its upper surface is approximately flat, which often seems to be the case. In some beds, the stratification is vaguely defined, as if it had been partly destroyed during reworking of the beds, before they were consolidated. Many contortions are distinguishable, but it is difficult to follow any particular stratum.

Another explanation is that the beds may not have had sufficient consistency to fold and may have simply broken into lumps that rolled back upon themselves or slumped and piled up in disorder in a matrix resulting from the redeposition of the fragments put into suspension by the slide. Such slumping contemporaneous with sedimentation has been recognized in all sorts of more or less argillaceous or marly rocks.[1] These folded masses can be distinguished from tectonic folds especially by the perfectly regular bedding of the strata above and below them. If slumping recurred from time to time in the past, producing the same effects, a whole series of similar zones will likely be found to succeed one another in a given section. Whereas tectonic folds generally tend to emphasize stratification, here the latter is often irregular. The tendency to form elliptical loaves is a marked difference from real folds.

Contrary to what would happen if such intense folds originated in an already consolidated rock, there is no sign of crushing or slickensiding. At times folding by slumping and certain intraformational breccias formed by reworking of recently deposited sediments have formed together, but the origin of these breccias cannot be mistakenly attributed to tectonic phenomena.

Independent of any errors that may be introduced by complications attributed to tectonic dislocations, they have great stratigraphic interest; the occurrence of slumping, which indicates a sloping bottom, could have caused certain horizons on top or slopes of ridges to disappear, to increase in thicknesses at the foot of slopes, disturb the normal succession of fossiliforous zones, and mix the facies that were originally deposited in very different depths.

Differential compaction of sediments may also be expressed in features that might be attributed to tectonic phenomena if examined superficially. It is known that at the time of deposition, some sediments or some particular layers in a sequence are formed of more or less clayey or calcareous muds having a very high water content. Later, most of the water escapes under the pressure of overlying sediments, and since the mineral content remains approximately constant, the beds frequently thin to a quarter of their initial thickness or, in the case of coal, to a twentieth of the original thickness. In other sediments, such as sands or gravels, however, compaction is negligible.

Sediments deposited with their surface remains horizontal may not remain so if the thickness of underlying clayey mud is not uniform. This may be due either to the intercalation of sand or gravel lentils, which do not shrink, or to inequalities of the bottom that will be reflected, more or less attenuated, in the character of the overlying beds, even if sedimentation had completely obliterated these irregularities during deposition (Fig. 47).

The dips of beds that originate in this way, and which always remain very slight, are of great importance for localizing certain petroliferous horizons in flat-lying regions, such as the North American mid-continent, but they are no indication in deformation of the earth's crust. They must not be confused with the "posthumous movements," such as those that produced certain undulations in Mesozoic beds of the Paris Basin, which seem to indicate that movements of the deep substratum took place along the same lines as those of the Paleozoic, but with much smaller magnitudes.

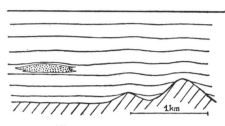

FIGURE 47

Formation of undulations by subsidence of beds deposited horizontally on an uneven bottom or above an incompressible lentil (sand). Each of the beds shown represents the same thickness of the initial deposit.

During glacial retreat, masses of ice are often buried under morainal and fluvioglacial materials, usually under the well-bedded gravels deposited by streams emerging from the glacier. The subsequent melting of the ice causes subsidence in these gravels, which is often clearly indicated by the presence of small faults having throws of about one meter.[2] Often such subsidence produces closed depressions or kettle-holes occupied by lakes. Here, too, clear signs of mechanical displacement do not indicate tectonic deformation but simply express the evolution of this exceptional sediment, a mixture of ice and gravels. This type of displacement seems only to have been described in Quaternary sediments.

In other morainal regions (in particular, south of Lake Garda), larger displacements have been observed, which often exhibit folds having an amplitude of several meters. Small overthrusts caused by the pressure of the glacier on the underlying terranes have also been observed. The dimensions of the folds and their situation generally make it possible to recognize the origin of the very localized pressure. Similar deposits occur in the Netherlands; at Maaru (east of Utrecht), beds of sand and gravel in a section several hundred meters thick have been strongly tilted and displaced by the pressure of glaciers.

Superficial deposits may also be disturbed by the melting of ice that formed within them during severe, prolonged cold periods. This ice may occur either in horizontal lentils or in vertical wedges. During melting, overlying beds subside into these wedges, yielding a visibly displaced filling, in which stratification and the long axes of pebbles are often vertically arranged (Fig. 48). The

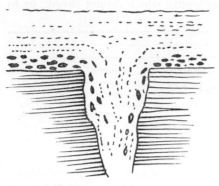

FIGURE 48

Wedge-shaped cleft filled by overlying alluvium.

origin of such wedges is unmistakable, but this is not the case when the displacement is greater; beds of sand, clay and gravel may be folded and contorted in an extremely capricious manner. When such displacements are observed in tectonically quiet regions, as in the valley of the Oise (Fig. 49), or in the environs of Bordeaux, it is quite evident that the cause of the movement could only have been surficial. The alluvium must have lost all cohesion after repeated freezing and thawing, with the result that a very slight slope was probably sufficient to promote a slip. In view of the frequency of such displacements, we must be cautious before coming to a conclusion of Quaternary tectonic movements.[3]

Movements in superficial beds are related to the very general phenomenon of solifluction. Altered superficial beds or vegetal soil may slide slowly down slopes, especially when aided by alternating freezing and thawing in depth. The freezing makes the terrane altogether impermeable; earlier, however, the lentils of ice thickened through capillary action of the water. During superficial thawing, the excess water cannot migrate; thus, it transforms the soil into a plastic mass. Solifluction is a common phenomenon in certain climates. It is accompanied by the complete distortion of a thin superficial layer and greatly complicates observations; evidently no account should be taken of dips measured on blocks that have been affected by solifluction.

On a fairly steep slope, running water carries away movable elements too rapidly for them to cause real solifluction, but the rock in place, perhaps

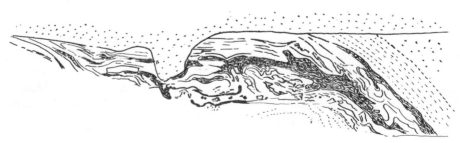

FIGURE 49. *Example of earth flowage (solifluction) simultaneously affecting the Eocene and the Quaternary. Valley of the Oise (length: 28 m). [After Patte, Bull. Soc. géol. France, sér. 5, no. 11, p. 297, 1941.]*

FIGURE 50

Creep of beds on a slope. Left, Example observed at the west foot of the Petit-Saint-Bernard pass.

somewhat modified by weathering, is gradually displaced down slope, as expressed by bending of the stratification (or of the schistosity), which may even amount to a complete overturning (Fig. 50). The apparent dip, along the slope, is then completely different from the dip at depth. A careful examination is necessary to recognize this phenomenon; the careful observer should seek deep sections in transverse ravines and compare dips on opposite banks, and, above all, verify the agreement of the measured dips with the general structure. Creep is often one of the principal phenomena that hinders precise tectonic study.

Superficial movements may also take other forms, such as slumps (Fig. 51), which affect clayey formations to a certain depth, with the formation of lenses of very variable dimensions, or much more severe landslides in which whole mountain slopes, breaking up in the course of the movement, come down to the valley bottoms. These phenomena are generally quite easy to recognize, if only by their topographic forms. They have played an important role in forming the relief of certain mountainous regions, and their study is therefore important.

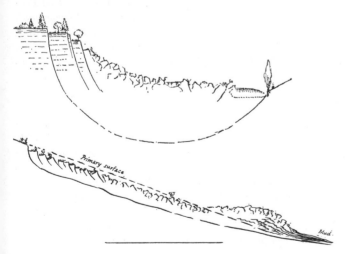

FIGURE 51

Two examples of earth slides. Above, Deep slip, in the glacial valley of the Ain (Pont de Poitte). Below, Superficial slip (based on the Valdrome slide, in Aptian marls, Drôme, France).

Some surface phenomena have been observed that are intermediate between slides and landslips and may be difficult to distinguish from tectonic movements. Whole slabs of hard rocks, resting on plastic clays, may be displaced by a progressive slip with little if any fragmentation. Only a regional study shows that in the segment under study all the beds are lower than in nearby areas; to explain this arrangement we may often hesitate between a slide and a fault (Fig. 52). Calcareous beds that form part of an anticline may even slip as far as the adjacent syncline, forming what may be mistaken for an overthrust.

FIGURE 52

Collapse of a calcareous segment by subsidence (Valley of the Estéron, Alpes-Maritimes).

The hesitation at times felt between assigning a given complication of detail to a superficial slide or to a tectonic deformation is really due to the fact that there is a continuous passage between certain deformations of tectonic flow and the greatest of these slides, which we shall look into later on (Chap. 13). So it is quite useless to place on the definitions a clear-cut limitation which does not exist in the phenomena. Only convenience justifies a boundary; it is often clearly defined, but at times may seem arbitrary. If it is possible to distinguish a first phase, in which the tectonic structures originated, and a second phase, in which these structures were deformed by slides related to

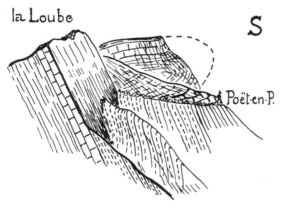

FIGURE 53

Overthrust (?) of Poët en Percip (Drôme). Foreground, South side of the anticline that forms the summit of the Loube, plunging is regular. Background, A limb of the anticline can be seen clearly sloping to the south. In the interval, at the village of Poët, a mass of Jurassic limestones, considerably broken, rests on a section of the Cretaceous benches. A mechanical shearing of these benches would not be very probable; it looks as if the Jurassic had slipped on what was then an erosion surface, very high above the present bottom of the valley. But it is impossible to say in which measure tilting of the anticline had preceded this movement, which might be considered an overthrust from the strictly structural point of view.

FIGURE 54

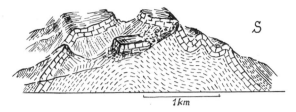

North anticline of Lure, 11 km to the east of Séderon (Drome). The structure may be interpreted as follows: In a first stage, there was formed, under a Cretaceous cover, perhaps still thick, an anticline whose form is indicated in the background. Following the channeling, which determined a wide inlier of Oxfordian marls, a section of Upper Jurassic limestones, 500 m wide, slipped on the Oxfordian marls and came to rest in the axis of the anticline, clearly lower than the flanks; this section is fissured throughout its whole mass.

the present valleys, there are no difficulties. Another criterion that may be used is the fact that during tectonic deformation, the rocks remain compact. On the other hand, a slide near the surface is always accompanied by a certain fissuring, and the fissures remain open. But in doubtful cases where, without being able to gather the elements of an answer, the question is asked whether a certain mass of Jurassic limestone, quite pulverized but with some recrystallization of the calcite, resting on a Cretaceous syncline not far from an anticline, represents an overthrust remnant or the remains of an old landslip that was probably produced when the relief was very different from the present relief, it may be said that the question makes no sense because the two phenomena pass continuously one into the other (Fig. 55).

Even when slides of hard beds resting on clays do not produce such complex displacements they may distort the outcrops of hard beds resting on the

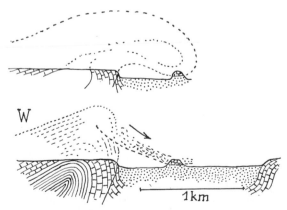

FIGURE 55. *The two interpretations of the overthrust of Montmeyan (Var). A remnant of Upper Jurassic limestones resting on the Upper Cretaceous in the middle of the syncline may be interpreted either as a remnant of a folded bed, or, much more likely, as the result of a slide from the neighboring anticline before the latter was leveled by erosion.*

FIGURE 56

Keuper of Lorraine (Gironcourt). Section showing how the blocks of flagstone dolomite have slipped on the slope to a level below that of the sandstone and the underlying coal.

clays and subside in large blocks. These slides can be recognized in outcrop, inasmuch as the thickness of the hard bed will be greatly increased, and its base will seem to drop below its expected level. In the Lorraine Keuper, there is a coal bed situated a few meters below the "flagstone dolomite," an intercalation a few meters thick that occurs in the middle of the Keuper (variegated marls). Prospects placed above the base of the dolomite, on the basis of outcrops, were found to be, in fact, below the coal (Fig. 56).

Sloping clay bed may not only facilitate the slip of overlying limestone beds, but they may also be laterally displaced by their own weight; isolated blocks may thus be buried in the clay that flows back around them. Serious errors might be made in judging the mutual relations of two such rocks in outcrop. Marcel Bertrand has pointed out that in Provence, for example, bits of Lias belonging to an overthrust unit rest on the sandy Upper Cretaceous.[4] A similar occurrence has been observed near

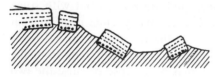

FIGURE 57

Subsidence of blocks of Burdigalian calcareous molasse resting on Eocene sands (Bonnieux, near Apt, Vaucluse.)

Apt, where blocks of calcareous molasse rest on Eocene sands or on Oligocene[5] clays (Fig. 57).

Such movement may take place even on a much larger scale. Several times it has been pointed out[6] that a thick bed of clay, cut by valleys and elsewhere overlain by resistant beds, has been driven toward the valleys, thereby producing near them a swelling that tilts the underlying beds and gives the appearance of an anticline (Fig. 58).

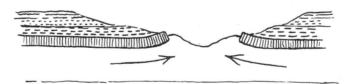

FIGURE 58. *Uplift of clays in the axis of a valley, under the weight of neighboring plateaus.*

Certain bentonitic clays take up water and swell as soon as erosion brings them into contact with the air. According to Woolnough,[7] this is probably the explanation for the superficial displacements that made any accurate geologic survey impossible in New Guinea and put an end to a search for oil there.

Woolnough also mentions a fossil swelling of an argillaceous bed that made up the foot wall of a coal bed in New South Wales. Neither the lower bed nor the foot wall was affected by the swelling which was localized in narrow wrinkles and was probably produced before the deposition of the Trias, after erosion had cut down to within a short distance of the bed.

Much more frequent among the displacements due to the alteration of certain sediments are those that result from the solution of salt or gypsum and from the hydration of anhydrite. It is known that the latter is accompanied by a one-third increase in volume; thus, when the anhydrite is associated with another rock and, for example, alternates with beds of dolomite, its hydration causes the complete disintegration of the dolomite and the formation of a true breccia. This is one of the possible origins of certain cellular dolomites (cargneules, in French; cornioles in Swiss). The origin of certain samples of gypsum that show regular and fine folds of a few centimeters, although the details of the mechanics are not very clear, may be explained in the same way.[8] The swelling of anhydrite is one of the reasons why it is almost impossible to study the details of the structure of certain gypsiferous formations. We shall mention others later on.

Salt or gypsum always dissolves in a nonuniform manner, thereby producing very irregular subsidence of the overlying terrain, tilting certain sections and, at times, giving an appearance of a quite sharp but rather short-waved folding. When working above a salt or gypsum formation, this hypothesis should be kept in mind if rapid variations of dip are noted that do not seem to be in accord with the general structure. The accident that took place near Paris in 1900, during the digging of the Mcudon tunnel, was due to the rupture of the layer of marls that separated the roof of the tunnel from the water-bearing sands of the Stampian, which were thinned as a result of local folding that followed the solution of a lentil of gypsum. Although limestone is much less soluble, some cases of the collapse of overlying beds into karst cavities have been reported.[9] If a drill penetrates one of these areas of subsidence, which are always very localized, it will indicate altogether abnormal depths to the tops and bottoms of the different beds.

Let us mention again the appearances that the concretions may produce. According to Woolnough, very large concretions in Australia probably produce the appearance of measurable dips in some outcrops. Similarly, we may interpret curved color lines in a Jurasic limestone of the Paris Basin which have sometimes been taken for traces of folds.

Notes and References

1. Goguel, J., *Glissements sous-marins dans le Crétacé inférieur du SE,* Bull. Soc. géol. France, vol. 8, 5e ser., p. 251 ff., 1938.
————, Bull. Carte géol. France, vol. 44, no. 215, Chapter 2, 1944.

2. ————, *Dislocations dans le Quaternaire près de Bellegarde (Ain),* Bull. Soc. géol. France, 5e ser., vol. 13, pp. 261–262, 1943. Very analogous complications of detail can be observed in the alluvium of the Drac (Hautes-Alps) on the right bank of the Séveraisette (unpublished).

3. Note an observation by Bersier, who recorded a true fault affecting the Würmian moraine at the same time as the underlying molasse (*Un mouvement quaternaire en Molasse sub-Alpine,* Ecolgae géol. Helv., vol. 37, no. 2, p. 423, 1944).

4. Bertrand, Marcel, *Comptes-rendus de la Réunion extraord. de la Soc. géol. France, Oct. 5, 1891,* Bull. Soc. géol. France, 3e ser., vol. 19, p. 1169.

5. Goguel, J., *Comptes-rendus des Collaborateurs, 1932, feuille Forcalquier,* Bull. Carte géol. France, vol. 18, no. 190, p. 150, 1933.

6. Hollingworth, S. E., Taylor, J. H., and Kellaway, G. A., Large-Scale Superficial Structure in the Northampton Ironstone Field, Quart. Journ. Geol. Soc. London, vol. 100, pp. 1–44, 1944.
Prentice, J. E., and Sabine, P. A., Some Superficial Structures in the Cornbrash of Northamptonshire, Geol. Mag., vol. 84, pp. 89–97, 1947.

7. Woolnough, W. G., Pseudo-tectonic Structures, Bull. Amer. Assoc. Petrol. Geologists, vol. 18, pp. 1098–1106, 1933.

9. Abrard, R., *Un effondrement à forme de bétoire dans les sables de Fontainebleau à Dannemois* (Seine-et-Oise), Soc. géol. France, Comptes-rendus, 1945, pp. 23–24.

8. See Fig. 357 in Rinne, *Etude pratique des roches,* Paris (Lamarre), second edition, 1912.

CHAPTER NINE

Geometric Presentation of Results

Present forms of mineral masses and reconstruction of parts carried away by erosion—Extrapolation of observation; case of faults—Use of thickness of beds; search for a simple form to explain outcrops of beds; cylindrical folds—Sections—Structural map, panorama, perspectives and block diagrams—Their tracing—Interpretation of geologic maps—Extension of a section in depth—Limits of applicability of the geometric method.

WE HAVE DEFINED the object of tectonics as the study of the movements and deformations that have affected the earth's crust and, therefore, as the historical reconstruction of past phenomena. But tectonics may also involve the study of the present form of deformed rock masses. From a technical point of view, only the present form matters, and it might seem that this aspect, in a way static, would suffice.

We shall see later on that the historical analysis of tectonic phenomena clarifies and makes more precise the representation of their products. Even if we have a purely practical objective, we should not limit ourselves to the geometric viewpoint of the problem, which is the subject of this chapter. Geometric study does not even constitute a first approximation, but only a first phase of the general study; it is somewhat artificial to separate geometric study from the kinematic and dynamic studies that we shall consider later on, since these are closely tied in with the former in practice.

It is enough merely to state the problem we are facing to show to what extent it is indeterminate: given the results of observations made on the surface of the ground (at times a very complicated surface), and at few

111

points underground, to find the form of rock masses in depth. The problem thus stated is nearly always completed by seeking to formulate a hypothesis regarding the form of the rock masses destroyed by erosion. Far from introducing a supplementary difficulty, this extension of the problem facilitates its solution. To make a tectonic interpretation, it is necessary to exclude the effects of erosion from the imagination in order to visualize the structure in which the relief was carved. H. B. de Saussure made a remarkable discovery when he arrived at the idea that the Matterhorn is only a remnant left by the erosion of a continuous mass, of which the mountains that surround it originally formed a part. Today, an analogous reconstruction, in our minds, of the terrane that has been carried away by erosion constitutes the ABC of every attempt at tectonic interpretation. We may even at times conceive of a block, indeterminate toward the top, in which the erosion surface may be at almost any depth. Here, of course, it is merely a question of simplification, which simply means that the surface that existed during deformation is irrelevant to the structures of interest.

This hypothesis needs no justification, in that deformation is often accompanied by uplift, following which erosion may attack the rocks very rapidly and to great depth. Nevertheless, the limits within which this simplification may be applied seem often to have been exceeded. Certain tectonic phenomena are much better understood when we take into consideration the position of the surface during deformation. However, this consideration is more especially interesting from the dynamic point of view examined in Chapter 12, and does not influence the geometric study that concerns us here.

This geometric problem implies an extrapolation, in depth, of the observations made at the surface. If we know nothing, *a priori,* about the geometric form of the boundaries between different rock types, we can only prolong the observed contacts in a straight line, but this approximation is valid only for a slight thickness. Such would be the case, for example, for an intrusive mass of eruptive rock.

In the study of sedimentary terranes, however, we can assume that the thickness of the beds has remained unchanged, except perhaps in certain fault zones and in crushed or stretched zones, whose presence we have learned to recognize in outcrops. The tracing of faults implies an original accordance between the points where they have been effectively observed. If we can identify outcrops that correspond to either edge this will permit us to indicate the trace accurately, even in places where a fault is not directly observable. Except where observations are to the contrary, an observed fault may be prolonged in a straight line; that is, we may determine its direction wherever outcrops permit. In the absence of these conditions, or if a fault has been observed in only one outcrop, it is best to assume that the fault parallels other known neighboring faults.

These elementary rules should not be considered as laws, although the general character of certain fault systems seems to justify them. It is only suggested that they be used as first approximations, which may be modified very profoundly as more complete observations are made. Too often the systematic application of these rules has led to the map depiction of a geometric grid of rectilinear faults, when in actuality each fault is based on only one or two exposures, between which the accordance is not proved. If we fail to realize the arbitrary character of such representation of fault systems, there is a danger of seeing therein a confirmation of the applied rules that would justify their use in other cases. There may also be approved by mutual agreement, a style of representation of fault systems (or at times other tectonic features) only distantly connected with reality. Thus, observation points must only be connected with great caution; when in doubt, use should be made of the conventional sign "doubtful fault," which indicates a fault that probably exists but whose exact location and direction are unknown. In like manner, we should not draw faults on the basis of observation points that are merely in the neighborhood. If, on two sides of a plateau whose cover makes observations uncertain, the margins show a certain number of faults, no one will doubt that approximately as many exist under the plateau. To make a real representation of them, however, may be so complex that it is impossible, in which case it is better not to attempt to do so.

Once a set of faults has been mapped and their throws have been calculated according to the normal stratigraphic interval between the beds that they bring into contact, their dips, which are necessary to extend them in depth, remain unknown. When the dip is uncertain the faults may be shown as vertical, but we should not take what is only a first approximation for the affirmation of a fact. Often, not enough importance is attached to the real dips of faults, which are, of course, usually difficult to determine. The interpretation of other surfaces of discontinuity, such as overthrust surfaces, poses more difficult problems for which a dynamic and kinematic interpretation is required in addition to a geometric interpretation.

Outside of discontinuity zones, observations made on outcrops enable us to determine the structure at depth if the thickness of the beds that separate the different horizons is known. When the dip of a certain bed has been measured at a given point, it is possible to deduce therefrom, at least as a first approximation, the position in depth of other beds on the normal to the observed bed, as well as the former positions of the highest beds that existed on this same normal before erosion. It is thus possible to determine a whole series of points for each of the beds under consideration and to delineate their form, both below the surface and in the parts eroded away. In carrying out a construction based on these principles, we usually limit ourselves to a plane section perpendicular to the strike of the beds. More or less ingenious geometric methods have been proposed for constructing the outline of beds that are assumed to be parallel to one another and whose dips are known at all surface points where measurement was possible. However, simple freehand sketching is almost always sufficient, since the thicknesses of beds are usually either roughly determined or are too variable to permit a strict application of the method just indicated. On the other hand, the thicknesses of the different beds can often be determined indirectly by introducing the idea of continuity into the geometric reconstruction and assuming the beds to have the most simple possible forms. More precisely, the forms imagined will appear satisfactorily if they conform absolutely to their intersection with the surface of the ground, which may be considered to cut them at random.

We shall clarify these ideas, since they may seem somewhat obscure, by using the following artificial example, which is deliberately made simpler than anything encountered in practice. On the flanks of a valley that cuts across a mountainous region, such as the Jura, the Appalachians, or the sub-Alpine chains, the same sedimentary beds appear at various points at very different elevations. Since the different beds are of very unequal hardness, the shape of the valley is very irregular, narrow in places, wider in others, and has gentle slopes and little side valleys (Fig. 59). Nevertheless, on observing its slopes, we note that the outcrops of a given bed, which form an almost continuous rocky wall, form here a sort of vault, there a curve concave upward; if these outcrops rise and fall alternately, it is natural to think that the same thing occurs in this bed at depth; and that the other beds should have parallel forms.

Let us imagine a structure involving the overall mass of the bed under discussion. In general, it is possible to choose a relatively simple structure, the irregularities of the topography being sufficient to indicate the complications observed at the outcrops. This structure should also show the dips that were measured. Very often the most simple structure imaginable approaches, in first approximation, a cylindrical form of successive beds all parallel to a

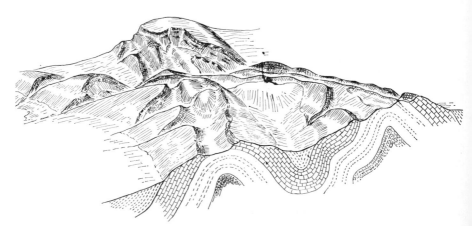

FIGURE 59. *Relations between topography and structure. A hard bed in each fold determines a ridge. The exposed side of the valley in the background gives an indication of the structure, which is not at all identical to a normal section.*

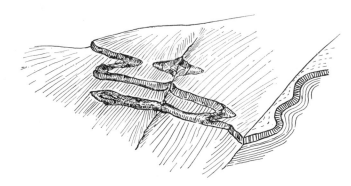

FIGURE 60. *Outcrops of Nummulitic limestone to the east of Blégiers (Basses-Alpes). The section shown on the right indicates the actual attitude of the bed, cut almost tangentially by the topographic surface.*

given direction. This structure may be confirmed by comparison with that deduced from the study of the neighboring valleys.

It must be kept well in mind that the appearance of a slope can give only a very remote idea of the transverse section of the folds; the topographic surface may cut the cylindrical beds in a very erratic manner. The examples in the figures are not likely to involve errors, since it would be hard to imagine that beds had folded along the line of the outcrops (Figs. 60 and 61). But there is danger that much more insidious errors might be made when the difference between the transverse section of the folds and their intersection with the topographic surface is less marked. In addition, errors due to per-

FIGURE 61. *Outcrops determined by a series of parallel groovings in a monoclinal series. [Inspired by south side of Mont Ventoux.]*

spective might result; thus, we should always seek to observe a slope from several different points. In order to avoid such errors, we should always endeavor to think of the forms of beds as they would appear in space rather than as a function of the picture given by the slope examined. We should seek to relate the outcrops of both slopes of a valley or both sides of a mountain to the same structure.

If it is possible (at least as a first approximation) to understand observations by assuming a cylindrical form for the beds, this form may be completely defined if we use as section a vertical plane normal to the strike of the generatrix, thus showing the true dip. Such sections are much used in describing tectonic forms. If there is a valley side-slope approximately perpendicular to the direction of the folds, the appearance of the outcrops therein exposed is quite similar to the way they would appear in the section, which thus assumes an intuitive significance.

If it is exactly normal to the direction of the folds, such a section represents each stratigraphic unit by a belt whose width represents its thickness. We should observe immediately that if the section were oblique to the direction of the folds this would no longer be true for the inclined parts of the beds, whose thickness would appear increased.

The consideration of such structures leads immediately to the definition of two essential elements. An anticline corresponds to the zone in which each bed is at a maximum elevation, and the beds on opposite sides dip away from each other. In a syncline, the elevation of each bed is at a minimum, and on opposite sides beds dip toward one another. In various forms, these two essential elements are involved in the description of all structures. The very simple structure that we have just studied and which is formed of cylindrical folds corresponds little with reality. The transverse section of folds may, if we shift along their direction, change either in shape or height; an anticline may diminish and disappear or another may form alongside. Sometimes an anticline widens and then splits through the appearance of an intermediary syncline. The dispositions that result from such changes will be studied in the following chapter.

However, we do not always have before us a sheaf of folds that are approximately parallel to each other and which may be described graphically through a series of parallel sections echelonned at known distances and whose forms vary progressively from one to another. If we are not going to publish our data, but are simply making a single representation, we may, instead of reducing all the sections to a single plane, arrange them in their natural positions on sheets of cardboard cut to the contour of the topography, or we may depict the structure using vertical sheets of glass or transparent plastic whose intervals reproduce in scale the actual distances between the sections. Such models have often been constructed to represent the ore body worked in a mine, but they may be useful for many other purposes.

It may be difficult to fully represent the structure of a region by a series of parallel sections. At times there are found in a given region folds with different directions whose points of contact may present complications. Or else the form of a fold may vary, not progressively, but abruptly, a fault separating two blocks that are quite different from one another. Sometimes the forms of the two fragments are quite alike, in which case the fault that separates them has simply shifted them apart vertically or, more commonly, in a horizontal direction. We may then assume that the fault is younger than the fold and that the blocks were simply split off from it. But such structures are often more complex; for instance, the forms of folds are different on opposite sides of a "transverse fault." The formation of folds and the accompanying fault action are two inseparable aspects of the same phenomenon, that is, of overall deformation. When deformation is this complex, a section, or even a series of sections, is altogether insufficient to define the forms of the rock masses under study.

Another mode of representation that may be applied to the most complex cases consists of what is called a structural map, on which contours are used to define the form of the chosen horizon. Finally, in order to grasp the structure of certain details, it may be convenient to show its shape in perspective from suitably chosen angles. This perspective, whether depicted in a photograph or a drawing (panorama), may correspond to an actual viewpoint. It thus condenses the observations made and may be very useful as a confirmation for any record of facts independent of interpretation.

These panoramas are sometimes tinted with the conventional geologic color symbols, and prepared in this manner, make very interesting records. Examples are to be found in most of the volumes of *Matériaux pour la Carte Géologique de la Suisse*. Several students of M. Gignoux[1] have published, side by side, a photographic panorama and a colored drawing in conventional colors, a practice which makes it possible, in a way, for an individual to repeat the observations that the author used as a point of departure.

No geologist should be satisfied with merely accumulating observations; it is necessary to make a synthesis of them and to indicate the form of the mineral masses deduced from observations. To do this, we may use, along with sections and a structural map, properly chosen perspectives that are usually replaced by a parallel projection, the observation point being pushed out to infinity. Such a perspective may be combined with sections by representing a rectangle of the terrane bounded by four vertical planes; this gives us what is called a "block diagram." The direction of the projections may then be oriented so as to emphasize any given feature. If the beds outline cylindrical folds having inclined axes, a perspective whose projections are parallel to these axes will show the form of these folds independently of any irregularities of relief. If the folds are not exactly cylindrical, it is often possible to choose a direction such that the projected form of the folds will appear approximately in the same manner, provided the irregularities of relief and the changes of form of the folds do not conceal their general character.

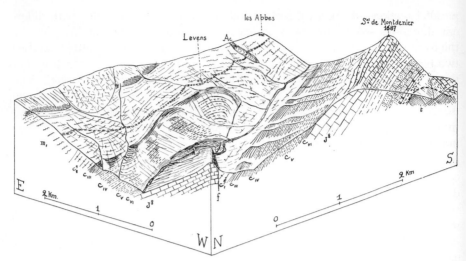

FIGURE 62. *Example of block diagram, seen parallel to the direction of the axes, so as to give sensibly the position of a section ("cylindrical view"). The Levens Fault, Basses-Alpes. [Goguel, J., Description tectonique de la bordure des Alpes de la Bléone au Var, Mém. Carte, Fig. 51, 1937.]*

We call such a perspective a "cylindrical view." It gives approximately the same effect as a section, but is more objective than the latter, which would lead us to represent in a given plane details of form of the folds observed in many outcrops, that is, in different transverse planes (Fig. 62).

To apply these different methods of representation, we begin with observations entered on a map and subject them to the necessary geometric transformations. Then, on these drawings, we express graphically the synthesis whose principle we have indicated; parallel to a given bed observed at the surface, another given bed is placed at a given distance. The sense of continuity makes it possible to connect these indications.

In drawing a section whose trace is given on the map, the representation of the topographic surface raises no difficulty; it is sufficient to measure and record the horizontal distances and to record the elevations read on the map. When it is only a question of representing variations of thickness, or of the facies of a horizontal sedimentary series, it is possible to exaggerate the vertical scale. But this practice is formally outlawed from the tectonic point of view, since it causes a distortion of the section, in that the thickness of a bed is modified as the dip changes. Inasmuch as the constancy of the thickness of beds is the first of the basic principles used in geometric reconstruction, it is indispensable to maintain it by the methods of representation employed.

There is no difficulty in recording on the section the observations made in the plane itself. But we must also take into account all the other observations. A section is not an end in itself but a means for recognizing certain results of a general tectonic synthesis.

One method consists of tracing, not an isolated section, but a series of parallel sections. After having recorded the surface observations made in the plane of each section, or in the immediate vicinity, we shall seek a form of folds that slowly varies from one section to the next (in the case where there is no transverse fault), satisfying all the surface observations and the known thicknesses of beds. If the thicknesses are not known, a carefully drawn section, showing the exact dips and the parallelism of the different beds, makes possible a graphic determination of the thicknesses. With practice, it is possible to include on single section observations made outside its plane, as if a whole series were being traced simultaneously.

Various methods have been devised for constructing the oblique projection of a block diagram starting from a topographic map. The following method seems to be the simplest (also see Fig. 63). Place on the map a piece of transparent, gridded tracing paper or plastic and orient it so that one axis is parallel to the direction of view. Let c be the side of the grid, expressed on the scale of the map. At the bottom of the proposed diagram, draw a horizontal scale, and divide it in the same way as the axis of the abscissas of the grid, the unit being the length c, represented on the scale of the diagram. Use a movable ruler, parallel to the vertical of the sheet (it is convenient for this to be lined), having two scales: Above, the heights on the scale of the diagram, and below, the ordinates counted downward, the unit corresponding to the length c multiplied by the relation that defines the inclination of the projection.

To represent a point, its x and y coordinates are read from the grid and its elevation, z, from the map. The edge of the ruler is passed through point x of the basal scale; point y on the ruler is brought opposite the basal scale and the point is marked at the height z. Thus, no construction is necessary, and

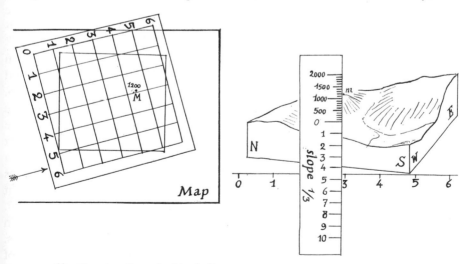

FIGURE 63. *Construction of a block diagram.*

it is easy to make a number of rulers corresponding to the different possible projection inclinations. The use of special pantographs for automatically making block diagrams has also been proposed.[2]

In general it is satisfactory to represent on a block diagram the outcrop terranes and lateral sections constructed according to the principle indicated above. However, if we wish to represent the form of a determined horizon, there is nothing to prevent deducing its position in depth from the strata observed at the surface and representing it as if it had been completely cleared of overlying rocks, or preserved from erosion, where it was originally above the surface of the ground. It is also possible to modify a block diagram in order to obtain more or less simplified diagrams. Experience has shown that it is easier to trace a diagram by generalizing the indications furnished by a detailed perspective than by tracing directly.

We have assumed so far that the structural geologist was working on his own observations. It goes without saying that in order to locate these observations exactly, each one of them should be carefully recorded on a topographic map, which is the basic record of every geometric study.

In order to transform any given set of observations into a geologic map, the indication of the continuity of the rocks between the points observed and the outline of the contours imply an interpretation of the deep structure. Depending on the care exerted in the survey and the density of the observations, the part of interpretation may be more or less great, but it is never zero. On the other hand, although the geologic map constitutes the most objective synthesis of a set of observations, it cannot exhaust their substance. It is difficult to indicate all the visible dips or the exact form of fold axes, and above all, reading the map offers no clue concerning the accuracy of the observations, which is a function of the quality of the outcrops.

Even the best map interpretation of the geology of an area cannot take the place of a direct study of the terrane. Nevertheless, it is necessary to know how to deduce tectonic structure from a geologic map, which often constitutes the only available record. This operation does not really constitute a tectonic interpretation, but is rather a reading exercise through which we repeat the thinking of the geologist who mapped the geology; moreover, it is indispensable that this reading become almost instinctive through repeated exercises. At the same time, these exercises familiarize the mind with the different kinds of tectonic structures.

Sometimes a careful examination of a map will suggest an interpretation that may have escaped its author. Almost always this will of necessity cast doubt upon certain parts of it that may be assumed to represent rather accordances by continuity than the result of close observation. The study of some topographic maps may convince us that conditions for observation were not very favorable in certain zones. But it is evident that such an interpretation, implying doubt of certain indications of the map, can only serve to set up a program of verification in the field which will eventually result either in correcting the old map at crucial points or in presenting a choice between two interpretations.

In its classic form, the reading of the geologic map should permit the rapid sketching of cross sections, block diagrams, or perspectives. The object of classic exercises is to familiarize the students with these operations.[3] The first stage, which cannot be overemphasized, should be perfect ease in reading the topographic map. This should enable the student to recognize all the details of the relief shown on a topographic map. Then, using a geologic map, a careful study of the stratigraphic succession should be made, distinguishing the discordant masses from one another and seeking to recognize the topographic role of the different formations that correspond either to ridges or to depressions.

To locate the anticlines and synclines, it will be sufficient to compare with the relief the outcrop belts of the oldest and most recent terranes in order to make sure that they do not correspond simply to the deepest erosion zones or to elements spared by erosion; follow the variations in height of the outcrop of a given horizon in order to recognize its high points and its low points.

If a section is to be drawn, remember that measurements or constructions should not be limited to those made in the plane of the section, but it should express a three-dimensional interpretation of the region traversed, following the principle outlined above.

In making a geometric interpretation, whether it is made on a map or from observations on the ground, we cannot limit ourselves to tracing the form of a key horizon that might be represented by a structural map, but we should consider the overall form of the sedimentary succession.

Let us first consider a transverse section of a fold, or of a sheaf of folds, that we assume to be approximately cylindrical. If the thicknesses of the beds are constant in spite of the deformation, a second horizon should be found at a constant distance from the first. Its section is parallel to the section of the first.

By definition, two curves are parallel if all normals common to both curves are of the same length (Fig. 64). For the arcs CN and PQ, the difference between the lengths of the arcs is equal to the

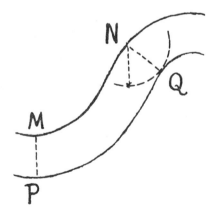

FIGURE 64

Properties of two parallel curves.

length of the arc of the circle whose radius is equal to the length of the normals ($MP = NQ$), included between radii respectively parallel to MP and NQ. In particular, if the common normals between which the lengths are measured have the same direction, the lengths of the two curves are the same. The area included between the two curves is the product of the distance that separates them times the mean of their lengths.

Thus, if we consider the section of an anticline and trace the successive key along the parallel curves, not only the thicknesses, but the lengths of the beds and the areas of their sections (and thus their volumes) are the same as before deformation. All these properties make very probable the correctness of the positions of different horizons traced along parallel curves.

But this can be applied only to a series of limited thickness. If we start from the curve that represents a certain horizon in a given section, then when parallel curves are drawn, there comes a moment when the center of common curvature is reached. The outline of the curve then presents two cusps and two branches that cross each other (Fig. 65).

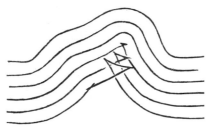

FIGURE 65

Geometric outline of curves parallel to the section of a key horizon.

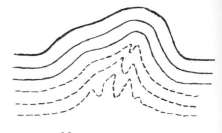

FIGURE 66

Possible outline of geologic horizons under the key horizon of Fig. 65.

Folds in which the thickness of beds is not preserved are called disharmonic; that is, the forms of the folds on opposite sides do not exactly correspond and may differ greatly (Fig. 66). For this reason, simple geometric considerations are not sufficient to determine the form of the beds; we shall have occasion to return to this problem to show the precision that kinematic or dynamic considerations may introduce. Disharmony does not refer to the heart of the fold only. Perhaps one limb of an anticline, usually the one on the side toward which the fold is inclined, may be stretched or faulted. The anticline then becomes an overthrust. In order to study such complications of detail, it is necessary to apply all kinematic and dynamic considerations with care. So many purely geometric syntheses have been proposed, implying more or less ingenious systems of overthrusts that later observations have not confirmed, that the greatest prudence is required in this field.

The purely geometric method involves only an extrapolation, a prolongation in depth of observations of quite limited amplitude. It is, however, a very frequently employed technique, and inasmuch as it is directly connected with all phases of the work on the ground, it is necessary to be completely familiar with the methods involved.

In the following chapter, we will describe several types of elementary complications of detail that can be reconstructed by geometric analysis.

Notes and References

1. Schneegans, D., *La géologie des nappes de l'Ubaye-Embrunais entre la Durance et l'Ubaye,* Mém. Carte géol. France, 1938 (see especially plates 1 to 7).

Barbier, R., *Les zones ultra-dauphinoises et sub-Briançonnaises entre l'Arc et L'Isère,* Mém. Carte géol. France, plate 4, 1948.

2. See, for example, de Sitter, L. U., Instrument for the Mechanical Construction of Block Diagrams, Leidsche Geol. Mededeel., vol. 8, no. 2, pp. 315–325, 1937 (history and bibliography).

3. Bonte, A., *Introduction à la Lecture des Cartes Géologiques,* Paris (Masson), 1945.

CHAPTER TEN

Some Types of Elementary Structural Forms

Absence of clear-cut types—Definitions of terms—Tabular regions—Different kinds of faults and flexures—Horst, graben, step—Folded regions —Anticlines and synclines, axis plunge—Transverse fault—Dejective and ejective style—Anticlines, upright, overfolded, overturned, recumbent— Isoclinal structure—Ruptured anticline, overthrust—Parallel folding and disharmony; minor folds—Salt tectonics; salt domes, diapir folds, extrusion—Overthrust mass; window, klippe, plunging front, root, involution, scales, basal planing.

WITHIN THE LIMITS of this book, a complete description of the structure of the principal mountain chains cannot be given. We are concerned with the methods to be applied in their study rather than with the results of their study. If we were to choose certain mountain chains as examples and describe them in detail, this might suggest that they represented structural types to which other mountain chains would conform more or less closely. The zeal with which geologists searched for structures analogous to those of the Alps, the earliest studied and best known of all mountain chains, has led them to make quite serious errors in the initial stages of the study of other orogenic structures. Throughout the course of tectonic investigations, we must maintain a completely free and unbiased attitude and should resort to making analogies with other regions only with great prudence. It is not possible for us to set up a sort of atlas that would include examples of all the possible structures, to which we could refer. Nor can we adopt the method employed by the biologist. The manner in which living beings reproduce leads to their grouping into clearly defined species to which names have been assigned. When a name has been defined on the basis of a complete description of a type organism, detailed information is thus made available on every individual of the same species and eliminates the need for any further description. However, structures produced by mechanical deformations cannot be arranged in such clear-cut categories. If certain types are encountered frequently enough with analogous characteristics, all the intermediary forms may exist too; quite frequently, unusual arrangements are found that do not fall into any of the usual categories and which it is very difficult to describe with current words. That is why tectonic descriptions are often difficult to interpret and convey only a vague notion of the objects described. A list of fossils furnishes us almost as much information on a bed as their figuration, but words are powerless, in tectonics, to replace the geometric figuration of complications of detail, as shown by outcrops and by reconstruction in depth.

Nevertheless, it is necessary to define the current terminology as clearly as possible. However, these definitions do not constitute a systematic lexicon that, after search for priorities and recourse to types, for which the different terms have been created, would remove all ambiguity. Where possible, we shall illustrate the different terms that we are going to list by actual examples, but it should be well understood that the examples were only chosen to give an idea of the variety of possible structures and do not constitute either clear-cut categories or a restrictive enumeration.

The need for precise definitions of terms used in tectonic descriptions made itself felt a long time ago; to answer this need Emmanuel de Margerie and Albert Heim published, more than seventy years ago,[1] a trilingual *Essai de Définition et de Nomenclature,* which rendered great service. The definitions presented, based on a review of the literature then existent, have been very generally accepted since then and are to be found in all treatises on geology. Of course, new notions have been introduced since 1888, those of disharmony and diapirism, for example, and a small number of terms have been abandoned, but the work done by E. de Margerie and A. Heim has fixed the language used in tectonics. There is no question here of disparaging this fundamental work to which we can always turn with profit. Hereinafter, when we describe common structures, we shall mention, when possible, the authors of terms defined since 1888.

It is customary, from the point of view of their structure, to contrast tabular regions and folded regions. It is quite evident that this distinction depends on the age of the beds observed in relation to the time of deformation. Later beds rest on beds older than the movement with *angular discordance,* whose observation is of prime importance. Grabau[2] has defined two terms used to distinguish between two types of unconformity: *nonconformity* (an angular discordance) and *disconformity* (an interruption in the succession of sediments, in which no angular discordance is apparent). (See Fig. 67.) The general term "unconformity" indicates the stratigraphic gap (lacuna) cor-

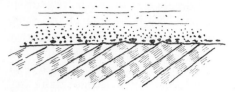 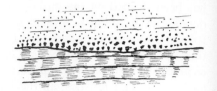

FIGURE 67. *Angular discordance* (*nonconformity*) *and interruption of the sedimentation* (*disconformity*).

responding to a transgression. At one time, A. d'Orbigny used the terms *discordance réelle* for an angular discordance, and *discordance d'isolement* for a stratigraphic lacuna, but unfortunately these terms have fallen into disuse.

By definition, in a tabular region, tectonic displacements affect only narrow

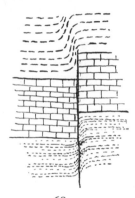

FIGURE 68

Passage of a fault (*in a rigid bed*) *into a flexure in the overlying plastic bed.* (*Based on the Oppedette faults, Basses-Alpes, affecting the Urgonian limestone, surmounted by a plastic, marly-sandy beds of the Mid-Cretaceous.*)

zones; these may be faults with a surface (often a plane) of discontinuity whose two margins have slipped in relation to each other or flexures if the continuity of the beds has been preserved (Fig. 68). The intermediate case in which faulting occurs together with marginal drag is rather common. However, faults or flexures also exist in regions of inclined beds and are found in all combinations with real folds.

Whether the beds are horizontal or not, an inclined fault is called *normal* if the upper margin has sunk and *reverse* in the opposite case (Fig. 69). If the beds are inclined, the position of a fault is defined in terms of its relation to their dip, by distinguishing directional or longitudinal faults that may be *conforming* or *contrary*, depending on whether they lower the beds in the same sense as the dip or not, *diagonal, oblique,* and *transverse* faults (Fig. 70).

The attitude of a fault is defined by its *strike* (the direction of a horizontal line in the plane of the fault) and its *dip* (definition similar to that for the dip of a bed). The *displacement* is a measure of the amount of the relative throw of the two margins. For certain technical problems (mining exploration of a bed affected by a fault whose prolongation must be sought along a horizontal gallery or through another working) faults may present certain geometric problems than can easily be solved graphically.

We must distinguish different sorts of displacement (Fig. 71). The true relative displacement of one of the margins with respect to the other may be represented by a vector *AB* situated in the plane of the fault. This vector may be broken down into two components, a longitudinal displacement, parallel to

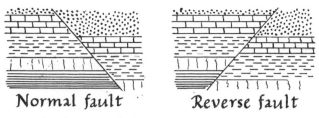

FIGURE 69. *Normal and Reverse faults.*

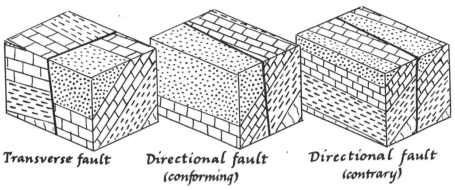

Transverse fault   Directional fault   Directional fault
                           (conforming)   (contrary)

FIGURE 70. *Transverse fault, conforming directional fault (French, faille directionelle conforme), and contrary directional fault (French, faille directionelle contraire).*

the beds ($B'B$), very difficult to recognize for lack of a datum point, and a transverse displacement that may be measured normal to the trace of the beds (AB') or along the line of the greatest slope (AB''). It is often convenient to consider the vertical projection, or vertical throw, of this apparent displacement, which, if the beds are horizontal, corresponds to their difference of level (AH). The amount of the displacement naturally varies along the fault until

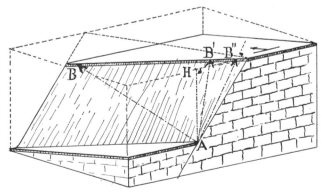

FIGURE 71. *Geometric definitions of displacement.*

it disappears at the extremities. It sometimes happens that the apparent displacement changes in sense along a given fault (Fig. 28).

Detailed studies have resulted in the recognition of important horizontal displacements for faults long considered as having undergone a displacement only approximately vertical; so the possibility of a horizontal displacement should never be lost sight of, especially for faults affecting folded zones. This notion may greatly enrich the tectonic interpretation of certain regions.

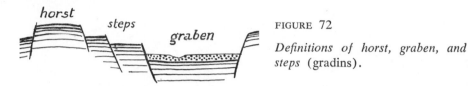

FIGURE 72

Definitions of horst, graben, and steps (gradins).

From an overall point of view, a flexure of beds, between flat belts, is approximately the equivalent of a fault with a transverse displacement. It often happens that, along a given complication of detail, certain beds are faulted and others simply affected by a flexure. But, whatever the plasticity of the beds, which may stretch a great deal, the overall dip of a flexure can scarcely correspond to any but a reverse fault, or at most a vertical one. There are all transitions in a fold, and it would be useless to seek a clear-cut limit. The term *monoclinal,* used only in English, is synonymous with flexure.

The groupings of faults or flexures frequently exhibit a particular pattern. Faults may be roughly parallel, determining a stepped structure or isolating uplifted *horsts* and depressed trenches or *grabens* (Fig. 72). On the east side of the Paris Basin, *double faults,*[3] spaced about 1 km apart, succeed one another for a distance of more than 20 km, in places, and include among them a sunken belt with a throw of about 100 m at a maximum.

We have seen that the apparent displacement of a fault may vary. It is said that two faults "relay" each other when they are approximately parallel along a part of their length and when their apparent throws vary inversely, such that their sum is approximately constant (R, Fig. 73). A fault may also

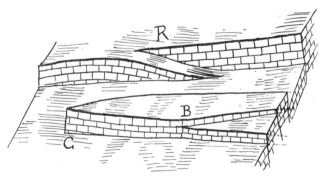

FIGURE 73. *Relay faults* (R) *and bifurcation or ramification* (B); *isolated wedge* (C).

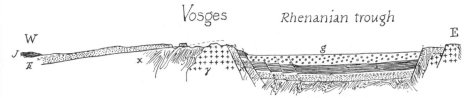

FIGURE 74. *Diagramatic section of the Vosges and the Rhenish trough.* γ*: granite; x; more or less metamorphic Paleozoic;* ₮ *Permo-Trias; J; Jurassic; g, Oligocene of the Alsatian Plain, and Quaternary, the general mass of deposits that are present in the basin limited by the faults. On the other hand, the Jurassic is missing on the Vosges and in the Black Forest (to the east) only because it has been carried away by erosion after the movement of the faults.*

ramify (as shown in B), or two faults may join at an acute angle, thus isolating a wedge (C) without producing any deformation beyond the apex of the angle.

Faults may also cause the subsidence of an approximately circular basin within a volcanic massif, thus producing a caldera (explosion calderas also exist). During the time of action of circular faults, radial fissures that display more or less marked displacements may also appear.

Certain faults, during their period of activity, may serve as limiting features to sedimentary basins (boundary faults). Such faults may be difficult to distinguish from those in which erosion has removed the beds on the adjacent uplifted section (Fig. 74).

In folded regions, geometric forms may be much more complex, especially since the variety of faults just discussed may be superimposed on the folds. Let us begin by analyzing the forms that a given sedimentary horizon may assume; in field surveys, a particularly well-marked bed is usually chosen as a datum, inasmuch as the form of such a bed can easily be traced. The whole nomenclature is dominated by the frequent statement that the surface often presents a series of irregular, roughly parallel undulations, and therefore presents a constant strike. The range of this uniformity, however, must not be exaggerated, since the surface of the reference horizon is seldom cylindrical, and the strikes of adjacent structural highs may be notably different.

In the analysis of forms, the fundamental elements are the longitudinal structural highs (anticlines) and lows (synclines). (See Fig. 75.) We shall

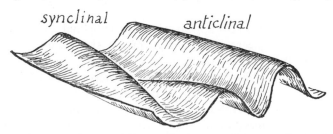

FIGURE 75. *Definition of an anticline and of a syncline; anticlinal relays.*

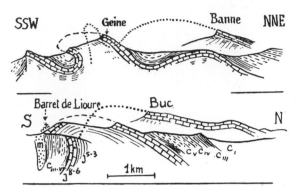

FIGURE 76. *Sections showing the form of the anticline north of Lure (Drôme), on both sides of each of the transverse faults of the Banne and Gresse. The profile of the Upper Jurassic is indicated by the broken line in front of the fault and by the dotted line behind it.*

return later to the special features that may be studied on a transverse section. We shall define the "axis" of an anticline or of a syncline as the longitudinal line formed by the high points or by the low points of successive sections through these structures. The axis is not necessarily horizontal; it may be affected by a more or less marked plunge. The plunge of the axis may have different meanings. In a first case the axis of an anticline plunges in a given direction, but this is not the case for the axes of adjacent synclines. The relative height of the anticline diminishes and ends by disappearing, often presenting a *periclinal plunge.* Often another anticline originates where the first fades out; we say that it relays the first. A syncline may fade out in a similar manner in what is called a *perisynclinal termination.* A very short anticline whose axis plunges at both ends constitutes a *brachyanticline;* if the longitudinal and transverse dimensions of an anticline differ little, it is called a dome. In the same manner, we define the term *brachysyncline,* or *cuvette.*

FIGURE 77. *Example of ejective style; section passing through Rosans (Drôme, Hautes-Alpes); the heavy line indicates the top of the Jurassic.*

But another case may also appear when the anticlinal and synclinal axes of a whole sheaf of adjacent folds plunge in the same sense; this sense may change, and the individual folds may successively traverse zones of transverse increase (or axial increase, or diametrical or, according to Gèze,[4] transanticlinal increase) or zones of lowering (axial depression or, according to Gèze, trans-synclinal depression). Such axial displacements may be traces of regional deformation. Where more or less deep erosion has occurred, we may be able

N

1 km

FIGURE 78. *Dejective style; section across the region of Comps (Var).*

to study both the high and low parts of the folds and consequently reconstruct their form to a very great height, if we can assume that their form does not vary with the axial displacements.

Of the faults that may affect the reference whose form we are analyzing, let mention, in addition to the varieties already studied, *transverse faults,* which are, in general, transverse to the folds. The fault margins are not simply wedged away from each other, but are folded in different ways (Fig. 76), having acted independently of each other at the time of deformation.

Anticlines and synclines may be somewhat crowded together. Stille[5] proposed that the term *ejective style* be applied to narrow anticlines separated by wide synclines (Fig. 77) and that the term *dejective style* be applied to the inverse (that is, wide, tabular anticlines separated by narrow, pinched synclines), as shown in Fig. 78. By doing this, the term congruent can be reserved for anticlines and synclines of comparable widths. These notions, which could depend on the horizon taken as reference, are interesting only when the corresponding characters are very marked.

Let us now examine the geometry of the various kinds of anticline as they appear in cross section. Anticlines may be upright, symmetrical, or, if the dip of one limb is greater than that of the other, *asymmetrical* or *overfolded.* If one of the limbs of an anticline has gone beyond the vertical, it is said to be *overturned;* if the inversion goes so far that the limbs approach horizontality, the anticline is then referred to as *recumbent* (Fig. 79). The term *coffer fold* indicates a relatively wide anticline with nearly vertical limbs.

If the opposite limbs of a fold are approximately parallel, the structure is called *isoclinal.* This holds true even for upright or slightly overfolded folds. If in a succession of similar folds erosion has removed the anticlinal hinges, all the visible dips will be approximately the same; thus we must turn to

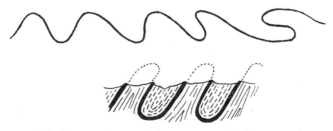

FIGURE 79. *Possible forms of an anticline; symmetrical or upright unsymmetrical, overfolded, overturned. Below, Isoclinal structure.*

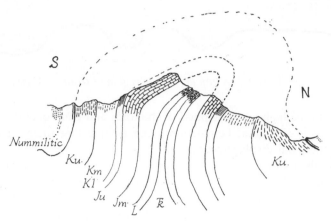

FIGURE 80. *Gourdan anticline (Alpes-Maritimes). Example of an upright fold with parallel sides overturned in its upper part. The observation of the outcrops (zone indicated by patterns) imposes the outline in depth of contacts as dictated.*

stratigraphic analysis to distinguish between anticlines and synclines. Daly[6] has suggested the term *homocline* with a sense very close to isoclinal. The term *accordance* has been employed to indicate the parallelism of dips that results from a very severe tectonic deformation. An isoclinal, upright anticline may overfold at its upper part or, more rarely, exhibit a fan-shaped form. Isoclinal synclines are also found, some of which are pinched or, at times, closed (strangled). (See Figs. 80 and 81.)

All these forms may be observed when the continuity of the reference horizon has been preserved; but quite often, one side of the anticline is

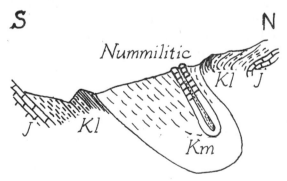

FIGURE 81. *Nummulitic syncline in the valley of the Estéron (west part of the Alpes-Maritimes). The two limbs of the syncline are resting upon each other along a great length; the fact that the Nummulitic limestone on both sides of the syncline rests on quite different horizons of the Middle Cretaceous shows clearly that the two limbs, now in contact, were deposited quite far apart, since the syncline is deep.*

stretched, at first thinning out and then disappearing, replaced by a fault quite different from those that have been considered in the case of a tabular region and producing a broken anticline. When a limb disappears through stretching, it is always the overturned one. Stretching may appear in a slightly overfolded fold as well as in a recumbent fold (Fig. 82); the degree of stretching of the overturned limb and the degree of inversion of a fold are largely independent. If the overturned limb of a fold has been truncated by a fault such that a series of sediments which succeed one another in normal sequence are thrust over more recent sediments (Fig. 83), the fold constitutes an *overthrust*. At the fault contact, more or less stretched and discontinuous fragments are often found, which are remnants of the overturned limb. Termier proposed that we distinguish between *first-order nappes*—the exaggeration of a recumbent fold, in which the overturned limb is preserved (*nappe-pli couché* of Gèze) and *second-order nappes*—the exaggeration of a fold-fault or an overthrust fault without an overturned limb (*nappe-écaille* of Gèze). Inasmuch as all intermediate cases may appear, there is little to be gained in making this distinction. The complications that may be associated with such nappes will be discussed later.

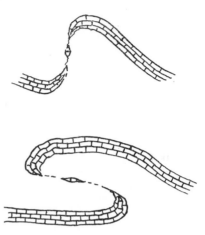

FIGURE 82

Stretching of the limb of an anticline. Top, Section based on the Vibre anticline (Basses-Alpes). Below, Overthrust in the southwestern Alpes-Maritimes, such as that of Caussols. In both sections, the horizon represented is Upper Jurassic limestone.

The foregoing statements are concerned only with elementary forms. The complex manner in which elementary forms may be grouped is indicated in Fig. 84, which shows the configuration of a rather thin bed of hard limestone (Upper Jurassic) lying between thick marly sequences, in Vanige Mountain, which is located at the intersection point of three anticlines.

But we must not be satisfied with studying the form of a key horizon. It is the overall character of the sedimentary series that must be clarified. Observation shows in quite a large number of cases that the initial thickness of beds in the sedimentary series has been preserved, such that deformation is reduced to a distortion of the surface (Fig. 85). Insofar as this is exact we may deduce the thickness of adjacent beds from the form of a reference horizon, since they remain parallel with the reference horizon. It is often possible to accurately define the axial plane (or surface) of an overfolded anticline. This plane is inclined in the same direction as are the limbs of the fold. The surface that

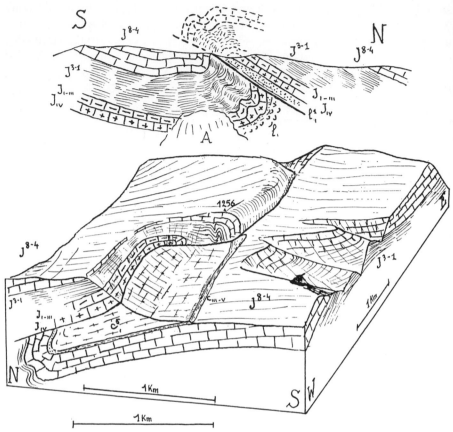

FIGURE 83. *The overthrust of the Audibergue (Alpes-Maritimes), eastern end. The section shown above represents the right bank of the valley of the Loup, which passes just behind the block diagram; it is thus seen in inverse sense to the block diagram. The amplitude of the overthrust, which results in the shearing of the tilted limb of an anticline, diminishes progressively from west to east.* [*Goguel, J., Description tectonique de la bordure des Alpes, de la Bléone au Var, Mém. Carte Géol., p. 260, 1937.*]

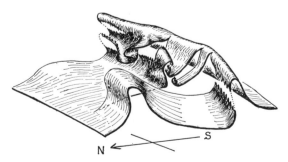

FIGURE 84

Form of the Upper Jurassic, assumed cleared of later sediments and the parts carried away by erosion re-established, in the region of the Vanige (Drôme). Bull. Carte Géol., no. 223, t. XLVI, Fig. 18, 1947.

contains the culminating points of the different beds is called the *crest plane*. Theoretically, this plane would be vertical if the folding were perfectly parallel, but it may be inclined in the same sense as the axial plane as a result of an

incipient disharmony. This is of great practical importance in petroleum exploration. If a well is to be drilled into an anticlinal structure, the well should be located toward the gentler flank if it is hoped to reach a deep bed at its highest point. It is easy to see, in a fold of any sort, that the beds can remain parallel to each other for only a limited distance; toward the crests, they curve more and more sharply until it is no longer possible to trace parallel surfaces. The beds must have been

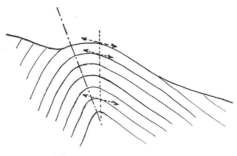

FIGURE 85

Theoretical form of an anticline. Axial plane and crest plane.

deformed in a manner such that their original thickness was not preserved. Such folding is called *disharmonic*. Simple geometric considerations are not sufficient to determine the form of the lower horizons. We shall see in the following chapters how other dynamic and kinematic considerations furnish complementary indications. Let us indicate at once that the disharmony is often due to the relative independence of an undeformed socle and its sedimentary cover. If the form of the latter is completed by tracing the successive beds left parallel to one another, this operation becomes impossible beyond a certain bed; it is then possible to record that the mass of the cover approximately outlines the form of an unfolded platform whose height may vary according to the points chosen (Fig. 86). Disharmony is sometimes expressed simply by a change in the thickness of certain beds in which quite irregular secondary folds can often be seen.

Folds may be distinguished on the basis of size; some correspond to major

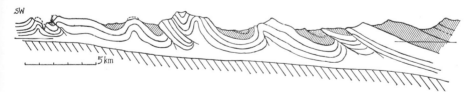

FIGURE 86. *Section of the region of Sénez (Basses-Alpes). (Description tectonique de la bordure des Alpes, de la Bléone au Var, Mém. Carte, 1937, pl, 2, coupe 3.) In tracing the outlines of the beds parallel to one another (taking into consideration stratigraphic variations of thickness), we should stop at the base of the Lias, but we assume the position of an unfolded sole (slant lines), doubtless corresponding to the Lower Triassic. Tertiary: stippled; Cretaceous: closely spaced lines; Jurassic and Trias: unshaded.*

complications, that is, they are elements of regional architecture that affect the whole thickness of the visible terranes. On the other hand, within a given formation, individual beds may exhibit numerous little folds of short radius that succeed one another from bed to bed but which do not extend beyond the boundaries of the formation under consideration. These are often called minor folds. In some rocks, folding may be observed on a still smaller scale, such as that of a hand specimen of thin section.

These minute secondary folds are very obvious, since they can be observed in outcrop, whereas the major folds can usually be identified only after laborious study of a whole mountain chain. For this reason, it would be to our advantage if we could use secondary folding in interpreting general structure. To this effect, some authors propose that the same mechanical principles can be used to explain the geometry of similar folds on different scales. However, this postulate has no rational basis. In Chapter 12, we shall note the important restrictions that a dynamic study will impose upon this postulate.

English-speaking geologists often apply the term *competent* to beds that fold harmonically and whose study enables us to determine the general structure, as contrasted with *incompetent* beds, which are susceptible to folding in an independent manner and which thus produce disharmonic folds. We shall try to state these notions more precisely in the dynamic and kinematic study.

It should be noted that special forms develop in certain terranes such as saliferous formations, which are characterized by a relatively high plasticity.

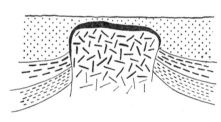

FIGURE 87

Theoretical section through a salt dome.

In certain regions, such as along the Gulf Coast (Gulf of Mexico) and in Northern Germany, cylindrical masses of salt penetrate undeformed horizontal strata. These salt masses are usually several kilometers in diameter, but some exceed ten kilometers (Fig. 87).

These *salt domes* were long unrecognized, inasmuch as the small number of those that pierce the surface (called *salt plugs*) were not correctly interpreted. But the localization of oil pools on their periphery provoked very active investigation of them. Geophysical prospecting has been successful in locating nearly 300 in the Gulf Coast region, about 100 in northern Germany, one or two in Alsace, and several in the Aquitaine. The subsequent study of well logs has been useful in enabling geologists to determine their form (Fig. 88).

In the plains of northern Germany and in those of the Gulf Coast (Texas), masses of salt several kilometers in diameter have risen to within a short distance of the surface. Actually, their upper extremities are not formed of pure salt but of quite complex rocks that contain a solution residue of salt, pro-

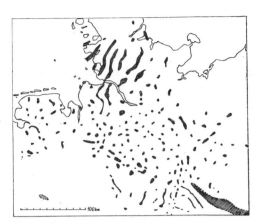

FIGURE 88

Salt domes in Northwest Germany.
[*After H. Cloos.*]

duced by the circulation of water through the superficial beds forming the *cap-rock*. The adjacent beds are more or less upturned at the contact with the plug, thus producing structures favorable to the accumulation of oil.

The surface may remain completely horizontal at the site of such a dome or it may rise slightly. Above certain Gulf Coast salt masses, the combination of circular uplift and concentric sinking due to solution of the salt has created a quite characteristic but not very marked relief.

Though the domes we have discussed are far removed from any mountain chain, some have been found in folded zones, for example in Laristan province (Persian Gulf) and in southern Algeria.

The salt that constitutes these domes always originates in a very deep horizon; in northern Germany, Permian salt beds are the source. Along the Gulf Coast, the horizon of the undisturbed stratum has never been reached; it probably lies at a depth beyond 4000 meters, hence the salt bed must be very thick.

Later on we shall study the mechanics of formation of salt domes, and we shall see that they are not formed as a result of forces of deep origin, but are due to the plasticity and the low density of the salt. Perhaps they should be included among the deformations of nontectonic origin, which were studied in Chapter 8.

Salt domes must not be confused with diapir folds, although the plasticity of the salt, or of the gypsum, is responsible for formation of both. Diapir folds result from the intervention of tectonic forces and may be of small dimensions; the difference in density between the salt and the adjacent sediments does not play an essential role in their formation. Actually, in the Basses-Alpes, there are diapir apexes of gypsum with a width of little more than ten meters.

When folding affects a series containing a saliferous bed, the latter, being subjected locally to great pressure, escapes along a fissure or an overthrust fault and may even pierce the overlying strata. Thus, the salt may intrude younger beds of any age without the intermediate strata taking any part in the diapir structure.

Mrazec[7] has given the name *diapir folds,* or simply *diapirs,* to such structures and has referred to them as "folds with a piercing core."

Gignoux[8] summed up his definition of diapirs as follows: ". . . a core, or a belt, of older [strata] . . . surrounded on all sides by a surface of abnormal contact separating it from the more recent [strata] tilted and stretched along this surface."

Usage seems to have clarified this definition, restricting the word diapir to folds within which the piercing core is formed of a plastic rock such as rock salt or a saliferous series (although Mrazec, in his definition, insisted that diapir folding could be observed in other than saliferous rocks). When a core of hard rock pierces a less resistant cover, which does not become entrained, we may apply the term used by Viennot,[9] namely, *extrusion.*

One property of diapirs, mentioned incidentally by Mrazec, is so striking that it might have been included in the definition, namely, that they are not regular in the sense in which we say that the very continuous undulations of a calcareous series are regular. Some are blade-shaped, whereas others are elliptical or circular in cross section. In any case, their form may change very rapidly from one cross section to another; therefore it is, in general, foreign to the tectonics of the terrains into whose midst it pierces, which may show more or less elongated undulations. This lack of structural continuity is characteristic of diapirs.

Diapirs of all sizes have been found. Some are very small, having diameters on the order of tens of meters, whereas salt domes are always of great dimensions, but vary in average diameter according to the region. Small diapirs could not have been produced as a result of a difference in density between the salt and the adjacent strata, but have instead been produced by active tectonic forces. Figure 89, from Mrazec's original publication, shows some of the forms of diapir folds observed in the Neogene of Romania—a series

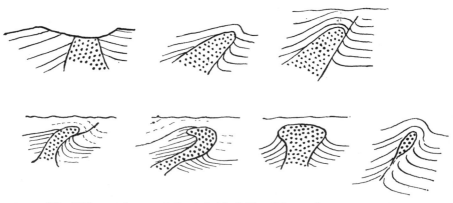

FIGURE 89. *Different forms of diapir folds.* [*After Mrazec.*]

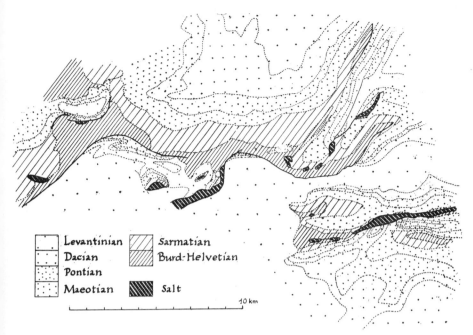

FIGURE 90. *Geologic map of a part of the sub-Carpathian region (Roumania), showing the relative independence of the saliferous diapirs in relation to the anticlines of the underlying Miocene series. [After Grozescu, H., Ann. Inst. Géol. Roum., vol. 8, 1918.]*

more than 2000 m thick, formed of plastic terranes. The salt seems to have come from the underlying Miocene, but its origin is open to some discussion; it is certain that the salt, during its movement, was separated from the strata with which it was originally associated and was somehow mechanically concentrated.

In Fig. 90, which shows a map of a Romanian region, that is particularly rich in diapirs, we can observe the discontinuous character that these structures typically exhibit, as well as the frequency with which they mark out abnormal contacts that are prolonged on both sides into the terranes of the cover. This is characteristic of diapirs; in many regions, diapirs are seldom observed other than in the form of salt points that mark surfaces of abnormal contact. The relative displacement of the two margins evidently produced mechanical conditions that were favorable to the movement of salt, or of plastic rocks in general. Such injections of saliferous Keuper along surfaces of abnormal contact are very frequent in the Alps, the Jura and the Pyrenees. If the diapir apexes are adjacent to a surface of abnormal contact, as is often the case in certain points of the Basses-Alpes, we may assume that they progressed along this surface to pierce through undeformed strata only along a short length.

The Triassic piercements of Aquitaine were described by Dupouy-Camet[10] from an examination of cores obtained in a number of wells drilled for oil. Our knowledge concerning these piercements was greatly advanced as a result of this study, since a complete range of domes and diapirs deserve becoming classic. Four of them are true salt domes, several kilometers in diameter, but little elongated, implanted vertically. However, some seem to be joined to an anticlinal wrinkle, which may have initiated their emplacement. Others correspond to anticlines of the covering terranes, more or less regular or faulted, through which the Triassic core pierced more or less widely according to the positions varying with different cases. The Triassic core may remain buried at depth and be revealed only by well-logs, in the absence of which the structure might be taken for a simple regular anticline, as in the case of the anticline of Saint-Marcet, whose piercement core was revealed only by the numerous wells drilled for gas. Or, the Triassic core may have reached the surface; it is frequently seen that the Trias has extravasated on the surface, flowing over the capping terranes. In certain cases, especially when it is a question of a faulted recumbent fold, the Trias injected into the fault forms a blade only about 10 m thick. The Trias may also inject a simple fault, at times even transverse to the folds.

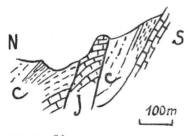

FIGURE 91

Extrusion of hard Jurassic limestone in the midst of the Cretaceous marls of the syncline of Gréolières (Alpes-Maritimes).

The study of lacunas, sedimentary breccias, reworked sediments, and the discordances of which they are evidence has made it possible for us to state precisely the chronology of the movements. Traces of Pyrenean movements have been found even in the foreland, but the ascent of the salt may at times have been produced or continued outside these principal phases of movement. It is the opinion of the author that, besides folding the cover, the faults affecting the platform may have played a role in localizing these domes, in some of which pre-Triassic shreds are involved.

We have seen that the term *extrusion* (Viennot) is reserved for the blade of a hard rock in the midst of a cover that is not entrained. These extrusions are in general of limited dimensions, as plates or without marked elongation, and are apparently due to great pressure at the heart of hard rocks, which has caused flakes to break off (Fig. 91).

In the Alps, and in certain similar mountain chains, among which the Franco-Begian coal basin should be mentioned, the abundance of overthrusts has produced numerous complications for which a whole special vocabulary has been created. A complete analysis of the present disposition of beds re-

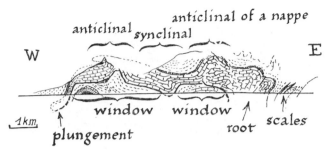

FIGURE 92. *Section of the right bank of the valley of the Guil (Hautes-Alpes), showing the different constituent elements of a nappe. This nappe contains Triassic limestones, overlain by a rather thin series of Jurassic, Cretaceous and Flysch. In the windows, from the top down, the rocks present are: Flysch, Cretaceous, Triassic (limestone and quartzite), and Permian andesite.*

quires a kinematic analysis of the succession of movements, some of which were separated by erosion phases which may have accumulated their effects on the same terranes. This analysis is presented in a later chapter, but we should present a certain number of definitions based on the present geometry of the beds.

Nappe de charriage (overthrust mass), or simply *nappe*, is the name given to large overthrusts, some of which have moved forward several tens of kilometers. This name is applied both to recumbent folds with preserved overturned limbs (and usually laminated) and to simple folds. However, it is not possible to set up a definition that would permit distinguishing recumbent folds and overthrusts from *nappes* strictly on the basis of the amount of forward movement undergone by the overthrust block. The nomenclature applied to these structures differs from one region to another and has been re-

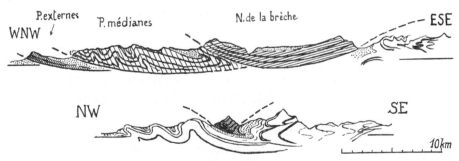

FIGURE 93. *Shreds (lambeaux) of overthrusts, and klippes. Above, Section of Haute-Savoie, to the north of Giffre. The Mesozoic of the different nappes that constitute the Prealps is indicated by a different shading and is left blank for the autochthon. The Tertiary is uniformly indicated by dots. Below, Section to the south of the Arve, through the Annes klippe.*

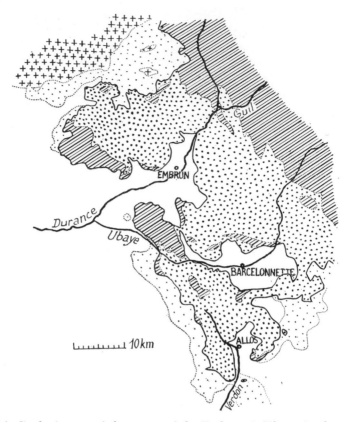

FIGURE 94. *Geologic map of the nappe of the Embrunais-Ubaye. In the autochthon, the crosses indicate the crystalline rocks (Pelvoux), the Mesozoic is left blank, and the Nummulitic is indicated by light dots. In the nappe, the heavy dots indicate the "flysch" of Upper Cretaceous or Tertiary (Nummulitic) age; and the ruled lines indicate the Mesozoic. Note the windows or half-windows of Embrun, Barcelonnette, Allos.*

peatedly revised in accordance with changes in interpretation. In some regions, all recumbent folds are considered as nappes, regardless of their dimensions. In other regions, such as in Provence, the smaller features are still referred to as overthrusts or recumbent folds, whereas the larger features are called nappes.

In certain regions, recumbent folds of the same stratigraphic series are found superposed one above the other. Usage has abandoned the terminology that E. Haug applied in Provence (Saint-Beaume, Allauch). Since certain beds of the sedimentary series exhibited disharmonies, evidenced in place by stretching, Haug distinguished a "Liassic nappe," a "Jurassic nappe," and an "Urgonian nappe," superposed, and constituting, in his mind, parts of the same stratigraphic series.

It should be very precisely stated that the terms relative to nappes essentially characterize relations of relative positions and not of form, since the stacking of nappes could have taken absolutely any form. We speak of a nappe anticline or nappe syncline to indicate the overall form of the series of nappes. We also use the terms culmination and axial minimum to define the form of nappes in the longitudinal sense. Changes in form of nappes play an even more important role than does topography in determining the manner in which they are carved by erosion, producing *windows* (or fensters), corresponding to the exposure by erosion of the substratum of a nappe, surrounded on all sides or almost surrounded by preserved parts of the nappe. The term half-window (*demi-fenêtre*) is used if the nappe is preserved on only a part

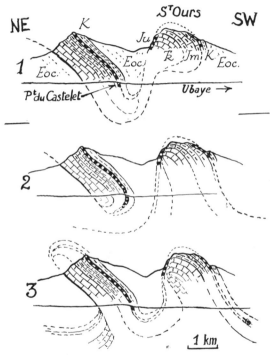

FIGURE 95. *The left bank of the Ubaye, at the Pont du Castelet (Basses-Alpes). Three interpretations are theoretically possible: (1) a fold of the frontal part of a nappe; (2) a plunging front and an autochthonous anticline; and (3) two autochthonous anticlines. The section of the right bank, along which it is possible to follow the prolongation of the series of the Pont du Castelet, which forms a nappe in accordance with that of the Guil (Fig. 99), makes possible the formal elimination of the third interpretation. The identity of the facies at the Rocher de Saint-Ours and at the Pont du Castelet makes the first interpretation much more probable than the second. The facies of the Jurassic of the lower series, visible a little farther up, are in fact very different.*

FIGURE 96. *Overthrust of Digne (Basses-Alpes); section made along the valley of
the Bes. In this structural feature, which by its dimensions would deserve
the name of nappe, the Trias (gypsiferous Keuper, in black) and the Lias
rest on the Tertiary. It is not possible to distinguish a root, the overthrust
mass being in continuity with the region situated to the northeast. In fact,
on this side, the whole Mesozoic sequence has slipped* en bloc, *owing to
the plasticity of the Keuper, which is laminated in places.* h, *Carboniferous;*
t_1, *Triassic sandstone;* t_2, *Muschelkalk;* t_3, *Keuper;* L, *Lias;* J, *Jurassic,
Middle and Upper (overlain in places by Lower Cretaceous, not shown);*
o-m, *Oligocene and Miocene.*

of its periphery. On the other hand, a shred (*lambeau*) of an overthrust is a
part of a nappe that has been entirely isolated by erosion. If its surface area
is small, it is called a *klippe.*

The front of a nappe corresponds to the hinge of a recumbent fold, which
may remain recognizable in spite of the stretching of the overturned limb. In
front of a window, only the front of a nappe may be preserved, in which case
it constitutes a *plunging head* (*tête plongeante*). (See Fig. 95.) Not too infre-
quently, the most recent beds of a nappe cannot be distinguished from the
substrata, thus a plunging head might be mistaken for an isolated anticline.
Only by following the head along the strike is it possible to indicate its relation
with the rest of the nappe.

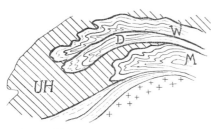

FIGURE 97

Hooding (encapuchonnement) *of
Helvetic nappes (Morcles, Diablerets,
Wildhorn) in the ultra-Helvetic series.*

The term *root* is commonly used apropos of nappe. However, it is also one
of the most difficult terms to define objectively. The root is the zone from
which a nappe arises, but according to
the idea formed of the kinetics of the
overthrust, it may correspond to different dispositions, such as a continuous
passage to a normal sedimentary cover
or a vertical plunge to great depth.

In superposed nappes, a fold of an
upper nappe may intrude itself beneath
a lower nappe. The intruding nappe is
called a *hood* or *involution* (*encapu-
chonnement*). Such complications are almost impossible to describe independently of the kinetics that originated them (Fig. 97).

The term scale (French, *écaille*) is employed with several different meanings; it may refer to a mass limited by an overthrust fault left in connection

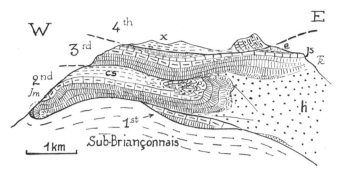

FIGURE 98. *The* écailles *between Briançon and Vallouise (Pierre Termier). Diagram of the mutual relations (composite section). First, second, and third scales (écailles) are shreds of the Mesozoic cover (Triassic limestone with Upper Cretaceous and Flysch) and of the Carboniferous, which rest on the sub-Briançonnais zone through a major overthrust. The fourth scale is a shred of a different nappe of more distant origin. h, Carboniferous overthrusting the sub-Briançonnais Mesozoic; ℞, Triassic (quartzites and limestones); Jm, Dogger; js, Malm (Guillestre marble); cs, platez marbles* (marbres en plaquettes) *of the Upper Cretaceous; e, Tertiary flysch; x, crystalline schists of the fourth scale.*

with its roots, which cannot be distinguished from a nappe of the second order, except by its smaller dimensions. The term may also refer to a nappe fragment that has been isolated between two other units and which is considered secondary from the point of view of the interpretation. Finally, it may refer to secondary nappes resulting from the subdivision of a major nappe through folding. Thus, the studies of P. Termier[11] have definitively imposed the names second-, third-, and fourth-*écaille* in the region between Briançon

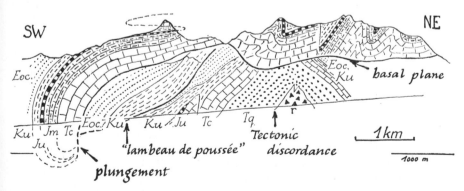

FIGURE 99. *Definitions relative to nappes. Section of the right bank of the Ubaye, upstream from the Pont du Castellet (situated on the plunging head), south slope of the Font-Sancte Massif. P, Permian; Tq, Triassic limestone; Jm, Middle Jurassic; Ju, Upper Jurassic; Ku, Upper Cretaceous; e, Tertiary flysch.*

and Vallouise respectively for two folds of the Mesozoic cover of the overthrust Carboniferous, and for an overthrust shred (*lambeau* or a *klippe*, considering its small dimensions) involving crystalline terranes of distant origin.

The term inversion nappe (*lambeau de poussée*) designates a scale whose origin lies in the substratum of an overthrust and which was torn loose by it.

The term *rabotage basal* (basal planing) has been applied by P. Fallot[12] to structures in which a folded, overthrust mass has been sliced by a less undulated overthrust surface, with the result that the lower ends are lacking in the synclines. The missing ends, however, should be found elsewhere along the surface of the overthrust as isolated scales.

The opposite of basal planing is the tectonic discordance by which the overthrust surface that constitutes the base of a nappe rests on the various members of the substratum and cuts across them at an angle. It is sometimes difficult to determine whether previous erosion had cut into the folds of the substratum before the overthrust formed, or whether the latter were torn away as a part of the substratum in the form of a *lambeau de poussée* (Fig. 99). Finally, it is very difficult to separate the definitions that we have just presented from the kinematic study of the generative movements.

Notes and References

1. Margerie, E. de and Heim, Albert, *Les dislocations de l'écorce terrestre, essai de définition et de nomenclature* (text in French and German, synonymy in French, German, and English), Zurich, 1888.

2. Grabau, A. W., Physical Characters and History of Some New York Formations, Science, new ser., vol. 22, pp. 528–535, 1905. (See especially p. 534.)

3. Abrard, R. and Corroy, G., *Etude de la double faille de la Marne et des régions voisines,* Bull. Carte géol. France, no. 165, vol. 30, pp. 17–24, 1927.

4. Gèze, B., *Etude géologique de la Montagne Noire et des Cévennes méridionales,* Mém. Soc. géol. France, new ser., vol. 29, no. 62, fasc. 1–3, Paris, 1949. (See especially page 8.)

5. Stille, H., *Injektivfaltung und damit zusammenhängende Erscheinungen,* Geol. Rundschau, vol. 8, pp. 89–142, 1917.

6. Daly, R. A., Homocline and Monocline, Bull. Geol. Soc. America, vol. 27, pp. 89–92, 1916.

7. Mrazec, L., *Les plis diapirs et le diapirisme en général,* Inst. géol. Roumanie, Comptes-rendus, vol. 6, pp. 226–272, 1927.

8. Gignoux, M., *La tectonique des terrains salifères, son rôle dans les Alpes françaises,* Soc. géol. France (livre jubilaire), vol. 2, pp. 329–360, Paris, 1930.

9. Viennot, P., *Première contribution à la connaissance des extrusions pyrénéennes,* Bull. Carte géol. France, vol. 31, no. 171, pp. 349–403, 1928.

10. Dupouy-Camet, J., *Recherches structurales sur les accidents triasiques du Sud-Ouest de l'Aquitaine,* Bull. Serv. Carte géol. France, vol. 49, no. 233, pp. 249–535, 1952.

11. Termier, P., *Les montagnes entre Briançon et Vallouise,* Mém. Carte géol. France, Paris, 1903.

12. Fallot, P., *Observations sur la tectonique de la zone subbétique dans la province de Murcie,* Bull. Soc. géol. France, 5e ser., vol. 14, pp. 11–28, 1944.

CHAPTER ELEVEN

Kinematic Interpretation of Tectonic Deformations

Conservation of volume in deformation—Conservation of length of beds in parallel folding—Stripping and slipping of the cover—Deformation of the basement, disharmony—Intercutaneous scale—Movement of a fault, contraction or corresponding extension—Rhenish trench—Deformations not parallel to a given plane—Transverse faults—En echelon folds; folds with obliquely faulted side—Study of deformation in a horizontal plane, representation by a grid—Succession of several deformations; folded faults, successive faults, successive folds—Folding of nappes—Erosion between successive phases—Diverticulations.

WE HAVE just seen what gross uncertainties can be introduced if we apply geometric considerations to the study of the present form of mineral masses by prolonging the observations made on outcrops. It may seem that by not limiting ourselves to the present state, but attempting to follow the evolution of forms during the course of time, we greatly complicate the problem before us. In reality we introduce supplementary data that make it possible to state present forms with some precision.

Let us consider, for example, a folded sedimentary series; we know that before deformation, its beds were practically horizontal. Since mass is conserved during deformation, and since the density of deformed rocks differs very little from that of the original rocks (it may increase slightly, owing to a reduction in porosity), their volume is conserved quite completely. If the thickness of a bed is maintained, the same will be true of its area and probably of all the lengths measured on its surface, at least to the degree indicated above, that is, to the ratio of the change in density. The length along the curved beds of a simple anticline, as seen in cross section, is greater than the straight-line distance between two points on opposite limbs; that is, the distance between two points situated on either side of an anticline is diminished during folding, which is accompanied by lateral contraction. According to what we have seen above, within a group of beds involved in parallel folding, the amount of contraction is the same for each bed. What appeared to us as a geometric consequence of the form of the folds is a necessity from the kinematic point of view. If a fold or a sheaf of folds is included between two undeformed regions in which the superposition on a given vertical of the different beds has not been disturbed, the lateral contraction corresponding to its formation, which is the distance by which the regions situated on either side have approached each other, evidently has a well-defined value. For all the beds that have undergone only a change of form (incurvation) without stretching in their plane, this lateral contraction is the difference between the length of a bed (measured on a transverse section) and the distance in a straight line of the extremities of the latter. It is to such beds that the term "competent" is applied.

For beds affected by parallel folding, this does not tell us much more than did the geometric analysis of Chap. 9. But with regard to other types of folding, kinematic considerations enable us to indicate the possible forms much more precisely.

As a first approximation (insufficient in many cases), we may assume that all movements took place parallel to a plane perpendicular to the axes of the folds. Then it is possible to make a complete study of the deformation by preparing cross sections.

If certain beds were stretched, or contrariwise increased in thickness by the lateral compression, evidently we cannot apply to them the calculation of the lateral contraction; but we know that (with an approximation related to the disappearance of the porosity) volume was conserved in the course of the deformation. This is not sufficient to determine the present form of the upper and lower surfaces of a stratigraphic unit, but it may suffice to remove an uncertainty. In the same way, if the anticline is broken by a longitudinal fault (for an oblique fault it is doubtful that the hypothesis of uniquely transverse movements can be applied), the equality of length of all the beds for which the thicknesses are conserved imposes on the tracing of the section a condition that permits excluding the possibility of certain conformations that might have been considered.

Beyond an incompetent bed which permits a disharmony, becoming deformed without the length and thickness remaining separately constant, but with conservation of the volume (area on the section), the amount of lateral contraction of competent beds will be the same as for the other competent beds, at least between two regions free of deformation (which may be difficult to prove).

Even in thin-bedded, incompetent formations, we can still apply the preceding considerations to the detailed contortions that affect it, but they are often difficult to completely unravel. We may attempt to study them statistically by evaluating the relation of lateral contraction (inverse of the thickening) to the detail of the folding. The study of the latter takes us back to the study of elementary deformation.

Let us apply the rule of the conservation of volume (or the area of a section) below a competent reference horizon of known form between two verticals situated on either side of a fold. The lateral contraction is the difference between the length of the folded competent bed and the straight-line distance between two points on opposite limbs of a fold. Let us calculate the depth of a bed such that, if there has been no change of form, the volume situated above this level may be the same before and after deformation. To do this, we divide the section of the intumescence (outlined by the reference horizon above its initial position) by the value of lateral contraction. This is an easy calculation to make with the aid of a planimeter and a curvimeter on a carefully drawn section after an accurate cartographic survey (Fig. 100).

It is impossible to affirm that the horizon whose depth is determined in this way is not deformed, but only that, if it was lifted above its initial position, it was also equally depressed below. Another horizon situated lower would have undergone essentially a subsidence. When trying to imagine what happens at more considerable depths we run into great difficulties. In numerous cases it is probable that the depth calculated as above corresponds actually to that of a horizon that has not been deformed and which consequently has not undergone the same contraction as had the overlying beds: the latter must have slipped on it, either on one side of the fold, or even on both sides of it, but for unequal distances. Kinematic analysis then shows us that the mechanics of folding of parallel beds can be applied only to a series of limited thickness, a "cover," to use an expression consecrated by use.

A whole series of considerations, certain of which will be found in the next chapter, show that the mechanics of slipping décollement of the cover have played an essential role in the Jura (as Buxtorf has shown), and in many other analogous regions, such as the sub-Alpine mountain chains. In order to effectively apply this method we must have a thorough knowledge of the form of the folds and in particular of the displacements of the faults that may be involved. It is not applicable to ruptured folds involving an overthrust fault of unknown amplitude, but it may be combined with the method whose principle was indicated in the preceding chapter and which consists of tracing the different stratigraphic units according to their known thicknesses. In this way, it is possible to determine the depth of the basement (socle) on which the "cover" has slipped as well as the stratigraphic composition of the latter.

In the Jura, in spite of the considerable variations of facies and of thickness of the Jurassic stages, the basement always corresponds to the same stage—the beds underlying the saliferous beds of the Trias. In the southern sub-Alpine mountain chains, an analogous identification can be made; in the

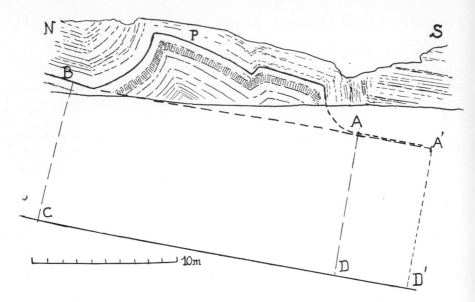

FIGURE 100. *Anticlinal fold and its kinematic interpretation. The section at the top of the figure, traced from a photograph, is visible on the left bank of the Calavon to the north of Céreste (Basses-Alpes). It affects well bedded Oligocene lacustrine limestones.*

The deformed zone is separated by a very clearcut limit from the blocks on both sides, which have remained unchanged; there is no progressive accordance, but an angle in the beds at the crossing of this limit. There is every reason to believe that outside these limits the beds remained rigid when they slipped in relation to each other in the deformed zone. At times, small hollow spaces are observed between them.

By prolonging one of the beds (traced in dashes), which may be very safely done from the attitude of the adjacent beds, we find that the unchanged blocks occupy positions that are the prolongations of each other (line BA). On the section, measurements show that the length of BPA surpasses the direct distance by 5.4 m, and that the area between PBA and the straight line BA is 51.4 m². Determining the quotient 51.4 × 5.4, we find that a horizon CD situated 9.90 m lower may have remained unchanged; we have APB = A'B and surface APBCD = surface A'BCD'.

By following the section more to the north we find, in fact, that about ten meters below the line APB, the calcareous sheaf rests on a marly mass; so it is probable that the flag limestone has slipped on the marls, undergoing a slight dislocation.

It is difficult to say whether it is a question of a gravity slip, aided by the slight dip, which continues very far toward the north, or whether the contraction of the calcareous bed does not result rather from the fact that the underlying beds are bent into a syncline with a very large radius of curvature.

The same method of interpretation may be applied to an anticline of large dimensions whose form will stand out in a detailed survey made on an accurate topographic base.

FIGURE 101. *Folds* (plis de couverture) *of the Alpes-Maritimes. The folds situated to the south of the Permian Dome of Barot indicate the slipping of the Mesozoic cover. The folds of the Muschelkalk to the north of the Barot Dome show, according to Bordet, that there has been a relative slip of the Jurassic cover. So it is probable that there has been an overall slip followed by the uplift of the Barot Dome.*

next chapter, we shall see what causes this localization. A confirmation of this interpretation results from the fact that older beds are never found in the heart of anticlines. But the height of the basement is not constant; undulations that are of great interest in understanding the localization of the folds of the cover may have formed prior to formation of the cover, but they also result from postdepositional movements. Thus, in the Permian Barot dome (Alpes-Maritimes) the basement has risen sufficiently to be exposed by erosion. It is thus seen that the basement forms a broad arched hump of an order of size entirely different from the folds of the surrounding cover and is itself not folded (Fig. 101).

The case of a horizon that favors slipping and of the unique disharmony that marks the base of the cover (at least tectonic, as from the stratigraphic point of view the basement may include sedimentary beds, such as the transgressive basal sandstones of the sedimentary series) is the most simple, but there may also be disharmony at other levels. It would be hard to explain why all the beds should preserve a constant thickness as they are deformed when their incurvation necessarily implies a change of form of the elements situated on the concave surface of a bed, on a convex surface, or on both.

Observation shows that certain beds (the marly and clayey beds in particular) that constitute thick, nonstratified masses undergo quite appreciable changes of thickness. For this reason, the calcareous beds that surround them do not have parallel forms (Fig. 102). That is the very definition of disharmony, but it may appear in different degrees. The folds of beds situated on both sides may correspond in general, but the minute folds of detail may not correspond; similarly, the forms of the principal folds may not be the same. For example, in the Massif des Bauges, Lugeon noticed that the anticlines were always irregular; they were sometimes split at the level of the Upper Jurassic, but were simple and regular at the top of the Neocomian (Urgonian). But, insofar as their position or general form is concerned, these anticlines correspond perfectly.

If the series that undergoes changes of thickness and presents disharmony

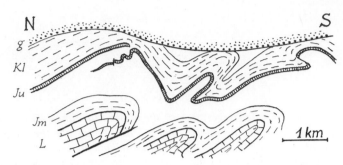

FIGURE 102. *Section of the folds between Chaudon-Norante and Barrême (Basses-Alpes). There is disharmony between the Lias and the Upper Jurassic, as well as between the Lias and the earlier terrains. The Oligocene (O) is discordant.*

is thicker, things may go farther. In the same Bauges massif (and also farther south in the Chartreuse—transverse valley of the Isère), the Middle Jurassic is never found in the heart of the anticlines; instead, only Oxfordian marls are found. It seems that the Bajocian or the Lias were not involved in the folding. This situation persists to the south of the Drôme, where the erosion never reaches, in the heart of the anticlines, a lower stage than the Callovian-Oxfordian marls (Fig. 103). The form of most of these anticlines, which are narrow and sharp, is such that, in a cross section, it is difficult to see how to include Dogger (Middle Jurassic) anticlines in the Drôme structures. Only the anticline situated to the north of the Montagne de Lure is wide enough to suggest that the Dogger should form an anticlinal structure below the level reached by erosion. Except at this location, there is a complete absence of correspondence between the folds of the Lias and the Dogger on the one hand, and those of the Tithonian and the Cretaceous on the other.

In terms of overall structure, the sedimentary units that show disharmony are those that are capable of undergoing a change of thickness in the course of deformation; this change of thickness is of course accompanied by an inverse change of length. As part of such a unit thickens, it undergoes lateral contraction in the same way as does the mass of the cover in the course of its folding, and if it is stratified, it may adapt itself equally by folds unrelated to

FIGURE 103. *Section in the south of the department of the Drôme. The anticline of the Buis (prolongation of the anticline to the north of Lure) is the only one whose form suggests that the Middle Jurassic should be included in its makeup.*

those of the adjacent units. These folds will of course be of very slight length and amplitude, since they are found only within the limits of a given formation.

We have seen above how to interpret minute folds, which are often quite visible in outcrop. They convey information not on the general structure, but on the local deformation of the mass, in much the same way that the deformation of fossils suggests the nature of elementary deformation in a sample of rock. Our efforts would be in vain if we were to seek a direct relation between the form of these minor folds and that of the major folds. In order to understand minor folds properly, it is necessary to consider them within a dynamic framework; the minute minor folds suggest the magnitude of the pressure to which the containing mass was subjected. We shall examine this aspect of the question in the next chapter.

Paul Fallot has noted a particularly interesting example of disharmony in the north of the Alpes-Maritimes for which he created the name of intercutaneous scale (*"écaille intercutanée"*).[1] In a zone where the Mesozoic cover is sheared off at the level of the Upper Trias and has slipped in its whole mass, an overthrust, which in places attains an amplitude of 5 kilometers and which brings the Trias to repose on the Neocomian, does not continue above this horizon. It seems to fade out in the mass of the Aptian marls, and the Upper Cretaceous exhibits folds of only slight importance or local minor folds (Fig. 104). The attitude of the overthrust in the Jurassic indicates a contraction of

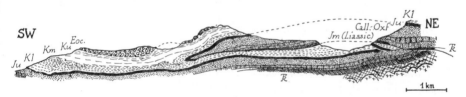

FIGURE 104. *The intercutaneous scale* (écaille intercutanée) *of La Roya.* [*After Paul Fallot.*]

the series reaching 5 kilometers. Since the movement certainly occurred follow deposition of the Annot sandstone (Oligocene), the Upper Cretaceous and the Nummulitic Paleogene evidently underwent an equivalent contraction, although it is not indicated by any important feature. Slips on the Aptian marls brought about the distribution of the contraction along quite a long distance; it must have taken place in the marls through a mass compression and in the heavily bedded Upper Cretaceous through minor folds.

The fact that a compression of such magnitude may escape a first examination, at least in certain beds, demonstrates the great care with which kinematic considerations must be put into operation, always paying strict attention to the lithological constitution. Here, the folds in the limestone of the Upper Jurassic indicate the deformations that the bed has undergone. It typifies the "competent" bed, whereas the Upper Cretaceous, and especially the Middle Cretaceous, behave "incompetently." The folds of the Basses-Alpes and of the Alpes-Maritimes furnish numerous examples of a disharmony in the same beds, which are, in general, less marked.

Paul Fallot pointed out later[2] that complications of detail described in different places in the Alps, which involve a division of the lower beds of an overthrust series into scales (*écailles*), might be considered as *"écailles intercutanées."* The presence of such *écailles* may furnish proof of an overall slipping of the cover.

The application of kinematic considerations to faults, and especially to systems of faults, might also provide interesting results. We have already seen how the movement of a fault seems to behave and seems to result from a series of very rapid shocks of very limited magnitude that may continue over a long period. The geometric nature of the relative displacement is evident, since it results from slipping along a fault plane.

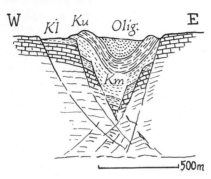

FIGURE 105

Transverse section of the Broves trench, near Comps (Var). An attempt has been made to suggest the stretching in depth of the faulted Jurassic to which the Lower Cretaceous remains connected. It is the Middle Cretaceous that admits a disharmony and the flexible subsidence of the Upper Cretaceous. Ku = Cretaceous; Km = Middle Cretaceous; Kl = Lower Cretaceous.

When a series of normal or reverse faults comes into play, presumably roughly parallel, the vertical throws may compensate one another, but the horizontal components are added together and cause an extension in the overall mass in the case of normal faults, a contraction if the faults are reverse. In the latter case, folds could have caused an analogous contraction; as a matter of fact, we often observe reverse faults closely associated with folds that may be broken and overthrust. On the other hand, normal faults produce an overall deformation of a sense contrary to that which would result from folds. Folds and normal faults are not produced concurrently. By virtue of the conservation of volume, the action of normal faults should, in general, cause a diminution of thickness together with an increase of breadth.

Among the deformations of the Mesozoic cover in the northern part of the department of the Var, which result from its slipping on an undeformed base, a certain number of complications of detail seem to indicate an extension that appears in the form of a series of relatively narrow north-south trenches, whose trend is perpendicular to the folds of the region and which lie between Jurassic plateaus. These trenches are bordered by faults that primarily affect the Jurassic and the Lower Cretaceous. The Upper Cretaceous, and the Eocene in places, outlines relatively deep synclines along their axes. It seems evident that these synclines do not indicate compression but that, on the contrary, the extension of the Jurassic may have determined a hollow, or at least a greatly thinned zone, above which the Upper Cretaceous subsided while being stretched (Fig. 105).

Along the edges of these trenches, the faults seem to be approximately vertical, but it is possible that their dip may change with depth, just as in the superficial slips of an argillaceous mass the surface along which movement takes place is, in general, a curve that becomes steeper upward and reaches the surface vertically (Fig. 51).

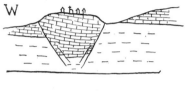

The absolute equality of height of the different horizons on both sides of each of the Comps trenches enables us to assert that they do not correspond to faults in the basement. This is an exceptional characteristic, inasmuch as normal faults generally seem to represent the surface repercussion of an analogous displacement affecting the whole of the crust. The Rhenish faults that delimit the Alsatian trench, whose throw probably reaches 4000 meters, are about 40 km from each other (Fig. 74). If we compare the subsidence, and the east-west extension, that results from their action, we find that conservation of volume would only be assured by relation to a surface situated at a depth of 20 km if these faults have a dip of 45°, or at a depth of 34 km if the dip is 60°. There is no reason to assume that a series of this thickness slips on an independent base. On the contrary, it is probable that the breaks affect the whole crust, even to a thickness of 30 to 50 km;

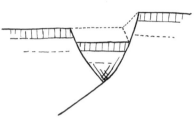

FIGURE 106

Top, Section through the village of Chateau-Chalon to the north of Lons-le-Saunier (Jura). The Middle Jurassic limestones form a wedge in the midst of the Lias (Lower Jurassic) marls. Bottom, Theoretical figure showing how, if a deep fault is tilted as it approaches the surface, conservation of volume requires the complementary subsidence of a wedge.

following the action of isostatic equilibrium, an uplift of the margins compensates in part for the subsidence of the basin (Chapter 14). This by no means indicates that such a fault traverses the deep terranes and their sedimentary cover in a straight line. In the Ledonian Jura, that is, along the margin of the Bresse, north-south belts, dropped between two normal faults, commonly separate plateaus of different levels (Fig. 106). Such a feature may be interpreted by assuming a deep fault of moderately steep dip (45°, to set a figure), and by assuming that in stratified sedimentary terranes, faults tend to approach the vertical; the conservation of volume may then be assured by making subsidence greater in the sedimentary terranes than in the underlying platform, at least along a certain extension.

Up to this point we have limited ourselves to the study of exactly transverse deformations which take place parallel to a plane and that can be studied in a plane section. This is never more than an approximation; many structures can be understood only if we take into account the fact that deformation took place in three-dimensional space, in which displacement could take place along in any direction. Such is the case for transverse faults that cut one or several anticlines, usually in a direction oblique to their axes. Generally the forms of folds on opposite sides of a fault are quite different; thus, we cannot assume that folding took place before faulting, since this would simply have displaced the two blocks relative to one another. When we compare the deformations undergone by the two margins, it becomes evident that the relative displacement varies in direction and amplitude from point to point. The fault has permitted the two margins to be folded differently. In particular, the anticlinal axes do not correspond. Let us assume, as is frequently the case (Jura, Grande Chartreuse, Fig. 107 and Fig. 108),[3] that the faults are oriented at 45° to the fold axes and that the displacement of the anticlinal axes is in the sense indicated by Fig. 109. We realize easily that the action of the fault is expressed by an elongation along the direction of the folds, whether the anticlinal axis was continuous at its origin, or, since the anticlines did not originate in a mutual prolongation, whether the mutual displacement in the region included between their axes is directed as indicated in the figure. We cannot

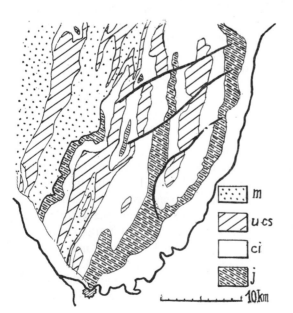

FIGURE 107

Geologic map of the Grande-Chartreuse Massif, showing the three transverse faults that cut the most internal folds. m, Miocene; u-cs, Urgonian and Upper Cretaceous; ci, Lower Cretaceous; j, Jurassic.

m

u-cs

ci

j

10 km

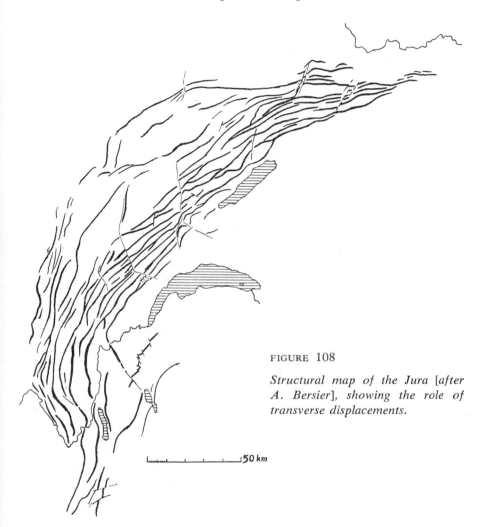

FIGURE 108

Structural map of the Jura [after A. Bersier], showing the role of transverse displacements.

⌊_____⌋50 km

dissociate the ensemble of folding and transverse fault, which were produced together and whose kinematic result was a transverse contraction that took place at the same time as the elongation along the direction of the folds.

In the Jura, a whole series of displacements are arranged in the manner just indicated; the elongation along the axes of folds may be related to the

FIGURE 109

Diagram of a displacement, with indication of the relative offset of the two margins.

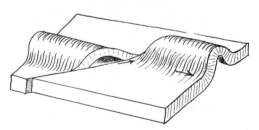

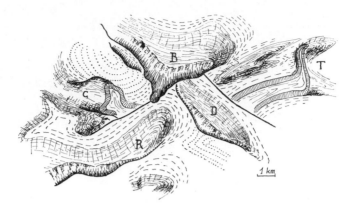

FIGURE 110. *Structural sketch of the environs of Castellane (Jurassic indicated by continuous heavy lines, Cretaceous by dashes, Tertiary by dots). The two anticlines of the Cadieres de Brandis (C) and of the Teillon (T), each of quite complex form with tilting to the north, are limited by two oblique transverse faults. In the wedge thus determined, the two anticlines of Rougon (R) and of Destourbes (D) have radiating strikes and seem to be related to the lateral compression undergone by the median wedge at the time of the advance of the anticlines C and T on its sides. In the north, the overthrust of the Braches (B) conceals the end of the median wedge.*

curve of the mountain chain, the arc evidently being longer than its chord. This tends to confirm the overall slipping of the folded cover and enables us to specify that it is the south-east side of the sheaf of folds that was displaced, the plateaus situated to the northwest and west having remained immobile.

The arrangement of transverse faults may be very complex; thus, near Castellane (Basses-Alpes), two transverse faults separate two strongly folded regions from a median compartment into which these folds are not prolonged (Fig. 110). The advance, on the sides of this median wedge-shaped compartment, of the zones that were folding brought about a contraction that was expressed by the appearance of radial folds.

During the formation of a regular cylindrical fold, the relative displacement of the regions situated on both sides is exactly normal to the elongation. A slight obliquity of this relative displacement may be expressed by different sorts of irregularities. Instead of a single fold, a series of folds may appear, each of which is normal to the relative displacement and relaying each other (folds "en echelon," Fig. 111).

To the north of the Buis (Drôme), a particular anticline exhibits one nor-

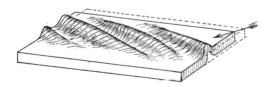

FIGURE 111

Diagram of folds en echelon with indication of the relative displacement.

mal side; the other is cut by a series of oblique faults, in all of which the displacement is horizontal and of the same sense. An experiment with a sheet of paper suffices to demonstrate that this arrangement expresses a relative displacement oblique to the general elongation (Fig. 112). The question that is posed in this case, as in the case of a sheaf of an echelon folds, is why anticlines normal to the relative displacement did not appear. This relative displacement no doubt had a different direction in an early phase; the broad fold that originated then continued to act later on at the time when the relative displacement of the two parts of the cover that it separated was taking place along a different direction.

When a fold is broken and an overthrust fault develops, there is no reason to believe that the relative displacement

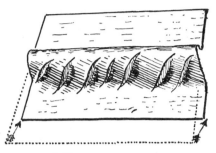

FIGURE 112

Relative displacement of the two sides of a fold when one of the sides is affected by oblique faults (experiment made with a sheet of paper).

is exactly normal to the elongation. More rarely, a vertical fault extends along a straight anticline, following its axis or one of its sides; this exceptional arrangement may result from the fact that the relative displacement of the two sides of the anticline involved a longitudinal component or that the fault antedated the anticline, as we shall see later on (p. 000). The two cases may be difficult to distinguish.

In dislocations of detail there is a tendency to produce either faults or flexures. When a combination of the two is observed (Fig. 113) it will often be the indication of a longitudinal component of the displacement which cannot happen in a flexure.

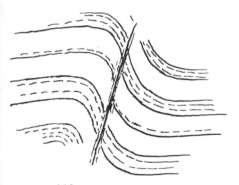

FIGURE 113

Combination of a flexure of beds with a fault whose displacement is probably longitudinal.

A careful study of the form of the tectonic features enables us to specify the direction of relative diplacements which have caused each of them. In the south of the Drôme, it is easy to recognize that a certain number of folds result from displacements oblique to their direction. We shall see later on how to interpret the latter as marking the location of earlier complications.

The analysis of such complex deformations, in which the direction of the relative displacements vary from point to point, is difficult to conduct. The magnitude of the relative displacement of numerous complications cannot be directly determined (such as faults with a horizontal displacement, or over-thrusts).

The fact that the present form of reference horizon, which is assumed not to have undergone notable changes of thickness during the course of deforma-tion, was derived through the sum of these displacements from a continuous flat form may enable us to remove these indeterminations. Let us suppose we cut up a map, following all the structural complications (transverse faults, anticlines, overthrusts), and separate the pieces from one another at a suitable distance and in the right direction, the divisions being separated by complica-tions for which it has been possible to evaluate the relative displacement (which moreover may not be the same the whole length of the complication); it often happens that the data are sufficient to determine the relative positions of all the fragments into which the map has been cut. From these positions, it is possible to deduce an evaluation of certain relative displacements that remained undetermined.

To express the result of such a reconstruction of displacements in plan it is possible to imagine a horizontal projection of a kilometric grid, supposedly traced on the reference horizon before the tectonic deformation. The relative positions of grid fragments corresponding to the basins and synclinal depres-sions result immediately from the reconstruction of their mutual positions, as indicated above. The form of the folds enables us to draw the projection of the grid, supposedly folded in the same way as the beds to which it is con-nected (Figs. 114 and 115).

If we fold a sheet of paper so that it assumes the form of the known com-plications, we can see how the complications whose detail we have been un-able to clearly define may appear. Such an experiment shows that this method can only be used in very simple cases. If a sheet of paper is very flexible, it is

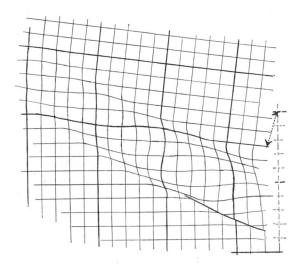

FIGURE 114

Representation by the projec-tion of a grid supposedly traced on the reference hori-zon before deformation of an anticline attenuating toward the west and passing, in the east, to an overthrust toward the south.

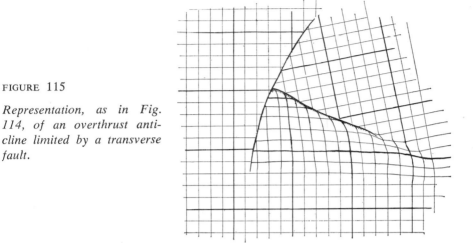

FIGURE 115

Representation, as in Fig. 114, of an overthrust anticline limited by a transverse fault.

absolutely inextensible in its plane. Aside from the tears and breaks that might occur, its form is that of a developable surface, in the mathematical sense of the term. On the other hand, a sedimentary bed, even if it is relatively resistant and does not appreciably change in thickness, will assume forms much more varied than will a sheet of paper when subjected to stress; a better representation would be obtained with a thin sheet of plastiline or tin.

In order to study a somewhat complex deformation in which the form of the beds differs from a series of parallel cylindrical folds other than by the action of some faults, and to employ the method that has just been indicated, we have been led to consider only the deformation of a reference horizon. If we can transpose into three-dimensional space the consideration of the overall deformation of the series in the study of a plane section and not merely of a single reference horizon there is no doubt that very important precise data would result. However, the problem needs further investigation. As will be indicated in the next chapter, another method, which takes into consideration the forces that come into play, produces very important results.

So far we have attempted to follow the progress of a given deformation without being able to specify its rate. Kinematic considerations are of greatest importance when they enable us to reconstruct the spacing in time of different phenomena, such as distinct deformations by faults or folds, which are eventually separated by phases of erosion or sedimentation. In the latter case, the presence of dated sediments enables us to distinguish quite easily the successive phases of movement, according to whether they do or do not affect the deposits. We shall return in Chapter 17 to the determination of the age of movements by comparison with the age of sediments that are or are not affected.

Masses are frequently found of such form that their deformation cannot be

FIGURE 116. *Section of the Carboniferous basin of Liége. The veins of coal are indicated by different sets of dots and dashes, the faults by unbroken lines: distinguished are a first series of faults with very little dip that were folded at the same time as the beds and affected by later faults. [After Humblet, E., Revue Universelle des Mines, 8ᵉ série, t. 17, no. 12, Liége, 1941.]*

simply explained except by the succession of two phases of movements of quite different character. Thus in the Franco-Belgian Carboniferous basin, it has been possible to follow incontestable fault surfaces that are not flat but are curved approximately in the manner of the surrounding beds (Fig. 116). The interpretation is evident: in the first phase these faults acted along planes; in the second phase, the series was folded. The same explanation is valid for the celebrated Grenchenberg section in the Jura (Fig. 124).

Succession in time is no less clear when two faults cut across each other; we can readily distinguish the order of faulting, that is, determine which fault evidently came into play before the other (Fig. 117). Things are a little more difficult when the successive structural complications, instead of being a fault and a fold or two faults, are two folds. However there are numerous cases in which the genesis of quite complex forms can be explained by the succession of simple movements, comparable to those whose development we have just analysed.

Often we must take into consideration the erosion that has taken place between the phases of deformation. However, the necessity for this did not occur to geologists until relatively recently. It was seen that a convenient first approximation in tectonic reconstruction consisted of considering the folded mass as being undetermined toward the top. In order to take into account the effects of erosion, on the contrary, we must try to determine the position of the topographic surface at each of the phases of the deformation, which is

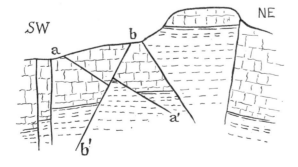

FIGURE 117

Faults affecting the base of the Urgonian limestone, Pas de l'Inferney (Vercors). It is evident that the fault aa′ is anterior to the fault bb′. Note that the displacements are not necessarily in the plane of the section.

somewhat difficult to do. But the results obtained in this way are well worth the effort.

Although we cannot claim to have exhausted the variety of structures to which the superposition of different deformations may lead, we are going to try to review the results of the succession of two faults, of faults superposed on a fold, of folds of faulted regions, of two folds, of folds and nappes, of several nappes, and then we shall examine the effect of erosion during the course of the deformations.

We have seen, in Fig. 117, examples of the succession of two faults in which the order of faulting is evident. The succession of faulting has especially been studied in connection with mineralization, the nature of which almost always varies with time. In mining districts in which different sorts of veins exist, it is almost always possible to determine the order of mineralization by observing the intersections where one of the veins, the younger, displaces the vein-filling of the other (Fig. 118). However, the intersections are often marked by a particular mineralization, which is generally richer than the vein mineralization; for this reason, miners carefully seek the zones of intersection or crossings (*"filons croiseurs"*).

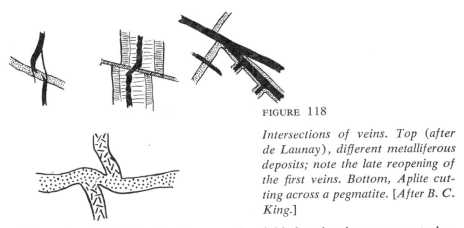

FIGURE 118

Intersections of veins. Top (after de Launay), different metalliferous deposits; note the late reopening of the first veins. Bottom, Aplite cutting across a pegmatite. [After B. C. King.]

The action of a fault affecting an earlier folded region is very easy to imagine. However, care must be taken not to confuse this case with that of a transverse fault contemporaneous with folding. In the first case, the two margins of the fault should have the same form, such that a simple reversal of the fault movement would be enough to bring the margins back into coincidence. On the other hand, if the forms of the two margins are different, the fault must have been active during folding, and it should be considered as a transverse fault, which does not exclude the possibility of its being active again later on. Transverse faults having the same age as the Alpine folds seem much more frequent than faults later than the folds.

If we consider more ancient folds, some of which were accompanied by a certain metamorphism and followed by erosion, the displacements resulting from recent movements, for example movements of Tertiary age in a Hercynian massif, are usually caused by faults. The existence of a sedimentary cover of intermediary age, which has been affected by faults but not by folds, often makes it possible to separate the two phases very clearly. This difference of behavior at the time of the two phases of deformation is essentially due to mechanical conditions; if certain beds of the block of old terranes are not indurated they may react other than by faulting at the time of more recent movements (see Chapter 12). Very frequently, a relation of position between recent faults and ancient folds may be due only to a difference in the mechanical resistance of the different strata.

The example shown in Fig. 116 corresponds to the subsequent folding of "flat faults," that is, of thrust faults. Glangeaud[4] has shown for the Jura the very varied modalities that may affect the folding of a region previously faulted. The subsidence movements of the Bresse and the Rhenish Trench are essentially of Oligocene age, and it is very probable, a priori, that they had numerous counterparts in the region now occupied by the Jura. Later, toward the end of the Miocene, the Hautes Chaines of the Jura were folded, primarily as a result of the slipping of the Mesozoic cover on the saliferous beds of the Trias. The existence of earlier faults disturbed the action of this phenomenon in different fashions. The faults that interrupted the mechanical continuity of the cover were transformed into transverse faults during subsequent folding, and their two margins folded in different ways. The folding by slipping of the cover assumes that the platform and the overlying saliferous beds were flat.

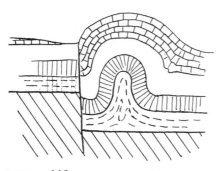

FIGURE 119

Localization of an anticline of the cover in contact with a fault affecting the platform, determining a sort of anchorage.

If they are broken through the action of faults the movement of the covering will be modified. The disharmonic action of plastic beds may lessen the effect on the cover of certain inequalities of the platform, but Glangeaud has described examples of folds adjacent to a vertical fault whose localization seems due to a sort of anchorage of the cover opposite a fault of the platform (Fig. 119).

But the effect of Oligocene faults becomes much more marked in the tabular Jura (Franche-Comté style described by Glangeaud, in contrast to the Helvetic style of the Hautes Chaines).

The lines of structural complications that separate the plateaus often present a quite complex structure, which Glangeaud has shown to be the result of the crushing of pre-existing fault zones. We have seen how groups of such faults often delimit a collapsed trench, which compensates for the greater dip of the faults in the cover than in

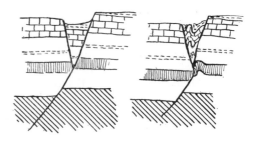

FIGURE 120

Diagram of a "pinch" resulting from the crushing of a collapsed belt between two faults.

the basement. The crushing of such collapsed or "pinched" belts, which may assume a folded character, produces varied complications (Fig. 120). The crushing of a sheaf of faults having the same sense may produce analogous complications (Fig. 121).

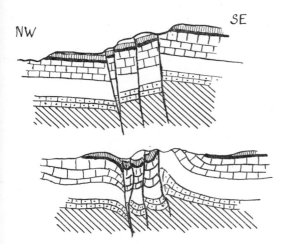

FIGURE 121

Structure of the Besançon sheaf [after Glangeaud]; posterior crushing of a faulted band.

If resistant beds on one fault margin face plastic beds of the opposite margin, certain complications may result. If a resistant bed is exposed as a result of erosion, the fault may be transformed into an overthrust fold as shown in Fig. 122 (fault fold of Glangeaud). To sum up, Glangeaud succeeded in explaining a number of characteristics of the Jura as being the result of the superposition of folds of Miocene age upon Oligocene faults.

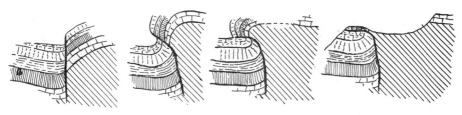

FIGURE 122. *Arguel fault-fold. (After Glangeaud.) Miocene pressure has twisted the plane of the Oligocene fault and determined a local overthrust.*

The superposition of two phases of folding rarely appears with simple characters. The profound reason for this will not appear clearly until the next chapter; we shall see that the cause of deformation by folding (from the mechanical point of view) lies in the stratified structure of the sedimentary series. After a first folding, the strata are greatly disturbed, thus the tendency of the series to fold a second time is greatly reduced. More than fifty years ago, Zurcher[5] tried to interpret the structure around Castellane by distinguishing a series of groups of parallel folds in each of which the folding was assumed to spread laterally from a central point. The manner in which the folds belonging to two distinct sheafs cut across each other would enable us to recognize the older, considered as having prevented the propagation of the most

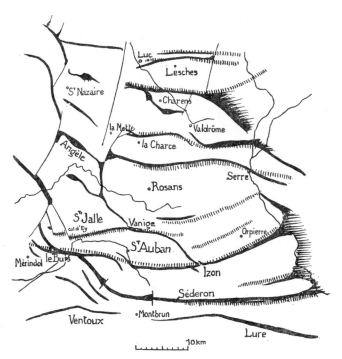

FIGURE 123. *Tectonic sketch of the Baronnies (south of the Drôme), indicating, in black, the post-Miocene anticlines and, by shaded belts, the earlier anticlines. The faults indicated by the fine lines are transverse faults. The uniquely post-Miocene folds run NW-SE, that is, they indicate a compression along a line running NE-SW. The existence of earlier folds of different direction (about E-W) has imposed this direction on a certain number of post-Miocene folds. This deviation is partially compensated, from the point of view of the overall relative displacement, by the action of transverse N-S faults, at times adjacent to an anticline. Note that, to the south of Valdrome, and to the south of Saint-Auban, the relay of the post-Miocene folds, which indicates the obliquity of the relative displacement in relation to the general direction E-W. (Cf. Fig. 111, Bull. Carte géol., no. 223, t. XLVI, Fig. 13, 1947.)*

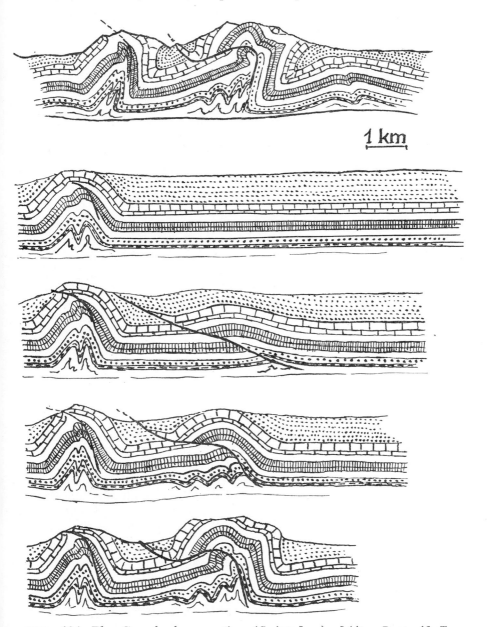

FIGURE 124. *The Grenchenberg section (Swiss Jura). [After Buxtorf.] Top, Present section from observations in the Granges-Moutier tunnel. Bottom, Successive stages of the deformation, showing (1) the action of the faults and (2) the folding which deformed them.*

recent fold. However ingenious this theory may be, it does not give very satisfactory results and has apparently been abandoned. But we must not eliminate the possibility that a similar method might give interesting results.

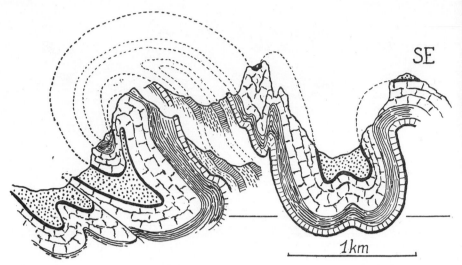

FIGURE 125. *Section of the Hundstein in the Säntis Massif. [After Albert Heim.] The heart of the anticlines is occupied by the Lower Cretaceous; the Urgonian forms the principal calcareous mass; and the synclines are occupied by the Middle Cretaceous. The genesis of such a structure is better understood if we accept that the fold of the anticlinal head (on the left) was produced in a second phase, following the formation of a straight fold. We might also ask if the movements of this second phase do not have the character of a "collapse structure" (see p. 106), resulting from a simple gravity subsidence, after erosion was already far advanced, without any deep deformation. In this hypothesis the dotted lines traced above the section would not at all indicate the form of the beds before erosion, but a simple stratigraphic accordance.*

Usually, however, the interaction between two successive folds takes place in an entirely different manner. In a slightly folded region a deformation by accentuation of old folds is quite easy, but the development of folds of different directions is very difficult. Consequently, there will be a tendency to folding along old folds, both by accentuation of the latter and through the aid of the thinning by erosion of the sedimentary series at the positions of the anticlines.

But the general direction in which the cover tends to be compressed may very well not be orthogonal to the old folds. Different complications may in

FIGURE 126. *General character of the nappe of* schistes lustrés *(shading) in Haute-Tarentaise and Haute-Maurienne (Raguin); the mass was folded after formation of the nappe. The crosses indicate Bonneval gneiss.*

SW

_{L____L____L____L____L____L}5_{_____L}10 km

FIGURE 127. *Diagrammatic section of the Ubaye-Embrunsis nappe, to the south of the Durance. [After Schneegans.] The autochthon is left blank, the flysch of the nappe is indicated by dots, and the Mesozoic by shading. Right. Frontal folds of the Briançonnais constituting superposed scales (écailles). (See Fig. 94.)*

part make up for this obliquity, such as longitudinal slip along the ruptured anticlines, transverse faults, and so forth. In the southern part of the department of the Drôme, an admirable example of this type of complication exists,[6] which is indicated by the appearance of a grid of anticlines limiting a series of oval synclinal cuvettes (Fig. 123).

When the first phase of folding has progressed to the formation of nappes, whether by accentuation of folded beds, or by the action of flat faults, the overall mass resumes a roughly stratified structure and may easily fold again. The folded faults of the Carboniferous of Belgium (Fig. 116) constitute an example of this case, as does the famous Grenchenberg section, in which it is evident that displacement along a flat fault preceded overall folding[7] (Fig.

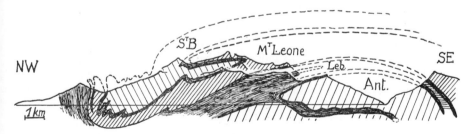

NW

1 km

FIGURE 128. *The Simplon section. [After Argand.] The patterns represent the cores of the different nappes that contain, at least in places, a strip of Trias and are enveloped in a mass of schistes lustrés (Bundschiefer in German) (shaded). Note the folds affecting all the nappes of Mont Leone and the Saint Bernard, which are evidently posterior to their emplacement.*

124). There are also relatively superficial folds whose genesis is more easily understood if separated into several successive phases (Fig. 125).

In the preceding chapter, we noted the special nomenclature used for nappe folds, which, in general, result from later movements, the emplacement of the nappe hardly being possible except on an approximately plane surface, even a descending one (Fig. 126).

Inversely, the region in which nappes originate may happen to have been previously folded. As we shall soon see, certain folds may constitute the embryonic shape of later overthrusts. If the folds existing in the region where the overthrust takes place are eroded, they will simply produce a tectonic discordance (Fig. 99). It is possible for non-eroded folds to be torn away from their base and carried into the overthrust; this is how Gignoux and Schneegans interpret the presence of a great mass of Mesozoic with sub-Briançonnais facies that occurs in the frontal part of the Ubaye-Embrunais nappe (Morgan, Ancelle), which is essentially Tertiary and Cretaceous flysch (Fig. 127).

Isolated nappes are quite exceptional; usually we find a series of superposed nappes. Their mutual relations lead us to believe that they were formed successively, generally beginning with the highest. At the time of formation of the most recent nappes, the structure of already existing nappes could have been refolded, which could be the cause of very complex arrangements (see Fig. 128); we have seen (Fig. 97) an example of involution in which an upper nappe (here, ultra-Helvetic) is pinched under one of the Helvetic nappes. Such an arrangement is very easy to understand if we reconstruct the series of movements that produced the different nappes. On the other hand, it enables us to establish the order of succession of the latter. In this case, since the most recent nappes were formed under the earlier nappes, erosion could hardly have acted during the movements. It is different in the examples that we are now going to consider.

We have already pointed out the possible influence of erosion on the folds of a first phase. In Provence (Lutaud), a certain number of folds, perhaps but little accentuated, seem to have been formed as early as the Upper Cretaceous and subsequently eroded, while continental sedimentation was taking place in the adjacent synclines. At the time of the second tectonic phase (Lutetian), the resistant calcareous beds of the Jurassic, were eroded along the anticlinal axis, and one of the flanks of the fold slipped, aided by the plasticity of beds of the Trias and passed above the other flank, over-

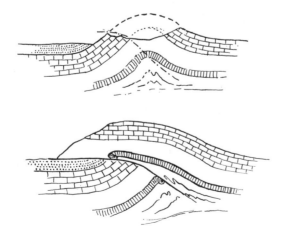

FIGURE 129

Diagram showing how erosion of an anticline (above) facilitates the rupture and the overthrust in a subsequent phase (case of Provence). [After Lutaud.]

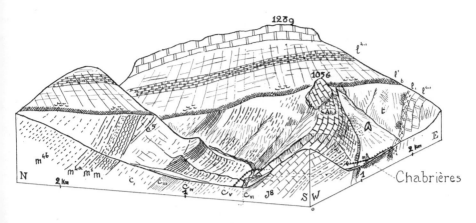

FIGURE 130. *Overthrust of the Cousson (Dourbes series), on the right bank of the
Asse (Basses-Alpes). The overthrust series (Lias and Upper Trias) rests in
discordance on the Jurassic, the Cretaceous, and the Tertiary, which outline an anticline; the Tertiary had been eroded before the overthrust, which
took place on the surface of the ground. But the harder Jurassic determined a projection that was shoved forward (hill 1056). (Tectonic
Description of the Border of the Alps from Bléone to the Var, Mém.
Carte, 1937, Fig. 37.)*

thrusting upon the adjacent syncline; thus, erosion had prepared, even permitted, the rupture of the anticline (Fig. 129). But naturally, the degree of
erosion must have varied from place to place, causing the lack of continuity
of these Provencal overthrusts in the longitudinal sense.

We have already seen the role of erosion, which can prepare a tectonic
discordance when an overthrust is extended to the very surface of the ground.
Such is the case of the Cousson overthrust around Digne (Basses-Alpes),
which rests on a leveled anticline in the valley of the Asse; however, a
remnant, corresponding to the hard horizon in the Upper Jurassic, was shoved
forward (Fig. 130).

Erosion causes even greater complications when it intervenes during the
formation of nappes. Lugeon[8] has given a remarkable example of this in his
description of the "diverticulations," certain complications of ultra-Helvetic
nappes (Fig. 131).

Above the Helvetic nappe of the Wildhorn (shown cross-hatched in the
figure), and folded with it, we find the three following nappes, from the
bottom up: Plaine Morte (Cretaceous and Flysch), Mont Bonvin (Jurassic
and Flysch) and Laubhorn (Trias and Lias). When the effect of the later
folds is removed, these stages appear in normal succession in each one of
these nappes. The hypothesis of diverticulations is based on the assumption
that these are elements of a given series, which were emplaced by slipping
one after the other, with the result that the oldest group of strata settled in

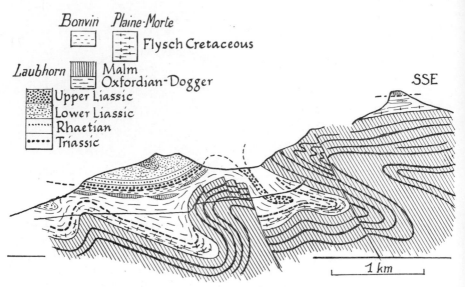

FIGURE 131. *Section of diverticulations of ultra-Helvetic nappes to the south of Lenk. [After Lugeon.]*

place above the others. The presence of flysch in several of these units probably resulted from the fact that their emplacement was contemporaneous with its deposition.

This diverticulation concept greatly simplifies the interpretation of a structure that would have been inextricable if it had been necessary to apply the hypothesis of distinct units. It may also shed some light on a number of other abnormal successions resulting from local slips. In this manner, Lugeon[9] proposed that the blade of granite caught in the flysch beneath the Morcles nappe was emplaced by a slide at the time of deposition of the flysch.

We shall see in Chapter 13 that emplacement by sliding under the influence of weight alone is not limited to units of small dimensions, but that it is the very essence of "tectonic flow" (*tectonique d'ecoulement*).

The question may be asked whether notions analogous to the diverticulation concept could not be applied on a much larger scale. In the Pre-Alps of the Chablais (compare Fig. 93), the Median nappe presents quite striking stratigraphic analogies with the Briançonnais strata, but it is overlain by the Breccia Nappe, whereas the Jurassic is composed almost entirely of sedimentary breccia. Analogous breccias are to be observed in Tarentaise in a more external zone (that is, more westerly) than that of the Briançonnais. Could the position of the Breccia and the Median nappes have been inverted relative to the position of the corresponding roots, comparable to the one produced in the diverticulations of the ultra-Helvetic units? If the block of Median slipped, under its own weight, to its present position (reckoning from Briançonnais units) and was subsequently uplifted, could the upwarping have progressed toward the west until it produced the slip of the Breccia Nappe, thus bending it back and bringing it to rest on the rear of the Median?

However rich kinematic analysis of the deformation and the distinction of successive phases may be, it could not suffice to explain such complex features; we have already alluded to the forces that have determined the emplacement of elementary nappes in the diverticulation. Dynamic analysis, which will be the subject of the next chapters, is necessary for a satisfactory understanding of tectonic deformation.

Notes and References

1. Fallot, P., *Les chevauchements intercutanés de Roya (Alpes-Maritimes)*, Annales Hébert et Haug (livre jubilaire Ch. Jacob), vol. 7, pp. 161–169, 1949.

2. Fallot, P., *Remarques sur la tectonique de couverture dans les Alpes bergamasques et des Dolomites,* Bull. Soc. géol. France, 5ᵉ ser., vol. 20, pp. 183–195, 1950.

3. Goguel, J., *La rôle des failles de décrochement dans le massif de la Grande Chartreuse,* Bull. Soc. géol. France, 5ᵉ ser., vol. 18, pp. 227–235, 1948.

4. Glangeaud, L., *Le rôle des failles dans la structure du Jura externe,* Bull. Soc. Hist. Nat. Doubs, no. 51, pp. 17–38, 1944.

———, *Les nouvelles théories sur la formation du Jura,* ibid., Bull., no. 52, pp. 5–16, 1948.

———, *Les caractères structuraux du Jura,* Bull. Soc. géol. France, 5ᵉ ser., vol. 19, pp. 669–688, 1949.

See also Extraordinary Session of the Société Géologique de Belgique, Sept. 25, 1947 in Bull. Soc. géol. Belgique, vol. 73, pp. 53–150, 1949.

5. Zurcher, Ph., *Note sur la structure de la région de Castellane,* Bull. Serv. Carte géol. France, vol. 7, no. 48, pp. 299–335, 1895.

6. Goguel, J., *Recherches sur la tectonique des chaînes subalpines entre le Ventoux et le Vercors,* Bull. Serv. Carte géol. France, vol. 46, no. 223, pp. 533–578, 1947.

7. Buxtorf, A., *Grenchenbergtunnel, Prognosen und Befunde,* Naturforsch. Ges. Basel, vol. 27, pp. 185–254, 1915.

———, *Theoretische Profile zur Erklärung der Tektonik des Grenchenbergtunnels, entworfen December 1915,* ibid., Verhandl., vol. 27, plates x–xiii, 1915.

8. Lugeon, M., *Une nouvelle hypothèse tectonique: La diverticulation (note préliminaire),* Bull. Soc. Vaud. Sci. Nat., vol. 62, no. 260, pp. 301–303, 1943.

9. Lugeon, M., *Hommage à A. Buxtorf, et digression sur la nappe de Morcles,* Naturf. Ges. Basel, Verhandl., vol. 58, pp. 108–131, 1947.

CHAPTER TWELVE

Dynamic Interpretation

Distribution of stresses—Relaxation—Fluid pressure—Deformations; elastic, elasticoviscous, reversible or nonreversible, plastic—Rupture—Mohr diagram—Different types of elementary deformations—Effect of the temperature and chemical composition of the fluid—Plasticity or viscosity —Distribution of forces during the deformation—Interpretation of refraction of the schistosity and of boudinage—Energy expended in deformation, principle of minimum work—Deformation by folding of a stratified mass—Disharmony—Mechanical properties of saliferous formations—Thresholds of principal types of rocks—Evaluation of relations between thresholds of two types of Rocks—Role of physicochemical conditions—Rupture—Method of propagation, shocks—Ruptures by traction—Heat released.

IT IS a general rule of geology that in order to clearly understand the present state of rocks, we must trace their past history as far as possible. That is why in the preceding chapter we made an attempt to follow the progress of deformation with time, instead of limiting ourselves to studying the geometry of present mineral masses. But this is not sufficient; if we really wish to understand deformation we must attempt to penetrate its determining factors. It is evident that forces must have acted to produce these deformations; for this reason, we are going to attempt to analyze their distribution.

At any given instant, there is present in the thickness of the earth's crust a certain distribution of pressures, that is, a state of stress. In order to analyze the state of stress, we observe that a force transmitted through an elementary surface is not, in general, normal to it; it can be demonstrated, however, that at every point there are three mutually perpendicular planes on which this force is normal; on two of these planes the force (or more precisely the pressure, which is the force per unit area) is respectively greater or smaller than the normal component of pressure on every other surface element passing through this point. Concurrent with the knowledge of the pressure exerted on the third plane direction ("median principal pressure"), the knowledge of the "minimum" and "maximum principal pressures," and that of the "principal directions" completely defines the state of stress at the point under consideration.

If two of the principal pressures are equal, the distribution of the pressures presents a symmetry of revolution.

But the case in which the three principal pressures are equal is much more important; the pressure exerted on a surface element of any given orientation is normal to it and presents the same value; the pressure is said to be hydrostatic; this is true of a liquid in equilibrium.

The stress that characterizes the mechanical state of the rock is then a complex quantity,[1] characterized by the magnitude and the direction of the principal pressures, or by six other parameters that enable us to calculate them. The stresses at the different points within the rock are evidently not independent, since they result from the transmission of force across the rock.[2] In particular, the weights of successive beds add up, thus increasing the stresses toward the bottom. The pressure exerted at the free surface is evidently zero (neglecting atmospheric pressure). The preceding considerations are insufficient to permit us to determine the stress at each point. A few examples will illustrate this.

If we pile bricks evenly into a square box, the horizontal pressure between them is evidently zero. If instead of bricks we pour sand into the box, a certain horizontal pressure is exerted (if there is a hole in the wall, sand will escape through it; a force must be exerted to block the hole). This pressure is less than the vertical pressure at the same point. If one side of the box is movable, to push it inward we would have to exert a pressure much greater than that required to hold it in place if we wish to produce any deformation of the mass.

Instead of piling up bricks, we might have constructed a vault and then filled the space under it with bricks. If we pile others on top, their weight will bear upon the supports of the vault and not on the bricks that are beneath.

Even if the external conditions are known, the distribution of internal stresses remains indeterminate. In the examples cited above, analysis of the manner of construction might remove this doubt. It would be difficult to apply analogous considerations to rocks in place, but other considerations might permit us to remove this indeterminacy in many cases. Since the same stresses apply during long periods of time, each rock element must have undergone a very slight settling under the action of these forces that tended to reduce the difference between the three principal pressures. If a mass is composed of horizontal beds of uniform densities and is bounded by a horizontal surface, this "relaxation of stresses" evidently has a limit; that is, if the distribution of the stresses is hydrostatic, settling can produce no further change.

If the surface is not horizontal, the distribution of stresses cannot be hydrostatic, but it still has a limit that can be calculated.[3]

In a mass in repose, there is every reason to believe that the limit thus defined has been reached and that the stresses are hydrostatic if the surface is horizontal. If the stresses are not hydrostatic, they are usually considered to be the result of the superposition of supplementary stresses on the hydrostatic stresses, due to the responsible agents of tectonic deformation.

Up to this point we have considered the crust as a solid. In reality, it is a more or less porous solid impregnated by a liquid that at each point has its own pressure. We must consider this liquid phase, which may be water or petroleum, apart from the rock. This fluid may move through the rock while undergoing a loss of pressure. If it is immobile, its own pressure varies as a function of the depth in proportion to its density.

Part of the external pressure exerted upon a rock element corresponds to the pressure of the liquid. Thus, only the difference between the overall pressure and the pressure of the liquid is actually supported by the mass of the solid rock. The rock may be represented as an open framework bathed in liquid; if we increase the pressure of this liquid, the load on the framework is not increased.

Since the density of the rock is always much greater than that of the liquid that impregnates it, the pressure undergone by the rock increases much more rapidly with depth than does the pressure of the liquid if the water is in hydrostatic equilibrium. But deep drilling has shown that water in some formations may be at a much higher pressure, sometimes nearly equal to the pressure of the overburden. In such cases, fluid pressure must be taken into consideration to understand certain ruptures.

In the course of tectonic deformation, the distribution of forces deviates, under the action of causes which we shall not indicate precisely for the moment, from the distribution corresponding to repose (that is, the hydrostatic distribution under a horizontal surface) and the distribution corresponding to a complete relaxation of the forces in all cases. Deformation then takes place. It is necessary to analyze the relations between these deformations and the stresses undergone.

First, let us briefly consider the case of hydrostatic force. Evidently, for reasons of symmetry, no change of form can take place, but only a change of volume; this may affect different modalities. The elastic change of volume is produced very rapidly, and it disappears entirely if the pressure is removed. An entirely reversible elasticoviscous deformation may also take place, but it will acquire its definitive value only progressively. The rock may also be compressible, in which case a part of the diminution of volume is irreversible and continues after removal of the pressure. This compressibility may appear immediately on application of the slightest pressure, or only when the pressure exceeds a certain limit. The change of volume is always limited; we may regard the compressibility as the result of the reduction in pore space, the constituent minerals being tightly pressed together. The change of volume by compressibility may take place either abruptly or gradually.

Heretofore we have considered the rock as a solid. Certain aspects of the phenomena are clarified if we take into account the contained water. At the moment the pressure is produced, the water does not have the time to escape; as a result, its pressure increases, and the solid part of the rock thus supports only a part of the external pressure. Then the water progressively escapes, as a result of the permeability of the surrounding rocks, and its pressure decreases. The pressure supported by the solid part of the rock increases by the same amount, and the deformation increases progressively; moreover, it may be a question of elastic deformation as well as of permanent deformation. At the time of the removal of the pressure, the same phenomena take place in an inverse sense; the elastic part of the deformation gradually disappears as the water pressure returns to equilibrium, a return that is slow if the permeability of the surrounding rocks is slight. However, it would be imprudent to assert that this mechanical process, which certainly plays an important role, is the only one that comes into the picture to delay the adaptation of the volume of a rock to the pressure that it is subjected to.

If the stress applied is not hydrostatic, things are more complicated. Industrial tests are conventionally made under conditions of unidirectional stress, that is, two of the principal pressures are zero. We should consider the change in length and the change in transverse dimensions of the test sample separately, since a rupture may result from several quite different mechanical processes that are distinguished by the direction and the aspect of the break. If we consider only the changes of length, we might find again the distinctions already indicated for variation of volume, between an elastic deformation (that is, one that is reversible and which may take place immediately or reach its definitive value only progressively) and a permanent deformation, which may be instantaneous or progressive, of limited amplitude, and which may develop slowly.[4] After removal of the load, the part of the elongation corresponding to the elasticoviscous deformation will disappear progressively. The principal difference from the hydrostatic compression is the possibility of an indefinite plastic deformation or of a rupture.

It is known that many rocks, when subjected to simple compression, behave like fragile substances, that is, they break before any permanent deformation takes place. Tests in traction or simple compression performed on other substances give us an idea of the complications that the law relating the deformation, stress, and the rate of change of applied stress may present, but it is necessary to consider the problem in all its general aspects and to seek the relation between a stress with three unequal principal pressures (none zero) and the behavior of the body, which may undergo simple reversible elastic deformation, rupture, or permanent deformation. But these representations must be stated in a more accurate manner.

Let us first introduce a method (Mohr circles) for representing the stress

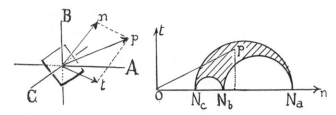

FIGURE 132. *Principle of the representation of stress by the Mohr diagram. Left, A, B, and C, are the principal stress directions. The element of surface under consideration supports a force p per unit of surface, which is broken down into a normal component n and a tangential component t. Right, Diagram showing that the point defined by coordinates n and t falls within the shaded area.*

at a point. Assume that at the point under consideration, a surface element of any orientation undergoes a pressure that may be broken down into a normal component and a tangential component (Fig. 132); we shall represent them in a plane in relation to which the surface element under consideration occupies a fixed position. It can be shown that the representative point is in this plane, in the interior of the shaded surface of the figure, which is limited by three semicircles. The extremities of their diameters, along the axis, correspond to the three principal pressures. The pressure acting on a plane passing through one of the principal directions has its representative point on one of the semicircles at angular distances from its extremities which are double the angles between the plane under consideration and the planes normal to the corresponding principal directions.

If the stress causes within the body a phenomenon produced along a surface (for example, a rupture), the stresses capable of releasing this phenomenon may be represented by an intrinsic curve that will depict the field of the representative points of these stresses on the Mohr diagram. The diagram representing the state of stress of the body shows immediately how many plane directions exist at the point under consideration by which the phenomenon may be produced. If one does exist, we can determine its position relative to the principal directions; we see immediately that, if such a plane exists, it passes through the median principal direction and that the value of the corresponding principal pressure has no bearing on the limit, which depends only on the extreme principal pressures (or, which amounts to the same thing, on their mean and their difference).

This conclusion is not strictly applicable to a phenomenon such as plastic deformation that does not take place along a surface but which involves the whole mass. The limiting condition for the appearance of such a phenomenon no longer depends on the mean pressure and the difference between the two extreme principal pressures, but on the mean of the three principal pressures (mean pressure) and on the quadratic mean of the three differences of the three principal pressures, taken two by two. These quantities do not appear directly in the Mohr diagram. But this distinction is of only theoretical importance, and as a first approximation, we shall hereafter combine the two types of limiting conditions.

Having thus characterized the stress, we can now study its effects upon a rock. With regard to rocks that break without deformation in the open air, such as the limestones, it has long been known that plastic deformation without rupture is possible in experiments "under triaxial compression," in which the test sample undergoes simultaneous lateral compression and longitudinal compression, naturally superior to the first; in the course of such experiments certain test samples have lost 10 or 20 percent of their length and have undergone a corresponding lateral expansion without losing their cohesion.

However, we should not be satisfied with merely observing the change of form or the rupture. It is necessary to try to understand the intimate transformations of the rock of which rupture or deformation are only the external manifestations.

From this point of view, the phenomenon of deformation is much simpler than that of rupture. A rock may be considered as a grouping of crystals that may belong to several mineral species. A crystal is held together by ionic or interatomic forces that act within the framework of the crystalline lattice. The nature of the force that bonds crystals to one another is much more obscure. The capillary tension of a thin film of liquid has been suggested in the case of cements shortly after their formation, or a thin amorphous film between the grains, but in many cases this force acts directly between crystals in contact.

For the moment we shall postpone consideration of reversible, elastic deformation in which the mutual arrangement of the different elements of the rock remains unmodified. A permanent deformation may result from the various mechanical processes that were described in Chapter 4. Let us enumerate them rapidly. There may be mutual displacement of crystals, which is hard to conceive without certain of their parts being broken; except for subsequent recrystallization, the resistance of the rock will be diminished. Deformation of the crystalline grains may also take place, either through deformation of the crystalline lattice (which may give rise to twinning or which may re-establish the initial orientation of the crystal) or by solution and recrystallization, aided by the contained liquid (even if only a trace is present). Solid diffusion could lead to the same result. There may also be recrystallization in the traction fissures that open, owing to the pressure of the contained liquid or to the pressure of crystallization of the material dissolved at the points where grains are most loaded. Finally, there may appear multiple shear fractures, immediately recemented. All these phenomena are expressed in an overall manner by a continuous deformation of the rock, but there rupture surfaces may also appear, either through shearing or through traction that will result in a discontinuous deformation.[5]

Each of the phenomena considered is evidently a direct consequence of the stress to which the rock was subjected and depends on the value of the stress. In particular, if the rock is isotropic, it is evident that the principal directions of the deformation should coincide with those of the stresses. If the rock is anisotropic, the relation is much more complex. Except for the case where it may be reduced to an alternation of isotropic layers of different properties, everything is still to be done in order to present an accurate picture of its nature.

To go further, it would be necessary to introduce other factors, such as temperature and chemical composition of the contained liquid. Experiments have shown that gypsum deforms much more quickly in the presence of water than it does when dry and that it deforms even more quickly if the water is acidulated. When warm and in the presence of solutions of carbonic acid, limestone may deform by dissolution and subsequent recrystallization without losing its cohesion.

These factors being determined, each of the types of deformation begins to take place if the stress goes beyond a certain limit, or threshold, which may be defined by an intrinsic curve on the Mohr diagram (with the restriction indicated above, p. 178). The deformation is then characterized by its rapidity, varying greatly according to the type of deformation and the manner in which it is distributed among the three principal directions. For certain modes of deformation, the rate is slow, even for a stress far surpassing the limit. For other modes, the rate of deformation is considerable.

Under given physicochemical conditions, the deformation will begin at a given rate. Then it may accelerate, if an earlier deformation diminishes the resistance (a rupture may finally occur), or it may be slowed by afterwork hardening. Experiment often shows that, under fixed conditions, the deformation increases as the logarithm of the time; that is, the speed of deformation is inversely proportional to the duration of application of the load. Things may be even more complicated; for certain steels, the resistance decreases at first, then increases as deformation proceeds until it exceeds the initial value. As soon as deformation begins at a given point, it develops easily up to the amplitude at which the resistance surpasses its initial value. It stops then, and other points deform in their turn. The volume that is undergoing deformation at a given moment forms a continuous belt, with its orientation determined by accordance with the intact parts of the test sample. These belts produce lines on the surface of the sample that are called Hartmann (or Luder) lines, which at times have been taken for the traces of slip planes. In reality, they are belts of finite width. An analogous phenomenon seems to come into play for certain rocks that present a clear-cut contrast between intact parts and intensely deformed parts.

If, after removal of the force, the sample progressively loses a part of the deformation that it has undergone, this may be due to the fact that certain particles were deformed, whereas others were greatly stretched; after removal

FIGURE 133

Hypothetical form of the intrinsic curves relative to rupture by traction (rt), *rupture by shearing,* (rc), *and by three modes of plastic deformation* (a, b, *and* c).

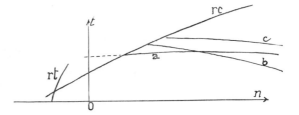

of the load, the particles apparently act upon one another and gradually become adapted.

It is an abstraction to consider a single mode of deformation by itself. In reality, several modes may be in operation simultaneously. If we trace, on a given diagram, the curve limits for all the elementary phenomena of deformation and of rupture, we may understand which of the phenomena takes place first, for a determined stress. It may be either a rupture or a plastic deformation but the latter may be more or less rapid. It may also be that the stress is such that two modes of deformation come into play simultaneously, but, in general, with unequal speeds (Fig. 133).

We are far from being able to trace experimentally the network of curves that we have just defined. At most, we are able to offer a few very incomplete explanations of their character. It seems that the intrinsic curve of rupture by shearing presents a quite wide open form; the intrinsic curves of deformation make a much smaller angle with the axis. Thus, they are the first to be recognized, when we increase the difference between the principal pressures, for a high value of the mean pressure, but rupture is likely to occur before any deformation under a slight mean pressure, especially in the open air.

In experiments performed on limestone at low temperature, the first plastic deformation takes place through the formation of twins; at high temperature and in the presence of carbonic acid, it is on the contrary the one that results from solution and recrystallization. The second type of deformation is always slow, and the first may be rapid. Experiments under triaxial stress are delicate, and only a very small number of them have been performed. Although certain experiments have lasted several weeks, it is evident that it has been possible to demonstrate only deformations that were produced at an appreciable speed. It may thus be asked whether, at low temperature, for a stress less than that which produces a relatively rapid deformation through twinning, a very slow deformation is not already being produced by an entirely different process; although not established by experiments of duration, in which the measuring devices have only limited sensitivity, such deformations might very well play an important role in tectonics.

Actually experiments made with simple compression in the open air using very sensitive measuring apparatus[6] have established a very slow rock deformation, *creep* (in French: *fluage*), of the order of one hundred thousandth in a few days for limestone under a load one half that which would produce rupture. This deformation increases as the logarithm of time.

For these very slow deformations, experiments on rocks are totally insufficient to establish the precise limit beyond which they begin to take place. Experiments on metals, however, are numerous; they show that the flowage for many metals is strictly nil over a broad field.

Recent experiments on steel [7] bearing on magnetic properties during traction tests have made it possible to establish, below the apparent elastic limit (24 kg/mm^2) a field (above 14 kg/mm^2) in which the phenomena are not exactly reversible. There seems to be a very slight permanent deformation at the limit of what the most sensitive instruments can establish. It is the measurement of magnetic properties that has made it possible to determine indirectly the lower limit of this field, that is to say the threshold for very slight deformations whose details cannot be directly studied.

It may be assumed that the same is true for most rocks and that there exists for slow deformation, as well as for rapid deformation, a threshold of plasticity to be expressed in the same manner. But the value of this threshold cannot be determined by laboratory experiments; it is by the study of tectonic deformations that we may expect to get an idea of the forces operating within the rock at the moment of its deformation, which must have gone somewhat beyond the threshold.

Deformation by recrystallization (rarely observed in the laboratory) seems to play an essential role in nature; it is probably much more sensitive to temperature than are the other modes of deformation. In fact, the ease of, or even the possibility of, recrystallization of a given mineral depends greatly on the temperature and doubtless also on the chemical composition of the contained water. When recrystallization takes place, it is expressed by the increase in the size of the grains, and if several minerals share in this evolution, it is manifested by metamorphism. The growth of the minerals that originate in this manner is influenced not only by the chemical conditions and the temperature, but likewise by the operating stress that acts on the form of the crystals. Deformation of the rock necessarily results, which no doubt takes place very slowly, but which in the long run may reach a notable amplitude if recrystallization continues. So we must keep in mind that under the physicochemical conditions that permit recrystallization of its constituent minerals, a rock should be able to undergo an easy, relatively slow deformation; that is, in terms of geologic time, a rock should be expected to behave as if it were quite plastic[8] during metamorphism.

In practice, if we consider only the overall result, we may regard the value of the threshold of plastic deformation (expressed by the difference of the principal extreme pressures) as independent of the mean pressure, at least as a first approximation for a given temperature. The corresponding intrinsic curve is then parallel to the axis (Fig. 134). As for the intrinsic curve relative to the rupture, quite numerous experiments have established that it presents

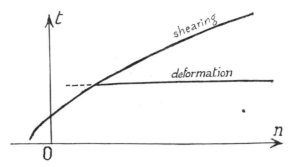

FIGURE 134

Approximate form of intrinsic curves for deformation and for shear rupture.

a relatively open form; it cuts the curve relative to the plastic deformation. But for a stress whose representative point is beyond the point of intersection, a mass may rupture in the course of slow plastic deformation.

The stress to be considered is that which operates on the solid framework of the rock. It differs from the external stress if the pressure of the contained liquid is appreciable. From the three principal pressures the pressure of the liquid must be subtracted, which, on the Mohr diagram, displaces the characteristic circle of the state of stress to the left; note that a strong liquid pressure may facilitate the shearing in relation to the plastic deformation (this is especially important for relatively slight depths and plays an essential role in the technical problems of the mechanics of soils). Owing to a sufficiently high liquid pressure, rocks sometimes break just from traction, the fracture being perpendicular to the weaker pressure, which, after subtraction of the liquid pressure, becomes a tension (see Fig. 133). If the liquid is supersaturated in a mineral susceptible of crystallizing, the crystallization pressure of the latter, which exceeds the pressure of the liquid, comes into play. Fractures produced by traction are often filled by a crystallized mineral under these conditions (Figs. 18 and 19).

The concept presented here evolves from the analysis of experiments performed on rocks subjected to triaxial stress, and from comparison with very numerous experiments performed upon other materials.

As indicated above, experiments teach us very little concerning the very slow deformations of rocks. They are not sufficient to exclude another concept implicitly contained in the theory of rock flowage brilliantly defended in recent years by Maurice Gignoux.[9] From the point of view of mechanics, this theory amounts to considering as null the threshold of slow deformations for rocks which would thus be included among viscous bodies, no longer plastic. Rocks might then deform very slowly under the action of stresses, even very weak ones such as exist under conditions of hydrostatic pressure.

We shall have occasion to return to this concept, especially in the next chapter, since it leads to an application of similitude that differs completely from the hypothesis of plasticity accepted here. It is essentially by comparing the consequences deduced from both theories with tectonic deformations actually observed, that we can establish good grounds for the hypothesis of plasticity, according to which a threshold exists beyond which deformation begins. As we shall see later, we may even attempt to calculate the value of the threshold according to the tectonic deformations actually recorded.

By using a simplified form of the results that have just been established, it is possible to represent in the following manner the mass of geologic formations in the act of undergoing a tectonic deformation that we shall assume at first to be very slow. Upon the mass under consideration, there operates on the one hand the weight of its different parts, and on the other, the pressures of the adjacent masses, concerning which we can say nothing *a priori*. Throughout the whole mass, there prevails a certain distribution of stresses in equilibrium with each other and with the external forces that we have just indicated. Wherever the rock is deformed, this stress reaches, or surpasses (generally by only a small amount if the deformation is slow), a value corresponding to the threshold of plasticity of the rock. Outside the field undergoing plastic deformation, the stress is inferior to the threshold; as we have seen apropos of the distribution of stresses in ground that is in repose, it is partially indeterminate.

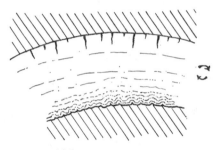

FIGURE 135

Secondary deformations (fissures, folds) that may have originated on the borders of a resistant bed in the act of bending following special values attained there by the stresses.

There is scarcely any need to point out that this distribution of stresses is too complicated for us to determine or to follow throughout the course of the deformation. If fractures appear, it is because the stress at a given point has reached the value corresponding to the intrinsic curve of rupture of the rock. As soon as it originates, the fracture develops rapidly; we can no longer avoid considering the forces of inertia, which are expressed by the appearance of vibrations that are propagated through the earth's mass (these are seismic waves). The distribution of stresses is so complex that its study can furnish interesting information only in simple cases.

Let us consider, for example, a relatively resistant bed (high threshold) included within a more plastic mass (low threshold) and in the act of bending (Fig. 135). The pressure that is exerted upon the separation surface evidently being the same in the two media, and the differences of principal pressures being equal to the respective thresholds, since there is deformation, the pressure that is exerted upon an element of surface normal to the limit is much less on the side where there is elongation (the extrados) in the resistant medium than in the plastic mass, and it may even be replaced by a tension which may be expressed by cracks. Inversely, on the compressed side (the

FIGURE 136

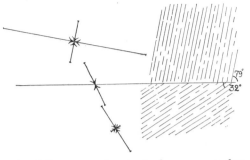

Refraction of schistocity at the contact between marly beds and limestone beds. The angle between schistocity and stratification is indicated at the right for both the limestones and the marls (Lower Cretaceous of the Basses-Alpes). The principal pressures are indicated to the left, in an arbitrary unit; the magnitudes and directions are shown vectorially. The differences of principal pressures that characterize the thresholds are in the ratio of 2.4, for the angles indicated. The pressure exerted on the contact is also indicated. (For the detailed calcualtion, see p. 272 of reference 1, p. 1.)

intrados), the pressure within the resistant rock is greater than in the plastic rock. It may produce secondary folds if the stratification is sufficiently marked. As affirmed earlier (p. 136), these folds are related to the particular system of stresses in operation at their point of origin, and they have no other relation to the general form of the folding.

The complete calculation of the distribution of stresses is possible in a certain number of simple cases and furnishes the explanation of actually observed arrangements.

In Chapter 4, p. 44, we called attention to the phenomenon of the refraction of schistosity, whose mechanical explanation is easily given (Fig. 136). If a mass formed of beds whose plastic threshold values differ from bed to bed is subjected to an oblique compression, it is obvious that the stresses cannot be the same in the different beds. The (oblique) pressure that is exerted on the surfaces of separation is evidently the same, but since the difference between the principal pressures differs from one bed to the next, the directions of these principal pressures must also be different, and we know that the schistosity that results from the deformation is perpendicular to the strongest principal pressure.[10]

The phenomenon of boudinage, described in Chapter 4, p. 59, at first sight appears under a very different aspect since it results from fragmentation of certain beds. The manner in which the stresses[11] are distributed among beds of different nature is not, however, very different from that which has just been studied. The difference is essentially due to the fact that the less plastic beds undergo rupture instead of plastic deformation.

Let us assume that the rock, in the midst of which there is a relatively thin rigid bed, is subjected to a stress such that the greatest principal pressure is normal to the bed (Fig. 137); the value of this principal pressure is evidently the same in the rigid bed as it is in the surrounding rock. The other principal pressures, parallel to the plane of the bed, assume very different values. Within the mass of the plastic rock, the amount by which these pressures

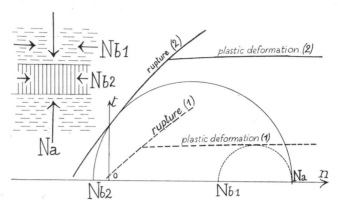

FIGURE 137. *Mechanical interpretation of boudinage. Left, Disposition and relative size of principal components of the stress for the resistant bed (2) and the surrounding plastic medium (1). Right, Their representation on Mohr diagram, showing intrinsic curves relative to the two media.*

differ from the normal pressure cannot exceed the threshold of plasticity as long as the rock does not deform. However, the rock cannot deform in the vicinity of the rigid bed unless it also deforms. The principal pressures (or one of them) in the plane of stratification become very low before this occurs; traction may even appear. Under these conditions, the Mohr circle attains the curve relative to rupture before touching the intrinsic curve of plastic deformation (or at least of rapid deformation), and the rigid bed fractures. Its fragments are then carried into the heart of the plastic rock undergoing deformation. Although the complete calculation is difficult, we realize that the space between the fragments is a zone of least pressure, in which crystallization of calcite or quartz sometimes takes place according to the composition of the impregnation liquid rather than the penetration of the surrounding rock.

It is possible to get an intuitive idea of the manner in which traction may appear in the rigid bed when we observe that by its presence it checks to some extent the plastic rock which would tend to spread. It is also possible to calculate the distribution of stresses if the greatest principal pressure is oblique to the rigid bed. When we observe bits cut obliquely, or tending to pivot, we can obtain certain accurate data on the nature of the stress that was in operation during deformation.[12]

In the case of boudinage, it is possible to calculate the distribution of forces up to the rupture of the hard bed. Then it becomes too complex, and we are able to obtain only a few intuitive indications. In general, this is the way things happen with ensembles that are somewhat less complex. However, here is an example in which the intuitive consideration of the distribution of the stresses furnishes an interesting result (Fig. 138). As a result of experiments on a reduced model, B. Willis[13] noted that if a resistant bed surrounded by plastic beds is in the act of bending to form an anticline under the action of a transverse compression, this hard bed, at the spring of the arch that it outlines, exercises a downward pressure under the action of which the lower beds will be driven laterally; by this trigger action, a second fold will form alongside the first anticline. This example is very diagrammatic. In the complexity of an actual case, there is but little hope that we can succeed in completely determining the distribution of forces and in following its evolution.

Happily, it is possible to obtain certain overall indications independent of the detailed distribution of stresses. To do this, it is sufficient to evaluate the energy expended during deformation in the form of work. The speeds being slight, there is no kinetic energy and the stored (potential) elastic energy is negligible. There are then only three terms to be considered. For a given portion of the earth's crust, the pressures exerted at the contact with adjacent parts do work if they displace their point of application. For example, if the field under consideration undergoes a lateral compression, positive work will be done. In the second place, the plastic deformation of an element of mass, owing to its resistance, always absorbs a certain amount of work, which is, for each unit of volume, the product of the deformation and the stress under which it was produced. If we take this as the threshold stress, and if we accept that the latter is independent of the mean pressure, this work is expressed simply by multiplying the total deformation by the value of the threshold, whatever may be the manner in which the deformation was attained. To the work done in deforming the rocks, we must add that absorbed by the friction offered by faults and thrust surfaces. The calculation of this involves an evaluation of the angle of friction (in movement) and the normal pressure operating on the fault at the moment it was in action. Finally, the third term concerns the work of gravity, which may be active or resistant. It may be evaluated very simply by determining the change in the height of the center of gravity of the mass under consideration. If the densities of all the rocks are the same (an approximation that is often acceptable), the center of gravity is that of the volume that they occupy, and its position depends only on the boundaries of the rock mass. It is then possible to evaluate the work of gravity by considering the volume lost by the mass under consideration and

FIGURE 138

In the horizontal compression of a hard bed that tends to form an anticline, the composition of the forces determines a downward compression at the spring of the arch, which may trigger a synclinal fold (indicated at the left).

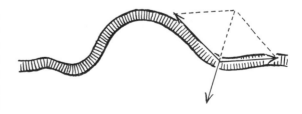

the volume gained (equal to the former if we consider the rocks as incompressible) and by multiplying the weight of the matter occupying this volume by the difference in height. We shall group the work of gravity with that absorbed by the deformation. If it is effective work, that is, if the center of gravity lowers we will consider it as negative; if it is resistant work, we will consider it positive.

The fundamental work equation expresses that the effective work (that of the pressures exerted within the limits of the volume we are considering) is equal to the sum of the resistant work of deformation (including the work of friction of faults) and of the work of gravity, taken as positive or negative.

If we know the initial and final states of an actual deformation, the absolute value of work of gravity can be easily calculated, but the work of deformation depends on the thresholds of plasticity. However, the values are doubtful. The principal interest in the formula just described is not that it enables us to calculate the work absorbed; it results from the following principle. For a given displacement of the limits of the mass under consideration, the deformation actually produced is the one that absorbs the least work (principle of least work) of all those that could be conceived.

In order to illustrate the application of this principle, let us consider a stratified mass undergoing a given lateral compression, ignoring the work of gravity (Fig. 139). We could conceive of a deformation resulting from regular crushing of all the beds, or involving a partial crushing, or parallel folding, in which the beds conserve a constant thickness but twist and slip upon one another. If the threshold of plasticity of the beds is notably higher than that of the layers that separate them, this latter mode of deformation corresponds to the least work, because the deformation has the least possible effect upon the most resistant beds and the most possible effect upon the plastic layers that separate them. If there had been a regular crushing of all the beds, the de-

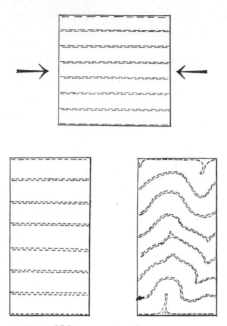

FIGURE 139

Deformation of a stratified mass by horizontal compression. Below. Two overall equivalent results, a homogeneous crushing and folding. It may be shown that if the mechanical resistance of the joints is very different from that of the beds, the folding (which implies a slip along the joints and a simple torsion of the beds without change of thickness) absorbs less energy than the homogeneous crushing.

formation would have been distributed equally among them. In this way is to be explained, by the difference of the mechanical properties of alternate beds, the deformation by parallel folding of sedimentary masses which we had presented as an experimental fact in the geometric analysis of deformation.

Mechanical analysis is of great interest in that it indicates the limits of application of this manner of deformation. Nonstratified masses, or those in which the stratification has no influence on the mechanical properties, may give way to disharmonies instead of folding regularly.

On the contrary, the beds whose threshold of plasticity is highest, and which alternate with beds much more plastic than they, will behave in a manner such that their own deformation may be the least possible; generally, it will be very minor in their plane, and will be reduced to a simple torsion. This expresses objectively on the plane of the mechanical properties the distinction implied by the terms "competent" and "incompetent" (see p. 136). It is incompetent beds that admit disharmonies; the application of the principle of minimum work makes it possible to specify the amplitude of the latter. When an incompetent series is contained between two competent series, it may either twist while preserving a constant thickness (in which case the folds of the beds which frame it are parallel) or it may vary in thickness. Calculations show that for undulations whose wave length is of the order of thickness, the work absorbed is no greater in the second case than in the first. On the contrary, for a much greater wave length, the work in a torsion of constant thickness would be appreciably less than for changes of thickness. Undulations of small wave length will thus be disharmonic on both sides of the incompetent series, whereas undulations of great wave length (relative to the thickness) will be parallel.

It was pointed out above that when a sedimentary cover shears or folds on itself, the shearing frequently occurs at the level of a saliferous or gypsiferous bed. This can be explained as follows: The salt and, to a lesser extent, the gypsum possess an extremely low threshold of plasticity; for monocrystalline salt, it is not even possible to recognize a threshold below which the deformation is rigorously elastic. For a crystalline aggregate, however, there seems to exist a threshold different from zero, as for gypsum. For gypsum, laboratory experiments seem to indicate that plastic deformation begins when the extreme principal pressures differ by about 200 kg/cm^2 (for a limestone the figure might be around ten times greater). We shall see later that it is possible to estimate at around one-half this value the threshold that effectively prevailed at the time of certain geologic deformations.

Be that as it may, these relatively low threshold values permit the slipping by plastic deformation of salt or gypsum with much less work than that which would have been absorbed by any other deformation of the sedimentary cover.

Saliferous or gypsiferous beds represent only the most extreme case of disharmony; a very strong deformation of a very slightly resistant bed absorbs less work than do much more moderate deformations of normal beds.

We can study tectonic deformation in the most precise manner by observing its effects on sedimentary beds. Since deformation is expressed essentially in the form of undulations of the beds, or by folding, we might be tempted to consider folding as the normal modality of deformation of the earth's crust. The foregoing analysis shows, however, that this is not the case. Folds are peculiar to stratified beds in which mechanical properties differ from bed to bed. A rock that does not present this character will deform in an entirely different manner.

We have indicated why the numerical values of experimentally determined thresholds of plasticity for a certain number of rocks could not be used directly in the study of tectonic deformations that no doubt occurred more slowly, and for which the value of the threshold may be considerably lower. On the other hand, for certain very resistant rocks, such as granite, the only deformations observed were produced by multiple ruptures; the corresponding stress (difference of principal pressures) would probably increase with the mean pressure, and the true threshold of plastic deformation would perhaps be higher.

So it is with reservations, and merely to establish an order of magnitude, that we give the following values:

	Difference of principal pressures producing a plastic deformation
Limestone: Carrara marble	1200–3000 [a]; 4000 [b] kg/cm^2
Solnhofen limestone	4000 [a]
Soft marly limestone, Low. Cret. Jura ..	500
Shale of the Lias (Basses-Alpes)	800
Chalk	45 (limited deformation)
Lutetian limestone (Paris)	60 (limited deformation)
Red Sandstone (Trias)	3000 [b]
Soft, calc. sandstone (Miocene, B.-Alpes)	1400
Gypsum	200
Rock salt	< 60–250 [c]
Talc	700
Granite	11,000 [d]
Quartz (monocrystalline)	> 120,000 [a]

(a) Griggs, (b) Karman, (c) Schmidt, (d) Adams and Bancroft. The other figures result from measurements made by the author (*Introduction à l'étude mécanique des déformations de l'écorce terrestre, Mém. Carte Géol.*, 1942, 2e éd., 1948), Chapter X.

It should be remembered that all these figures are the result of tests on dry, cold samples. At high temperatures, or in the presence of suitable solutions, the slow deformation thresholds might be much lower.

It is possible to obtain indications on the actual values of thresholds of plasticity by another method: When studying a deformation that is effectively completed (a slide, for example), it is often possible to calculate a limit for the threshold of the base bed. Knowing that, of several possible deformations, one is effectively produced, it is possible to obtain an approximate value of a threshold. It has been possible to evaluate[14] at 50 kg/cm^2 the difference of the principal pressures corresponding to the threshold for the saliferous formations of the Trias which permitted the basal sliding and folding of the Mesozoic rocks of the Jura, by comparing several anticlines successively lower and lower. It may be assumed that in the last phase of compression the distribution of the deformation among all the folds corresponded to the minimum of the work absorbed; from one fold to another the difference results especially from the difference in height (work of gravity) and the unequal length along which the slip should take place on the saliferous beds of the Trias. It is certainly possible to find examples on which such a calculation can be conducted in a more precise manner; thus we can soon hope to obtain a certain number of approximate values that correspond to actual tectonic deformations.

In addition to these absolute measurements, the ratio of thresholds of plasticity of different rocks may often be deduced from the character of the deformations in which they are all involved. We have seen the manner in which this relation may be deduced from the refraction of schistosity in the passage from one rock to another. The form of certain folds makes it possible to calculate the ratio of the thresholds relative to resistant beds and to other beds,[15] and we can certainly find many other arrangements of detail that will make it possible to calculate the ratio of plasticity thresholds.

Even without calculation, the character of folds facilitates the recognition of more or less plastic strata. When trying to represent a fold, one must guard against cases in which the plasticity does not correspond to the different sorts of resistance to which we are accustomed, such as crushing, rupture by shock, alteration in the presence of atmospheric agents, and ease of erosion. An especially typical example of this discordance is furnished by sands, which, even when unconsolidated, may strongly resist deformation when they are subjected to a pressure in all directions. A sand presents an internal angle of

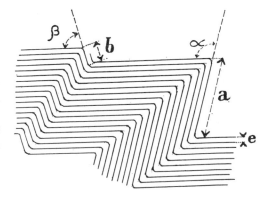

FIGURE 140

Example of limited flexures of a type common in the Upper Cretaceous of the Alpes-Maritimes. If two analogous flexures of different lengths are observed adjacent to one another, the angles are different (of course corrected for any perspective distortion).

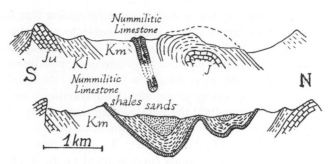

FIGURE 141. *Two sections of Nummulitic synclines in the Alpes-Maritimes (basin of the Esteron) a short distance from each other. Whereas the marls were finally completely expelled from the syncline in the first case, the sands (dot pattern) constituted a resistant mass that was relatively only slightly deformed. The character of the folding affecting the Jurassic shows that the compression is no greater in one case than in the other.*

friction high enough such that, at depth, its shearing (that is, its relative displacement of the grains) absorbs a great energy; quartz grains are extremely resistant. The western part of the Alpes-Maritimes furnishes examples that illustrate this remarkably. There we find a series of Nummulitic synclines several of which when they contained only marls were crushed to such an extent that the basal limestone of both sides frequently comes into contact; the marls were then very plastic. On the contrary, when the overlying sands were preserved, they resisted and formed quite voluminous cores[16] (Fig. 141).

A fortiori, massive sandstone, if not interrupted by marly beds, resists deformation very strongly, with a threshold that is no doubt higher than that of other sedimentary rock. When a sedimentary series begins with such a sandstone, its mechanical properties often cause it to remain solidly with the basement, the rest of the sedimentary series deforming in an entirely different manner.

On the other hand, in an alternation of sandstones and marls (or shales), the presence of the latter sufficiently facilitates the plastic deformation of the whole mass (Flysch of any age).

A conglomerate may be almost as resistant as a sandstone if its beds are not separated by plastic argillaceous beds. In the Mio-Pliocene conglomerates of the Basses-Alpes, there are pebbles that have been deformed and sheared by a fault at a point that has never been more than 100 or 200 meters below the surface. The pressure in force at this depth was sufficient to prevent the mutual displacement of the pebbles; since the pebbles were selected during the course of their transportation, they are always formed of quite resistant rocks.

We may acquire an understanding of the mechanical role of conglomerates on the periphery of the Alps, where they accumulated during the Miocene, at the mouths of the principal Alpine rivers (Fig. 142). Each of these old deltas constituted, at the time of the movements of the Upper Miocene, an abutment against which the folds stopped and were turned back on themselves.

In contrast to sands and conglomerates, which resist erosion poorly, limestones generally produce scarped reliefs. However, a pure limestone is a relatively deformable rock, owing to the ease with which twinning takes place in calcite and especially to the ease of its recrystallization by solution. Acid ground water no doubt greatly facilitates deformation.

Experiments indicate (and it should be the same for natural deformations) that a slight content of argillaceous impurities increases the resistance to deformation of the limestone. It seems that this increase is still appreciable for contents that render the limestone easily altered and reduce its morphologic role. The strong plasticity characteristic of clay appears only when the clay content is much higher.

In alternating calcareous and dolomitic beds, dolomitic beds are often found to be broken into angular fragments, whereas the limestone deformed plastically. This indicates a higher threshold of plasticity for the dolomite than for the limestone, but the difference was perhaps not very considerable, since the stresses could scarcely have risen above the plasticity threshold of the limestone and thus would not have reached the value corresponding to the dolomite. Under the viscosity hypothesis, the two rocks should have deformed together at different rates.

But the nature of the bedding and its spacing play a more important role than do the properties of the hard beds in facilitating the deformation of a

FIGURE 142

Accumulations of Mio-Pliocene conglomerates on the periphery of the Alps. Note their relation to the sinuosities of the peripheral folds.

stratified mass. The interbeds are usually formed of a more plastic rock than the hard beds but in a quite variable relation, which has nothing to do with the aspects of the outcrops that are due to alteration alone. The marly beds, which were eroded subaerially and which separate calcareous, rounded loaves and show a characteristic banding on the escarpments of the Lower Cretaceous of the sub-Alpine mountains, correspond to a relation of the thresholds of plasticity of 2.5 (by refraction of the schistosity), whereas in the Upper Cretaceous (Basses-Alpes, Alpes-Maritimes) the beds have a threshold about one-fifteenth that of the calcareous beds that they separate. This accounts for the frequency of the often very marked secondary folds that are completely lacking in the Lower Cretaceous.

Thus, when a wide range of properties exists between alternating beds, the overall resistance to folding scarcely exceeds that of the single more plastic rock. When marls, for example, permit a disharmony between two calcareous series, folded independently of each other, the absence of stratification in the marls is of more significance than a very low value of the threshold (which may be the same as for the joints of the calcareous masses).

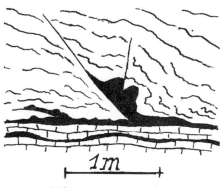

FIGURE 143

Injection of coal into a roof fault (Swiss Tertiary Molasse). [After A. Bersier.]

Coal often behaves like an extremely plastic material, even to the point of being injected into the fissures of adjacent hard beds (sandstones or conglomerates). The changes of thickness of folded beds and, in particular, the thickenings in the hinges are important for exploitation. A coal bed may permit a relative slip of its walls (Fig. 143).[17]

We could not speak of the mechanical properties of sedimentary rocks without recalling the essential fact that gypsum and salt, or, more generally, saliferous and gypsiferous formations, present an extremely low threshold of plasticity. It is also difficult to specify the phenomena that play an effective role: deformation of crystals, as in the laboratory; solution and recrystallization, which seem to play a less important role here than we might have expected; the properties of associated clays (in particular, their deflocculation). The plasticity of gypsum may result in a true filter-press effect, the gypsum being expelled from a formation that no longer contains anything but the marls and intercalated dolomites.

This phenomenon can be observed in a particularly clear manner in a section located in the valley of the Bès, to the north of Digne (Fig. 96). In the overall slip of the Jurassic series that forms the Digne overthrust, the Keuper was carried along and was reduced to a very slight thickness to the east of the Barles anticline. To the west of this anticline, the Keuper is represented by an accumulation of residual marls and dolomites, which owe their origin to the expulsion of gypsum from the Keuper. The latter accumulated in thick masses at the base of the overthrusting series some ten kilometers farther on.[18]

Anhydrite, a common form of calcium sulphate found at depth, poses a problem. Its resistance to crushing seems high, and nothing else seems to deform as easily as gypsum. However, some Triassic formations that contain anhydrite are highly deformed. I would suggest, with some reservation, that solution and recrystallization could have played an essential role if the conditions of temperature and pressure (the pressure of the contained water being, in general, less than that of the solid) were such that anhydrite would constitute the stable form of calcium sulphate.

In comparison to most sediments, crystalline rocks (except serpentine) behave as if much more rigid, owing to their lack of joints, which permit easy folding of sediments, and to their mechanical resistance. But we should never lose sight of the influence of physicochemical conditions. In a "climate" that virtually renders possible the recrystallization of some minerals, any rock may behave, in the long run, as if easily deformable. In particular, quartz, which does not possess slip planes or twin planes, has never been deformed in the laboratory. However, quartz seems to be very mobile in many deformed rocks, forming veins that make all the fissures conspicuous. Between crossed nicols, the earliest formed crystals show undulatory extinction; recrystallization plays an essential role in these deformations, both in veins, or in healed crystal fractures. Laboratory measurements give no idea of the pressures under which these deformations could have been produced. At the moment it undergoes metamorphism, a rock should behave as if particularly plastic, at least for slow deformations; however, this does not prevent it, later on, under different conditions and at a lower temperature, from behaving as if very rigid. It is necessary to take this into consideration in order to understand the deep deformation undergone by internal zones of the Alps at the time of principal tectonic phases accompanied by metamorphism, whereas in later phases these zones may have played the role of rigid masses.

Plastic sedimentary rocks (argillaceous rocks, for example) may also have been deformed and then have undergone metamorphism that transformed them into crystalline schists that are very rigid (at least at surface temperature).

In addition to the plastic deformation of rock, discontinuous ruptures also play an important role, especially at slight depth; their disposition is particularly important when they give passage to mineralizing solution (see Chaps. 4 and 18).

In current experiments on compression (and even traction), the ruptures form along a direction oblique to the axes, in general at an angle less than $45°$

to the direction of the maximum principal pressure. It is often observed that the fractures seem to start from the surface where they originate aided by very slight irregularities (polish diminishes their frequency); this phenomenon is evidently without analogy in rock ruptures produced in depth. The first stage of rupture is generally impossible to observe, but it is conceivable that, slightly later, a pressure whose tangential component is in a fixed relation (coefficient of friction at repose) to the normal component is transmitted through the corresponding surface. In the vicinity of the rupture, distribution of the stresses is modified: the stresses are increased in the prolongation of the fissure and consequently the latter extends laterally. But, parallel to the fissure, and in its vicinity, the stress diminishes. Although the initial distribution of stress is approximately uniform, this decrease on both sides of the growing fissure prevents the appearance of other fissures parallel to the first in its immediate vicinity. From an initially continuous distribution of stresses, a discontinuance system of fractures develops.

Each fracture tends to develop laterally; the tangential component of friction on the surface is insufficient to balance the stresses that affect its periphery. When the rupture has extended sufficiently, its two margins become displaced relative to each other; the fissure thus becomes transformed into a fault. This relative motion appears to us as the normal sequence to the rupture; thus it is difficult to interpret undisplaced fissures as being the result of an oblique fracture; compare especially with joints.

When movement begins, the tangential component of the pressure transmitted across the fissure suddenly diminishes, the coefficient of friction in movement being less than the coefficient in repose. The relative movement of the two margins assumes a notable velocity, for which the kinetic energy is no longer negligible. Owing to the inertia of masses in movement, the position of equilibrium may be passed. When the motion stops, a state of tension may exist, which may be very different from the initial state. But the repetition of the same causes (for example, slow movements at depth) will bring about the reappearance of the initial forces until the movement starts again. We see that for a slow deformation in depth, a fault will act through a series of rough jolts, separated by periods during which the margins move progressively back into tension; these jolts seem to be the principal causes of earthquakes.

For a given rock, a fault can, in principle, originate only above a certain depth, since below that depth (as shown by the Mohr diagram) the plastic deformation that would be produced before rupture took place would prevent the forces from reaching the values that correspond to the rupture. But things would be different for a very rapid loading, such as that which would result from the appearance of a fault in the adjacent strata; thus, a fault may spread under conditions in which it could not originate. That is, at a certain depth, there may be rupture due to rapid loading but plastic deformation with slow loading.

Despite the difference between the chronological development of faults and

FIGURE 144

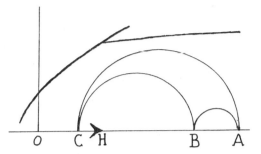

Mohr diagram of the state of stress of a rock. The position of the intrinsic curves shows that neither plastic deformation nor rupture by shearing is possible. But if H *is the pressure of the liquid, every pre-existent fissure perpendicular to the principal direction* C *tends to open.*

folds, respectively discontinuous and continuous, faults and folds are commonly observed to pass from one to the other. For example, if strata of very different mechanical properties are superposed, a vertical fault in the most rigid strata may pass into a flexure in more plastic strata, even if they are higher in the series. It is probable that the movement of the fault was then made by jolts of very slight amplitude.

We have pointed out earlier (Chap. 4) the existence of ruptures of a different type, almost unknown in experiments at atmospheric pressure in which the rupture plane is perpendicular to the principal direction of minimum pressure (which may be traction). These ruptures can be explained if we take into account the pressure of the contained liquid or, if it is not in chemical equilibrium, the crystallization pressure of the crystals that it is susceptible of depositing (Fig. 144). If this pressure exceeds the least of the principal pressures in the rock, every orthogonal fissure tends to open; it may be assumed that a multitude of small fissures exist that extend in all directions. Those that are oriented in such a manner as to open, extend progressively (see Fig. 18, where we can observe that the fissures are perpendicular to the principal direction corresponding to the weakest pressure).

The lentils of ice that form in a water-impregnated clay during winter are a very good example of this phenomenon. But we can also study it in innumerable veinlets of calcite and quartz in all deformed rocks.

The energy absorbed by plastic deformation, or by friction during faulting, is not stored up in elastic form, but is transformed into heat. If we know the thresholds of plasticity, and the specific heat of the rocks it is easy to calculate the rise of temperature that corresponds to a given deformation. It has been found that this elevation of temperature barely reaches a few tens of degrees, even for a very deep deformation, thus it cannot be the cause of appreciable modifications of rocks, such as metamorphism or recrystallization.[19]

It is only in the action of faults by friction that immediately after the movement, which is very rapid, the energy liberated is concentrated in a very thin film, which may attain a quite high temperature but only for a very short time. This particular characteristic may perhaps play a role in the formation of certain slickensides. It is in deep tectonics that the effect of this heating along faults should be most important, because the normal pressure is higher than at the surface, with the result that the energy absorbed, all other things being equal, should be higher. The recrystallization that is frequently observed in mylonites may be facilitated by this heating. If an injection of crystalline rock seems to outline a surface of abnormal contact, we may ask whether it is really an injection and not a re-fusion zone, or at least of total recrystallization aided by the local heating due to the slip.

The consideration of the forces involved in tectonic deformation is susceptible of furnishing many other indications. But whenever calculation alone fails to describe this phenomenon, we are led to represent it to ourselves intuitively, even by analogy with phenomena actually subjected to calculation; then the problem of scale presents itself, because our intuitive representations always involve models in the scale of our perceptible experience. In the next chapter, we shall see how to make the proper change of scale.

Notes and References

1. Mathematicians present this conception in terms of tensors.

2. The relations between the forces at the different points are expressed by the three equations of equilibrium.

3. See reference 1, Chapter 1. J. Goguel, *Introduction* . . . , Chapters 13 and 14.

4. The importance of this elasticoviscous deformation for bodies such as plexiglas has been shown by Albert Kammerer (*Les propriétés mécaniques des solides réels et la théorie de l'élasticité,* Paris (Hermann), Actual. Sci. et Industr., no. 1161, 1951). He showed that the elasticoviscous part of the deformation depends essentially on the change of volume, the change of form at constant volume seeming to be instantaneous. Although the explanation is quite different, there is in this something analogous to what may be expected for a rock whose pores are filled with water and which may be considered incompressible as a first approximation. The author likewise shows that certain experimental results can only be interpreted by taking into account the fact that deformation is not an exact linear function of the stress.

5. The deformation of a sand by relative displacement of the grains is one of the simplest facts that can be considered. The intrinsic curve along which the deformation begins to take place is wide open, which may be expressed by saying that the angle of internal friction is quite large. It may also be noted that the deformation of sand requires that the grains separate from each other, resulting in an increase in volume, which O. Reynolds has called "dilatancy." If an external pressure opposes this increase in volume, the sand will behave as if rigid. Thus there are two ways of expressing the same behavior.

Reynolds, Osborne, On the Dilatancy of Media Composed of Rigid Particles in Contact, Phil. Mag., ser. 5, vol. 20, pp. 469–481, 1885.

———, Experiments Showing Dilatancy, a Property of Granular Material Possibly Connected with Gravitation, Proc. Roy. Inst. Great Britain, vol. 2, pp. 354–363, 1886.

Mead, The Geologic Role of Dilatancy, Jour. Geol., vol. 33, pp. 685–698, 1925.

Raistrick and Marshall, *The Structure and Origin of Coal and Coal Seams,* London, 1939.

6. Griggs, D., Creep of rocks, Jour. Geol., vol. 47, pp. 225–257, 1939.

7. Langevin, A., Reimbert, E. Paul, and Reimbert, M., *Distinction entre la limite d'élasticité apparente et la limite de réversibilité apparente de l'acier en traction,* Acad. Sci. Paris, Comptes-rendus, vol. 230, Feb. 20, 1950.

8. Goguel, J., *Importance des facteurs physico-chimiques dans la déformation des roches,* Nineteenth Internat. Geol. Congr., Algiers, fasc. 3, pp. 133–142, 1953.

9. Gignoux, M., *Méditation sur la tectonique d'écoulement par gravité,* Univ. Grenoble, Lab. Géol., Trav., vol. 27, pp. 4–34, 1948.

————, *La tectonique d'écoulement par gravité et la structure des Alpes,* Bull. Soc. géol. France, ser. 5, vol. 18, pp. 739–764, 1948.

————, *Comment les géologues des Alpes françaises conçoivent la tectonique d'écoulement,* Geologie en Mijnbouw, new ser., vol. 12, pp. 342–346, 1950.

The same concept was developed by S. Warren Carey, using a more rigorous physico-mathematical approach. See in particular: The Rheid Concept in Geotectonics, Jour. Geol. Soc. Australia, vol. 1, no. 1, pp. 67–117, Adelaide, 1953. This treatment, however, calls for the same reservations; it is arbitrary to assume, *a priori,* that for all rocks, the threshold of strength is nil. On the contrary, many observations can be interpreted only by assigning the threshold a finite value.

10. See reference 1, Chapter 1, Goguel, J. *Introduction . . . ,* p. 272. The calculation shows that the threshold of plasticity relative to the two rocks is in inverse relation to the sine of twice the angle that the schistosity makes with the stratification.

11. See reference 1, Chapter 1, Goguel, J., *Introduction . . . ,* p. 281.

12. Goguel, J., *Observations sur la déformation d'un calcaire métamorphique,* Bull. Soc. géol. France, 5ᵉ ser., vol. 18, pp. 441–452, 1948.

13. Willis, Bailey, The Mechanics of Appalachian Structure, Ann. Rept. U.S. Geol. Surv., pt. 2, pp. 217–282, 1893.

14. See reference 1, Chapter 1, Goguel, J., *Introduction . . . ,* p. 394.

15. It has been proved (Goguel, J., *Introduction . . . ,* p. 320) that, with the notations defined by Fig. 135,

$$\frac{S_i}{S_j} = \frac{ab}{2e\,(a-b)} \times \frac{\cos^2\frac{\alpha}{2} - \cos^2\frac{\beta}{2}}{\cos^2\frac{\alpha}{2} + \cos^2\frac{\beta}{2}}.$$

For the Senonian of the Alpes-Maritime it has been calculated that S_i/S_j is of the order of 15 (S_i, threshold relative to the beds; S_j, threshold of the soft layers between the beds).

16. Goguel, J., *Description tectonique de la bordure des Alpes de la Bléone au Var,* Mém. Carte géol. France (thesis), 225 pp., Paris, 1936.

17. Fourmarier, P., *A propos du glissement des couches de charbon entre toit et mur dans le bassin de la Campine,* Ann. Soc. géol. Belgique, vol. 50, no. 8, pp. 236–239, 1927.

Duparque, A., *Le rôle des actions mécaniques dans l'évolution des couches de houille,* Bull. Soc. géol. France, 4ᵉ ser., vol. 28, pp. 455–491, 1928.

Bersier, A., *Phénomènes de plasticité dans les charbons molassiques,* Eclogae geol. Helvet., vol. 41, no. 1, pp. 101–112, 1948.

Petrascheck, W. E., *Verdickungen und Verdrückungen von Kohlenflözen und die Gesetzmässigkeit ihrer Lage,* Zeitschr. Prakt. Geol., pp. 172–175, 1937.

18. Goguel, Jean, *Tectonique des chaînes subalpines entre la Bléone et la Durance,* Bull. Carte géol. France, no. 202, vol. 41, pp. 189–236, 1939. (See especially page 202.)

19. Hubbert, K. and Ruby, W. W., Role of Fluid Pressure in Mechanics of Overthrust Faulting, Bull. Geol. Soc. America, vol. 70, pp. 115–206, 1959.

CHAPTER THIRTEEN

Applications of Mechanical Interpretation. Considerations of Similitude and Experiments on Models. Tectonics of Flow

Laws of similitude for the deformation of a model—Their intuitive application—Experiments—Influence of scale on actual deformations—The case of salt domes—Influence of scale on slides and landslips—Gravitational gliding tectonics—Influence of topographic forms at the moment of deformation—Difficulty of their reconstruction—Influence of erosion during deformation or between successive phases—The Prealps—Distinction between gravitational gliding tectonics and tectonics of deep origin—Delimitation of slides and landslips.

WE HAVE SEEN in the foregoing chapter that the mechanical phenomena produced during tectonic deformation are, in general, too complex for their direct analysis to furnish us useful information. We have thus been obliged to fall back on an overall method that lumps everything that took place during a certain interval of time, without our having to know all the details.

But the fact that the distribution of stresses at each instant and that of the resultant deformations may theoretically be considered as determined is going to furnish us very important results.

Let us imagine that, alongside the portion of the earth's crust, whose deformation we are studying, we can produce a similar deformation in what we shall consider as a model of the real crust. Evidently the model should be geometrically similar to the real on a given scale. Certain mechanical conditions must also be fulfilled for the resultant forces and deformations to be distributed in a similar fashion. If these conditions are met, the succession of deformations will be similar, although they will take place during different but proportional times.

What are the mechanical conditions that should be met? The pressures at homologous points on the model and on the earth's crust are in a given ratio, which should apply both to the exterior pressures and to the thresholds of plasticity of the different rocks and substances that represent them.

This ratio should likewise apply to the pressures that result from gravity. The pressure produced by a certain thickness of material is equal to the product of this thickness times the weight of the unit of volume. The ratio of the pressures is then determined. It should be equal to the product of the ratio of the thicknesses times the ratio of the densities, and (if the model is subjected to a gravitational force other than that which exists at the surface of the earth) times the ratio of the gravities (experiments with centrifuge).

Of course, this ratio should be verified for each of the substances used in the model to represent each of the real rocks. Theoretically, for each one of them, the whole system of intrinsic curves relative to rupture and to the various deformations should be similar (this brings into play only the relation of the pressures), but there is no practical interest in developing this last condition. Before presenting the consequences of the fundamental relation that imposes the same ratio for the thresholds of plasticity and for the pressures produced by the weight, for the homologous thicknesses of the model and of the crust, it should be remarked that we have found no condition relative to the speeds of deformation, at least as a first approximation, that is to say practically, if the deformations, both of the model and of the real, are very slow.[1]

It is essential to observe that both the rocks and the substances that represent them should be real solids that possess a threshold of plasticity below which a force produces no deformation. This reasoning would not apply at all if we considered viscous bodies for which the stresses are proportional to the velocities of deformation.[2] Within this hypothesis, and for a given substance, the duration of a given deformation increases if we diminish the scale of the model. It is, on the other hand, inversely proportional to the viscosity of the substance utilized. To construct a model that would allow us to observe a tectonic deformation take place within a reasonable amount of time, it would be necessary to use a substance of low viscosity (such as certain toothpastes, according to King Hubbert and Gignoux) in order to compensate for the change of scale and the reduction of the duration. In short, within the hypothesis of viscosity all rocks should flow like water, given enough time; the similitude specifies only the times that would be necessary.

The geologic consequences of such hypotheses have been developed in a very brilliant manner by M. Gignoux.[3] Perhaps, however, since his reasoning is essentially on an intuitive plane, he did not sufficiently stress the mechanical hypothesis that constitutes the basis of his interpretation, which is opposed by the hypothesis of plasticity that we have adopted here.

In such a field, any hypothesis *a priori* or based on laboratory experiments under conditions different from reality is open to criticism. So it is essentially by an *a posteriori* comparison of facts of observation with the consequences of various theories that we may choose among the latter. We shall have to return later on to this question in order to emphasize a certain number of facts of observation that can be very clearly indicated by the theory of plasticity, although that of viscosity cannot explain them.

The foregoing theory should furnish the basis for experiments on reduced models designed to reproduce real tectonic deformations in the laboratory. But a great many experiments that have been carried out using models do not take this theory into consideration. The rules of similitude are even more essential for the intuitive representation of tectonic deformations than for the interpretation of experiments. When we attempt to imagine the latter it is impossible for our thoughts to grasp the immense extent and we think of an image of it that is on our scale, like the map on which we coordinate our observations or the sections that we sketch. The fundamental relation of similitude shows us that we must not give the material of this model the properties of real rocks that we know from direct experience (at least in so far as concerns the limit of rupture and the stresses below the threshold of plasticity that leave the rock unaltered). Since our imaginary model should respect the real values of gravity and density with which long experience has familiarized us, we must imagine the substances that make up the model as possessing a threshold of plasticity that is, compared to that of the rocks, in the ratio of the scale. If a limestone begins to deform under the weight of a column 500 meters high and of constant section, the substance of the model must deform under the weight of a similar column reduced to the scale of the model. So it should seem to us, in the sense of our experiment, as very soft, susceptible of deforming under the action of very feeble forces, but also of conserving its form indefinitely if the forces to which it is subjected are sufficiently small. The idea that we should have of it can be put in concrete form by comparing it with modeling wax or toothpaste but not with grease, no matter how viscous it might be. Of course if we wish to represent the deformation of a mass of varied rocks, nothing prevents our imagining a model formed of assorted substances.

The theory of viscosity thus leads us, in the intuitive model, to replace the rocks by substances of very feeble resistances. For our actual experiment, the difference between such viscous or plastic substances is not very striking, but plastics can be modeled and will conserve their form indefinitely whereas viscous substances spread progressively. When we imagine their deformation, the consequences of this difference do not appear immediately. So it is only in a more indirect way that we shall be able to choose between the two hypotheses.

The first experiments on a reduced model far antedated the establishment of these laws of similitude. The best known of such experiments is the one by which it was shown that lateral compression can produce folds. Performed for the first time in 1788 by James Hall, it has been repeated a great many times in varying detail. In general, a box is used whose vertical sides can be moved by means of a screw; in it are placed a succession of horizontal beds more or less plastic; the movements of the base of this series can be facilitated by placing across it a strip of canvas or a stretched rubber membrane (Favre). When the system is compressed horizontally, the beds are seen to fold (Fig. 145). This result was very important in the time of James Hall. Later experiments of the same sort produced nothing much more positive, and are of little more than didactic interest.[4]

When the criteria of similitude are applied to these experiments, it is found that the materials used were always far too resistant; that is, the role of gravity in determining the form of the folds is much less important than in reality.

Somewhat different devices have been used in other experiments; for example, in order to study the distribution of complications of detail in a plane, a rubber membrane can be stretched after it has been covered with a layer of paraffin. The experiment has even been performed with a sphere in the hope of reproducing the arrangement of tectonic complications on the earth.

The only experiments for which the above stated rules of similitude have been used seem to be those of Griggs and Kuenen, whose object was to illustrate the manner in which the crust floats on a denser fluid magma and may deform under the effect of compression or movement of the fluid. Such experiments serve, especially, to give concrete form to the hypothesis that they are designed to illustrate, but they can hardly be considered as presenting a con-

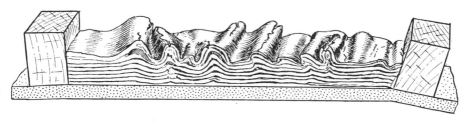

FIG. 145. *Experiment on folding. In the model, clay has been spread on a strip of rubber stretched between two blocks. When the tension on the rubber is released, the clay folds. The visible lines on the sides had been traced in advance but do not correspond to a stratification of the mass. [After Favre, Arch. Sc. Phys. et Nat., nouvelle série, t. 62, p. 193, Genève, 1878.]*

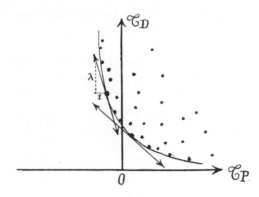

FIG. 146

Diagram of the work absorbed by gravity and the deformation for different types of overall equivalent deformations.

firmation of it. They present nothing that is not implicitly assumed by the mechanism put into operation.

Too often the results of experiments on models have been looked upon as confirmation, not only of the mechanism implied by the hypothesis put into operation, but of the hypothesis itself. It may almost be said that it is possible to perform an experiment that would support any geologic theory, even one that is completely inexact. On reading the reports, one is often confounded by the facility with which authors satisfy themselves with vague analogies between their experiments and reality. Perhaps some day test-model laboratories may render services to tectonics analogous to the advances made through the use of aerodynamic tunnels in testing airplanes, but that day has yet to come.

Let us return to the influence of the scale of a system on the manner in which it will deform. Consider two systems formed of the same rocks placed under similar conditions but of different sizes. We already know that, if we wish to represent them in a model of a given size, the substance used in the large system must be less resistant than the substance used in the small system. That is, the greater the dimensions of the system under consideration, the easier the deformation seems to be. We are going to make a direct and precise statement of this important conclusion.

For our two systems, we already know that there can be no similitude of resultant deformations, since in the larger of the two systems, the pressures due to gravity are greater than in the other. In a word, gravity will have greater influence. Since there is no similitude, let us return to the consideration of the work absorbed, which is composed of the work of deformation and the work expended against gravity. If now we multiply all the lengths by L, assuming that the deformation remains similar and that the threshold of plasticity is constant, the volumes are multiplied by L^3. It is the same for the work of deformation. As for the work of gravity, it is multiplied by L^4 (volume $\times$ height).

We have seen that if the mechanical theory does not permit us to determine the deformation that will be produced because of the complication of the calculations, at least it does permit us to choose, among several types of deformations conceived in advance, the one that will be produced and which corresponds to the least external work.

Let us imagine that we have considered all the possible types of deformation and have calculated for each of them the work of deformation T_D, and the work expended against gravity, T_P, for an imposed external deformation. On a diagram (Fig. 146) we can represent each of these deformations by taking T_D and T_P as coordinates; it is easy to see that the representative points are limited by a line having the form indicated. The real deformation, which corresponds to the minimum of the external work (sum of T_D and T_P), cor-

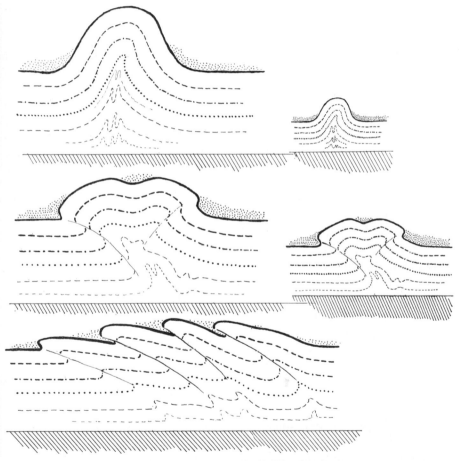

FIGURE 147. *The effect of size on the form of folds. Three deformations affecting a series of the same composition have been represented, below and to the right, on the same scale, and to the left on varied scales which bring them to the same dimension; for a given value of lateral contraction, the thicker the series is, the more the structures are flattened.*

responds to the point of contact with the limit curve of a tangent inclined 45°. The same diagram may be used to study the system whose dimensions have all been multiplied by L, since the work of deformation has become $L^3 T_D$, and the work against gravity has become $L^4 T_P'$. The minimum of the external work (the sum of these expressions) is obtained by drawing a tangent to the limit curve with the slope L. We see immediately that, at the point of contact, the work of deformation is greater (if $L > 1$), and that the work done against gravity is smaller than in the preceding case. That is, if we increase all the dimensions, the structural complications will involve more crushing and more flattening, at the cost of a deeper intimate deformation (Fig. 147).

Let us emphasize that this conclusion is valid for the hypothesis of plasticity; in the hypothesis of viscosity, the rate of deformation would play an essential role, the slowest formed structures being the most flattened.

Now, it is possible in Tertiary mountain chains formed of Mesozoic limestones (Alps, Jura) to study numerous structural complications formed of the same rocks. And in fact it is to be seen that the tectonic style varies according to the size; it is possible to construct a continuous series, beginning with the smallest anticlines of the Jura, which show no tendency toward flattening. The largest anticlines of the Jura are less narrow; in the Helvetic nappes, they are much more voluminous. The overthrusts and recumbent folds spread the deformation over a great width, which somewhat diminishes the height of the structures but at the price of very deep deformation of the rocks. Among the Helvetic nappes, different degrees of flattening are found, which vary according to the dimensions of the nappes.

This is not only a qualitative confirmation of the theory but it suggests the possibility of calculating at least the order of magnitude of the plasticity threshold of the rocks. In fact, if we know the form of a fold, it is possible to calculate the work done by gravity as well as the factor of the threshold of plasticity in the work of deformation; the only thing that remains is to determine the threshold in order that the work of the external forces may be, for the real deformation, less than it would have been for a deformation similar to those that have been observed on other scales. This calculation would require a very precise survey of the form of the folds, but the fact that the small anticlines are very little flattened by gravity proves that the threshold of plasticity of the rocks that constitute them is above a certain limit.

The importance of the influence of scale on the nature of tectonic deformations will appear if we consider several examples.

First, let us examine the case of the salt domes (Chap. 10). The deformation that has produced them, and which consists of an ascent of the salt in the midst of the overlying strata, is made without any intervention of external forces other than gravity. The salt (density 2.2) is lighter than most of the overlying strata (densities 2.5 to 2.7) and is at the same time very plastic.

Just as the superposition of a heavy liquid on top of a lighter liquid is unstable and cannot subsist, the superposition of heavier strata above the salt does not correspond to the most stable state possible and can subsist only due to the rigidity of the rocks. This rigidity is sufficient to prevent the deformation of a moderately thick bed of salt at slight depth (for example, the 100 or 200 meters of Triassic salt in the environs of Nancy at a few hundred meters depth). But if the nature of the rocks remains the same, and if we imagine that all the dimensions increase in the same relation, it is easy to see that the weights of the mineral masses increase as the cube of this relation and that the forces necessary to overcome the rigidity of the rocks varies approximately as the square only (that is, as the sections that would undergo shearing). So there should be a scale beyond which the irregularities of the surface of the salt can be accented, the salt rising in the high parts toward which it flows along the bed while the overlying terrains are sheared at the emplacement of the dome and subside all around.

It is possible to mechanically analyze the ascent of a salt dome, following the two methods whose principle we have indicated. If the distribution of forces is analyzed, it is seen that the pressure under the dome is less than that at an equal depth outside the dome, since the salt is lighter than the surrounding rock. In the salt bed, the salt should tend to flow toward the base of the dome, which will rise (Fig. 148).

It is likewise possible to consider the work going on. If the salt rises a given fraction of the depth, and if the surrounding heavier strata subside by an equal volume, the center of gravity of the whole mass lowers; thus, gravity supplies a moving work which (if the scale is varied by multiplying all the dimensions in a given relation) varies as the fourth power of this relation.

The resistant work, which should be equal to the moving work of gravity, since the other exterior forces do not effect any work, corresponds to the movement of the salt and to the deformation of the surrounding strata. If we consider the thresholds of plasticity of these different rocks as given it varies as the cube of the scale.

Let us consider a mass of given strata resting on a bed of salt. It is always possible to choose the dimensions of this mass (depth and thickness of the

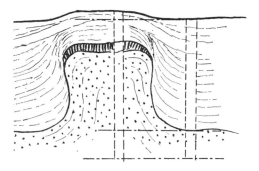

FIGURE 148

Calculation of the pressure, at a given depth, under the dome and outside it; the surface difference of level should be taken into account, since it increases the pressure under the dome and therefore opposes the movement.

salt) such that, for an embryonic dome of given amplitude (of height, for example, equal to one-tenth of the depth), the work of gravity may be at least equal to the resistant work and the movement may continue.

As the dome rises, the instability becomes more marked and the movement more rapid. Naturally our reasoning only enables us to reconstruct the first phases of the phenomenon (which we would not be able to recognize as such if we observed them), but it is easy to understand the role of the inequalities of the surface of the salt, which serve as triggers whether they are due to folding, faults or other factors. The movement, at first very slow, will gradually accelerate in the same manner as when water is carefully poured on the surface of a rather thick oil; the separation surface, originally almost horizontal, deforms very slowly at first, then more rapidly, and finally, all the oil rises to the surface. If the first inequality presents the form of an elongated ridge, it will begin at first by rising as a whole, but as soon as its height becomes irregular, the highest parts will rise more rapidly and will at the same time thicken. Starting from the linear ridge, there will soon be a change into one or more almost circular domes.

When the mass of the salt dome approaches the surface, there is danger of its deforming the latter and producing an intumescence of the surface, whose weight will check the movement. However, geographical conditions may tend to cause such swellings to disappear through rapid erosion or through deposition up to constant level. Such would be the case, for example, in a plain swept by the meanders of a stream and covered by its alluvium, or on the littoral platform of a sea sufficiently agitated to prohibit the formation of a shoal. Without being altogether necessary, such conditions must have been very favorable to the genesis of salt domes.

The movement having the tendency to accelerate, all the salt of the bed in the vicinity of the dome would tend to flow toward the latter. The bed will become thin and finally its pinching will prevent access toward a dome of the salt situated beyond a distance which calculation seems to indicate to be approximately of the order of the initial thickness of the bed. Each dome then can only be fed by a restricted zone.

Owing to the centripetal movement of the salt, the various beds are forced to compress laterally such that within the body of the dome they are extremely dislocated and are often folded with more or less vertical axes. Escher and Kuenen[5] have experimentally reproduced these particular details in a quite suggestive manner.

When the salt approaches the surface and reaches the zone of circulation of underground waters, it gradually dissolves. The residues of solution— marls, anhydrite, dolomite—accumulate at the top of the dome, forming a "cap rock" whose density is relatively high. The movement will slow down all the more, since the sediments near the surface are often only slightly consolidated and are of quite low density. The thickness of the "cap rock" may become such that equilibrium will be re-established, after which movement will no longer continue. This particularity explains why many salt domes produce a positive gravity anomaly; the cap rock, which is close to the surface and is surrounded by relatively light strata, masks the effect of the salt surrounded by relatively heavier strata that lie at greater depth.

The theory that we have just sketched explains why salt domes are always quite large, having diameters reckoned in kilometers. Domes of smaller size could not have formed. The size limit may vary from one region to another, depending on the nature of the strata overlying the salt or on the degree of irregularity of its surface.

Most known domes do not crop out, and nothing indicates their emplacement beneath a more or less uniform plain. In certain arid regions, however, the salt does outcrop. In the south of Algeria, at Djelfa, there is a mountain of salt that seems to represent a salt dome, although its structure is poorly exposed. In Laristan[6] (Persian Gulf), several salt domes crop out, even though the region is characterized by anticlines and synclines of enormous dimensions, in keeping with the thickness of the sedimentary series. One of these domes feeds a "salt glacier," which flows down the slope under the influence of its weight. This flow confirms the extreme plasticity of salt, which exceeds that of all other rocks, as is very easily established by laboratory experiment.

Harrison[7] has described a series of salt domes that give way to quite clear peripheral dips in the surrounding strata and which follow the gorges of the Colorado river. It is difficult to understand, from the morphologic point of view, why the river established its course precisely on the anticlinal arches; thus, the author proposes a different explanation. The domes probably developed after the scooping out of the valley, and were most likely localized along the valley as a result of the relatively greater axis pressure exerted on the salt in the zones beneath the neighboring plateaus. Within this very probable hypothesis we would be dealing with an intermediate case between real salt domes and upwarpings due to the movement of plastic beds toward the valleys, places of the least pressures (Chap. 8, p. 108). But, whereas clays do not seem to undergo such movements, except when they are actually cut into by erosion, the salt, being more plastic, was displaced from a bed situated far below the level of the river, piercing the beds of its cover. This movement did not continue all along the river, but became localized in a certain number of centers according to the constant process in the evolution of salt domes.

In the same way as do the complications of detail studied in Chapter 8, salt domes actually constitute paratectonic complications implying the intervention of no external exterior force other than gravity. But salt domes are always very large structures and could produce very deep dislocations of the surrounding strata.

The idea of a size limit for salt domes explains, for example, why there exist no such complications formed by the Triassic salt of Lorraine, the thickness of the salt not being sufficient. The theory of viscosity would by no means imply the existence of a size limit, but would simply indicate that the smaller were the domes, the slower would be the movements.

The existence of a size limit, below which deformation is not possible, is a general property of all types of deformation produced under the influence of gravity alone, that is, without the intervention of any other external force; this results from a consideration of the work done during deformation.

This applies particularly to gliding, landslips, and other superficial movements. Every day, we observe examples of such features extending over some meters or tens of meters; thus, we have acquired a somewhat intuitive feeling for the conditions under which they may have been produced. If, on the surface, landslips generally result from rupture, slides often correspond to the plastic deformation of a slightly resistant bed, especially if it is a question of somewhat deep slides. The foregoing considerations are then valid. They show that the more the scale is increased, the easier the slide becomes. So, with a change of scale, engineering experience is not enough to show what possible role gravity slides have played in tectonic deformations. Let us consider, for example, a slice of sedimentary strata resting on a plastic bed composed of a gypsiferous layer whose threshold may be estimated at 50 kg/cm^2.[8] Slipping will be possible on an 11° slope for a series 1000 m thick and on a 3.5° slope for a series 3000 m thick. Near the surface, slipping would not be produced by plastic deformation, but by shearing only.

At the time of a slip, there may be other deformations than that of the base bed; for example, the mass in movement may fold on contact with an obstacle. These deformations absorb an amount of work necessarily less than the work of gravity. The important role that may be played by such deformations, included under the designation of gliding tectonics (*tectonique d'écoulement*), was not recognized until quite recently. This term has been applied, by M. Lugeon, in particular, to the emplacement of certain nappes by sliding under the influence of gravity. But its meaning has since been considerably changed from the original. According to Gignoux,[9] to the idea of the motive role of gravity is added that of a rock flow in the manner of a viscous liquid, which is not necessarily implied by the gliding tectonics in the sense of M. Lugeon. According to Gignoux, this idea of rock flow involves not only the property of deformability, masterfully demonstrated by Albert Heim 75 years ago and accepted since without discussion, but also involves the assertion that this flow begins to take place, although very slowly, even for very slight stresses. We have had occasion above to discuss this idea.

The idea of gliding tectonics has been broadened in another direction by Van Bemmelen under the name of "gravitational tectogenesis." [10] Under this term are included all the phenomena in which gravitation intervenes, from the simple slipping of barely deposited sediments ("slumping") to isostatic readjustments on the continental scale, as well as a theory of the deep structure of mountain chains. Among the examples of tectonic slides in Indonesia, let us mention those that affect volcanic formations placed on poorly resistant and sometimes inclined Tertiary strata.

In order to understand the significance of the emphasis placed on the role of gravity in these recent papers, reference may be made to the results of the theory sketched above (p. 205). We have seen that gravity intervenes in the determination of structure whether aided by external forces or not, essentially by its work. With the exception of salt domes in which rocks of very different densities are involved, the work of gravity depends essentially on the form of the topographic surface before and after deformation.

We have indicated above (p. 112) that in the geometric reconstruction of the form of folds, we may sometimes go so far as to consider the present topographic surface as cutting at a random level a folded mass, undefined toward the top or at least continuing much higher; it is evident that such a point of view is totally incompatible with a consideration of the work of gravity. It may constitute a sufficient approximation in certain cases, that of the Precambrian, for example, or in a more general fashion, for the study of the depths of a deeply eroded mountain chain. It could not be satisfactory in the study of a recent chain.

The fact that, for the past ten years, the concept of gliding tectonics has remained in vogue is an expression of the geologist's awareness of the necessity for determining the level occupied by the topographic surface at the moment of deformation relative to present-day structures. In fact, this is the preliminary condition for understanding the influence of gravity, either in modifying the form of structures having another origin or producing along a slide or other structure. But to reconstruct the topographic surface as it was at the time of the phases of tectonic activity raises quite serious difficulties.

We still hear the opinion[11] expressed that folding takes place at depth, where the pressure makes rocks plastic, whereas higher up, the beds were less and less dislocated and the surface was not undergoing any disturbance. If such were the case, there would evidently be no question of tectonic flow. However, this concept can be formally rejected. From the kinematic point of view alone it is very improbable, since superficial beds must have undergone the same lateral contraction as the deep beds. Moreover, there are numerous complications of detail that we know manifested themselves at the surface; in particular, certain overthrusts formed on the surface of the ground (Fig. 129). As soon as tectonic movements tend to deform the surface, it is also attacked by erosion, or it gives place to landslips.

When an attempt is made to reconstruct the successive phases in the formation of a mountain chain, it is often difficult to determine how much sedimentary cover existed before the movement, since the most recent members were violently attacked by erosion and removed almost everywhere. Not always does there exist near the mountain chain a basin in which the sedimentation has remained continuous, and it is uncertain that the sedimentary series that

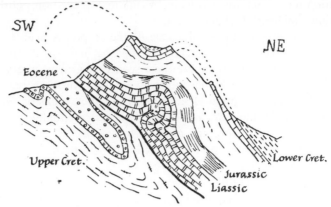

FIGURE 149. *Section of Mont Vial given as seen in the gully of the Hirondelles (Alpes-Maritimes). The turning back of the Eocene syncline shows here that there was no overthrust on the surface of the ground, but plastic deformation of the substratum of the overthrust. (Descr. Tect. bord. Alpes de la Bléone au Var, Mém. Carte, Figs. 173 and 177, 1937.)*

may have been deposited in such a basin was the same as in the region that was about to be uplifted.

At times, the most recent strata have escaped erosion only in the most pinched synclines, or else they have been protected by overthrusts that covered them. However, the compression may also have forced certain formations out of the synclines, or what seems to be an overthrust may be only a shearing surface within the thickness of the strata (Figs. 149 and 150).

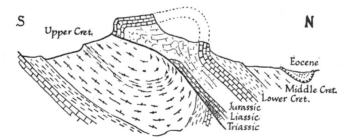

FIGURE 150. *Section of the Harpilles anticline (Alpes-Maritimes). Here there are two possible interpretations. As in the preceding figure, there might have been a simple shearing of the Cretaceous series, the overthrust, at least in the preserved part, not having reached the surface of the ground. But the Cretaceous substratum could also have been eroded following a first premonition of folding, although a more or less important part of the overthrust presently visible was probably produced on the surface of the ground. (Descr. Tect. bord. Alpes de la Bléone au Var, Mém. Carte, Fig. 156, 1937.)*

In order to determine the work done by gravity in a certain tectonic deformation, we would have to know the actual position of the surface in the initial stage and in the final stage; the work done can then be calculated from the vertical displacement of the center of gravity of a mass of known volume. However, later uplifts or sinkings could have masked initial relations of height. Thus, Lugeon and Schneegans are probably correct in attributing the emplacement of the nappe of the Embrunais, in the Valley of the Durance, to a gravity flow even though its base is today almost horizontal or is even lifted up in the direction of the movement (Figs. 94 and 127).

If erosion took place during the movement, it is convenient to divide the period of movement into short intervals of time and to calculate the work of gravity performed during each interval; however, we never possess the information necessary to correlate erosion with tectonic deformation. In general, uplifted regions are attacked by erosion, which thus diminishes the work done by gravity, especially the resistant work. It is the same as when erosion hollows out a valley which increases the value of the motive work in the movements toward this valley and may make it possible for it to overcome the resistances. But such movements are properly called slides or landslips rather than tectonic deformations.

The action of erosion between two tectonic phases may be even more important, not only because it reduces the relief that corresponds to the anticlines and thus diminishes the resistant work of gravity when movement is resumed, but it may also carry away such a thickness of strata that the work of deformation may be very noticeably affected. Even slightly marked folds, once eroded, constitute lines of less resistance along which later deformations localize. We have already mentioned (p. 172) the Provencal anticlines that result, as Lutaud has shown, from two successive movements, separated by a phase of erosion of the anticlines and sedimentation in the synclines.

We have seen that the effective calculation of the work of gravity in a tectonic deformation raises quite serious difficulties. Most of the time we shall have to limit ourselves to a few general indications, the most important of which, resulting from the application of the rules of similitude, has been noted above. The greater are the dimensions of a fold, more gravity tends to flatten it and thus lower its center of gravity, everything else being equal.

The role of gravity becomes much more evident when we have reasons to think that no force of horizontal compression has directly intervened in the production of a given structure. The best example of this case, apropos of which the idea of tectonic flow was put forward by M. Lugeon,[12] can be seen in the Prealps (Fig. 93). Here there is a series of thrust slices, separated from their roots by an interval of from 50 to 100 km, containing very high massifs (Mont Blanc in particular). The analysis of the dislocations has shown the absence of horizontal compression, blocks of hard limestones being scattered about,[13] and it would be very difficult to imagine an overthrusting bed of an amplitude of 50 to 100 km on whose normal flank a horizontal pressure had been exerted.

On the other hand, the hypothesis according to which a sheet (such as the group of the Prealps) would have slipped on a favorable slope appears much more probable. Considerations of similitude show, as we have seen, that a mass several thousand meters thick may slip as a result of plastic deformation of suitable strata on a slope of only a few degrees, which is altogether insufficient to initiate a slip on a small scale.

Moreover, it is not necessary to imagine a continuous slope presenting this inclination on a width of some one hundred kilometers (which would represent several thousand meters of drop or change of level). The detailed stratigraphic analysis of the Prealps shows that they are made up of a series of piled up units, coming from different zones. The initial emplacements of these units mark the stages of the movement which must have been broken into multiple phases, resulting from localized unwarpings of the basement. The movements may be explained by assuming that the basement was affected by a sort of intumescence, which spread step by step and on whose side, growing like a snowball, slipped the mass of sedimentary terranes that was to constitute the Prealps.

We have pointed out (p. 172, Fig. 131) the mechanism of diverticulations, in which the slipping of the different scales (*écailles*) under the action of their weight plays an essential role, since their mutual displacements imply that from the moment of their origin they were separated from their roots. It would be impossible to explain the arrangements observed as being a result of deformation in depth, or even as the result of a deformation in which the horizontal thrusts would constitute the principal moving force.

The counterpart of a slip of the cover of an uplifted mass should be the denudation of the latter, but it is very difficult to distinguish such a tectonic denudation from the simple effect of erosion; thus, the examples of these phenomena that have been indicated are not always convincing.

In the examples cited above, the slip under the action of the weight constitutes the only moving force of the movement. Lugeon and Schneegans[14] have been led to assume that slipping played an essential role in the formation of the Ubaye-Embrunais nappe in the region of the Durance (Fig. 126), since the mass of flysch that established the link between the roots and the frontal part seemed too feeble to transmit the compression necessary to assure the progress of the mass. In order to explain this progress by a slip, we have seen that it is necessary to assume that the general slope was modified after the event, since it is presently in inverse sense to the movement.

Another very fine example of the role played by gliding tectonics is that of the Apennines. They are characterized by the great development of the allochthonous formation called "argille scagliose" (scaly clay) as a covering on the autochthonous series that pierces into its midst in a series of anticlinal wrinkles. Scaly clay, properly so called, is an extremely dislocated clayey mass in which it is impossible to recognize any dip or original structure and which has visibly undergone a slipping en masse of very great amplitude. Its slight mechanical resistance is moreover emphasized by the fact that it presently causes a very great number of surface slides on the sides of the valleys (in Italian, *frane*) whose material is scarcely more dislocated than the scaly clay itself. Merla[15] has shown that, from the tectonic point of view, there must be attached to the complex of the scaly clay a series of fragments of varied terranes, ranging from a few meters to several kilometers and ranging from little scales of granite and important masses of greenstone ("ophiolite") to Mesozoic sheets with facies at times unknown in the autochthonous series and which seem to have originated in the region now occupied by the Tyrrhenian Sea. These sheets have been passively carried into the midst of the scaly clays.

From all the evidence, it is difficult to imagine an active tectonic impulse acting through a mass presenting so feeble a mechanical resistance, to explain its establishment on a breadth of overthrust that attains up to 200 km. Migliorini, Merla, and Trevisan have shown that the emplacement occurred through a gravity flow, not on a single slope for which it would have been necessary to assume an unlikely change of level of considerable amplitude, but thanks to a series of relays following the successive formation from west to east of a series of autochthonous anticlinal wrinkles on the east side of which a mass slipped, which had previously come to its emplacement and which could increase its volume en route from the scales (*écailles*) torn from these wrinkles. Even the base of the clayey mass seems to be composed of sediments deposited at quite varying epochs, such as during the emplacement, and perhaps at the very moment when these wrinkles were about to come into existence. The detailed stratigraphic study of the Tertiary sediments buried beneath the scaly clays, or carried along in their movement, and those that are transgressive upon them on the edge of the Plain of the Po, enables us to reconstruct the chronology of the movement, which extended over a considerable interval of time (Upper Oligocene, Miocene) if we consider it as a whole; but in the frontal regions, the sediments that transgressively cover the allochthonous formation, and those upon which it rests, are extremely close together in age. We are thus led to assume that the sliding took place on the bottom of the sea, scarcely interrupting the normal sedimentation there.

Attention having been drawn to these examples, different authors have sought to explain the highly varied dislocations in a similar manner. As always in such cases, once the first moment of enthusiasm is passed, there arises the problem of finding out within what limits the proposed explanation is valid. It is naturally difficult to give a precise answer, especially since the action of gravity and a horizontal tectonic compression of deep origin may combine in any proportion whatever. At least it is possible to show how extravagant certain interpretations could be.

We have seen that the origin of slips that characterize gliding tectonics must have entailed undulations of the basement, which may have had only quite gentle slopes; theoretically, these undulations could have resulted from purely vertical movements. So we might be tempted[16] (and this is approximately the position taken by Haarmann, in his *"Oszillations-Theorie"*) to reduce every tectonic deformation to vertical movements of the deep basement, and to the sliding by flow created by the latter in the superficial covering. But this would be disregarding the very numerous examples of compression in depth and, in particular, of overthrusting of deep crystalline masses on sedimentary terranes. It does not seem possible to interpret a section of the crystalline basement such as that of the Massif du Pelvoux (Fig. 158) as resulting simply from a slip on the sides of an intumescence of any sort. Such a section seems to establish the existence of a horizontal compression of the earth's crust. Moreover, even if certain evaluations of the horizontal contraction, based on the development of folds that were assumed to be continuous at the origin between roots and fragments of overthrust, are too high, it seems, nevertheless, that the development of the observable parts of the folds leads to a width far greater than that now occupied by a mountain chain such as the Alps. This proves that horizontal contraction took place.

It has been tempting at times to seek criteria that, from the very form of the folds, would enable us to determine whether they were formed by flow or by active compression. According to de Sitter,[17] the existence of superposed recumbent folds in which the overturned limbs are preserved is characteristic of structures produced by flow. Such criteria might be valid if the weight of the deformed mass were responsible for its emplacement, but they are evidently without value for complications resulting from the thrust due to the slip of the compartment behind them; their form is probably the same whether the action of a given thrust is due to flow or to compression by a scale (*écaille*) of the basement. Inversely, the criterion indicated by de Sitter is characteristic of the deformation that is produced opposite a depressed zone, and nothing would prevent such a circumstance from developing from a thrust of deep origin. Therefore, we cannot recognize directly whether complications are due to the tectonics of flow or to a thrust of deep origin, and in order to attempt an interpretation, we must study the overall structure to which they belong.

As "complications of the basement" seems to imply the intervention of horizontal compression, it is probable that, at least in a certain number of cases, the vertical uplifts of the basement that released the flow of the cover constitute only one of the aspects of the complications that are due to a horizontal compression and which may involve a more or less considerable horizontal component. This horizontal component of the movement of the basement was necessarily transmitted to the cover, which then must have undergone a horizontal compression before being carried away by the flow, unless the two phenomena were in operation at the same time. The tectonics of flow is not a panacea that can explain all the deformations of surface terranes. It is a very important phenomenon that suffices in itself to explain certain deformations, and it combines in most cases with the horizontal compression of the earth's crust, which constitutes the essential motive force of tectonics.

This role of gliding tectonics is sufficient for it to be necessary to examine attentively what its role can have been in the interpretation of every folded mountain chain and in particular the appearance of what types of structure it may have facilitated. In this examination, the consideration of similitude will play an essential role.

Just as the delimitation of the respective roles of gliding tectonics and of horizontal compression pose a problem, an analogous question is posed in connection with the limit between the superficial movements arising from gliding tectonics and slips or from ordinary landslides, which play an important morphologic role (see Chapter 8).

Actually, there is no essential difference in nature between these phenomena, and it would not be possible to support a criterion founded on the difference of scale.

From a study by M. Lugeon,[18] it seems that the following definition may be drawn: For the profile of the topography to be such that a slip may be produced in formerly stable strata, it is necessary for the profile to undergo a modification. Either slipping or an ordinary landslide will occur if this modification results from the normal action of the agents of erosion, such as from the undercutting of the foot of a slope by a river or from the accentuation of the profile of a valley by a glacier which at the time of its melting ceases to sustain

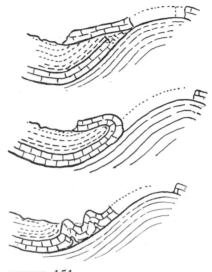

FIGURE 151

Examples of "collapse structures." Above. De-capping of a type very frequent in the Jura. Below. Overturning and crumpling. [After Harrison and Falcon.]

the wall by its mass. On the other hand, if the modification of the topographic profile results from a deep tectonic deformation, the movement arises from gliding tectonics.

But there are cases where this criterion may be difficult to apply. Without speaking of the difficulty that there may be in a particular case in reconstructing the details of phenomena that preceded the slip, erosion and tectonic deformation may combine their action. When tectonic movements are produced, they are accompanied by a resumption of downcutting by water courses, which tend to maintain their profile, as well as by the other agents of erosion. Erosion, then, may appear as the immediate cause of a slip, even if a tectonic deformation is its distant cause. For example, certain parts of the Himalayas have undergone very recent upheavals, as indicated by the violence of certain earthquakes; these uplifts may still be going on in our time; erosion is very active there, and landslips are very numerous.

We would hardly hesitate to consider landslips in which the rocks are fragmented as purely superficial phenomena. But superficial deformations in which the rocks undergo plastic deformation may be more difficult to classify. Examples are the "collapse structures" [19] in Persia and slips en masse, as in the uncapping (*décoiffement*) of the Jura, where a flagstone belonging to the side of an anticline has slipped onto the adjacent syncline (Fig. 151). However, this difficulty must not be exaggerated; usually there will be no hesitation in separating the manifestations of gliding tectonics, which are part of the general structure, from landslips or slides, which are of a local character. But, on the other hand, the role of structures resulting from superficial deformations (collapse structures), which may be of extremely varied types, has only quite recently been established. The detailed study of such structures may furnish many interesting results. The development of geologic surveys on a large scale will undoubtedly increase the number of known examples.

Notes and References

1. It will be noticed that we have implicitly taken the unit of force (or of pressure) as the fundamental unit. If we took the unit of mass as fundamental, a time factor would be introduced. But the time factor is only an intermediary for the definition of the forces and has no relation to the speed of development of the phenomena.

2. Among the authors who have developed this hypothesis (used by M. Gignoux) from the mechanical point of view, we may cite the following:

Maillet, M. and Blondel, F., *Sur la similitude en tectonique,* Bull. Soc. géol. France, 5ᵉ ser., vol. 4, pp. 599–602, 1934.

Maillet, M. and Pavans de Ceccaty, *Le physicien devant la tectonique,* 2ᵉ Congr. Mondial du Pétrole, Paris, 1937.

Hubbert, King, Theory of Scale Models as Applied to the Study of Geological Structures, Bull. Geol. Soc. America, vol. 48, pp. 1459–1520, 1937.

Koenigsberger, G. and Morath, O., *Theoretische Grundlagen der experimentellen Tektonik,* Deutsche Geol. Ges., Zeitschr.,vol. 65, pp. 65–86, 1913.

3. Gignoux, M., *Méditation sur la tectonique d'écoulement par gravité,* Univ. Grenoble, Lab. Géol., Trav., vol. 27, pp. 1–34, 1948.

4. See reference 1, Chapter 1, Goguel, J., *Introduction* . . . , Chapter 28.

5. Escher, B. G. and Kuenen, P. H., Experiments in Connection with Salt Domes, Leidsche Geol. Mededeel., vol. 3, pt. 3, ii, pp. 151–182, 1929.

6. Harrison, J. V., *The geology of some salt plugs in Laristan,* Quart. Jour. Geol. Soc. London, vol. 86, pp. 463–519, plates 52–58, 1930. (See especially plate 56.)

7. Harrison, T. S., Colorado-Utah Salt Domes, Bull. Amer. Assoc. Petrol. Geologists, vol. 11, pp. 111–113, 1927. (See especially page 118.)

8. See reference 1, Chapter 1, Goguel, J., *Introduction* . . . , p. 407.

9. Gignoux, M., *Méditations sur la tectonique d'écoulement par gravité,* Univ. Grenoble, Lab. Géol., Trav., vol. 27, pp. 1–34, 1948.

10. Bemmelen, R. W. van, Gravitational Tectogenesis in Indonesia, Geologie en Mijnbouw, vol. 12, new ser., no. 12, pp. 351–361, 1950.

11. A particularly clear expression of this opinion, then apparently very widespread, was given by Marcel Bertrand, ". . . Nevertheless, I accept the conclusion that mountains have been formed with their complex structures and all their folds without these showing at the surface except by a slight upwarping whose existence may even be questioned. For a long time I have been expressing this idea." (*Observations sur la formation des chaînes de montagnes,* Bull. Soc. géol. France, 3ᵉ ser., vol. 28, pp. 18–21, 1900.

12. Lugeon, M., *Sur la formation des Alpes franco-suisses,* Soc. géol. France, Comptes-rendus, pp. 7–11, Jan. 22, 1940.

13. Lugeon, M. and Gagnebin, E., *Observations et vues nouvelles sur la géologie des Préalpes romandes,* Bull. Univ. Lausanne, Lab. Géol., no. 72, pp. 1–90, 1941. (Also published in Mém. Soc. Vaudoise Sci. Nat., no. 47, vol. 7, no. 1.)

14. Lugeon, M. and Schneegans, D., *Sur le diastrophisme alpin,* Acad. Sci. Paris, Comptes-rendus, vol. 210, p. 87, January 15, 1940.

15. Merla, G., *Geologia dell' Appennino settentrionale,* Boll. Soc. geol. Italiana, vol. 70, pp. 95–382, 1951.

16. There is an excellent analysis of the different aspects assumed by the development of the idea whose main points we have indicated in: Moret, L., *Les idées nouvelles sur l'origine des chaînes de montagnes,* Revue Géogr. Alpine, vol. 38, fasc. 2, and also in: Univ. Grenoble, Lab. Géol., Trav., vol. 28, 1950.

17. Sitter, L. U. de, Gravitational Gliding Tectonics, an Essay in Comparative Structural Geology, Amer. Jour. Science, vol. 252, pp. 321–344, 1954.

18. Lugeon, M., *Question de mode en géologie et autres histoires, le décoiffement,* Annales Hébert et Haug, vol. 7 (livre jubilaire Ch. Jacob), pp. 261–274, Paris, 1949.

19. Harrison, J. V. and Falcon, N. L., Collapse Structures, Geol. Mag., vol. 71, pp. 529–539, 1934.

Harrison, J. V. and Leslie, N., Gravity Collapse Structures and Mountain Ranges, as Exemplified in S. W. Iran, Quart. Jour. Geol. Soc. London, vol. 92, pp. 91–102, 1936.

CHAPTER FOURTEEN

Some Types of Basement Complications

Basement and cover—Rarity of reference horizons in the basement—Absence of stratification; interpretation of deformations of the cover—Example of the Paris Basin; posthumous folds, readjustments, Alpine effects —Conditions of rupture of a homogeneous mass; ruptures and mylonitic zones—Overthrusting, strike slip, subsidence trough—African troughs— Great coal furrow—Division of basement into overthrust scales—Interaction with cover, involvement of scales (*écailles*)—Deformation of metamorphic terranes.

WE HAVE just devoted several chapters to the study of a particular case, that of the deformation of a mass of stratified terranes. This particular case is of dual interest in that, on the one hand, the existence of numerous reference horizons whose position is precisely known makes possible an accurate geometric analysis of the deformation; on the other hand, the differences of mechanical properties of the successive beds involve certain peculiarities of the deformation, the role of folding being in the first rank. Deformations of such stratified series may be designated under the general name of "cover tectonics." The other deformations will be grouped under the term "basement tectonics." The terranes that are affected may thus be of quite different natures; they may be eruptive rocks (granite, for example), or metamorphic series in which stratification that is susceptible of playing a mechanical role no longer exists (this by no means excludes the possibility that certain moderately metamorphosed series of very heterogeneous composition may behave according to the laws that govern cover tectonics), or they may be sedimentary rocks that were so strongly folded in an earlier phase that they are practically no longer able to fold through the movement of the beds upon one another. These different cases often combine, as can be seen in the deep parts of an eroded mountain chain, in which the rocks are not only folded but have also been more or less metamorphosed and injected with granite. Argand designated these old formations as "indurated," or hardened; a complex geologic history has eliminated the possibility of further folding. Finally, it is often convenient to group with the basement, thus conceived, the poorly stratified sandstones that often begin the series of transgressive stages (for example, the sandstones of the Permian and the Lower Trias in Provence), because they do not participate in the folding characteristic of the cover, but remain bound to the basement by virtue of their mechanical properties.

All these characteristics of the basement are essentially negative. If the distinction between the basement and the cover is a convenient one, it is still far from always being clear-cut. It is possible to find all stages between the typical cover tectonics and basement tectonics when the deformed mass is composed of an association of rocks having well differentiated mechanical properties, even when they do not form horizontal alternating beds. Thus, the Paleozoic of the Pyrenees, which was folded in the Hercynian epoch, behaves on the whole according to the laws governing the basement, insofar as Cretaceous and Tertiary deformations are concerned. But there are mechanically plastic horizons, such as the carbonaceous shales of the Silurian (Gothlandian). Although they no longer constituted horizontal beds at the time of the most recent movements, they were able to cause a certain local disharmony, even the formation of scales.[1]

It may also be quite difficult to trace a clear-cut limit between basement and cover tectonics if sedimentary remnants were transgressed by the latter. Sedimentary remnants share in the tectonics of the basement, but their peculiar mechanical properties may cause them in this passive passage to react in a more or less autonomous manner, at least in places, such that the characteristics common to the tectonics of the cover may combine in any manner whatever in the general framework of basement tectonics.

As we have seen earlier, it is possible to study deformations by two methods, either by seeking reference horizons whose initial form is known, or by seeking to recognize the intimate deformations undergone by the rocks. We shall return later on to the application of the second method, which, by the way, is not very accurate.

We seldom find usable reference horizons within the mass of the basement. We have seen (Chap. 6, p. 89) how it has been possible to make use of a granitic intrusion whose two parts were separated by a transverse fault to evaluate the horizontal displacement of the latter. For the Villefort fault, at the border of the Gard and the Lozère, we find, in this way, a horizontal displacement of some 10 km.

It is also possible to try to utilize the arrangement of zones of isometamorphism, assuming that they originally followed each other in a well-determined theoretical order on a given vertical. Moreover, it is often accepted that schistosity was initially horizontal. This led to the conclusion that important series in the Massif Central have been overturned because the mica schists plunge under the gneisses. But naturally these conclusions are valid only insofar as the hypotheses mentioned above are correct.

Here again, by far the most precise reference horizons are found in sedimentary rocks. But we must make a study of strata transgressive on the basement. The question will always arise whether their deformations actually reflect those of their substratum and do not indicate the structures of an independent cover tectonics.

If sedimentary terranes have not been eroded, it is possible to distinguish somewhat diagrammatically the following stages in their study and in that of the basement. A cover tectonics in which a disharmony separates the sedimentary terranes from the underlying basement is characterized by the fact that the anticlines are relatively narrow and have steep flanks. If we try to complete their section by reconstructing the form of the underlying horizons, we will be successful only to a certain horizon; the lower beds cannot exist in the hearts of anticlines. If it is possible to reconstruct the form of the synclines in an analogous manner, by using the thicknesses of the different stages measured in the anticlines, it will be possible to form a rather rough idea of the depth at which the basement would be found. By applying the same method step by step, it is possible to discover great undulations, but this process only furnishes an indication of the structure. Figure 96 shows how the structure of Mesozoic terranes to the north of Digne is sufficient to establish the existence of a structure in the Paleozoic basement several thousand meters in height. But it is impossible to indicate accurately the exact form of such a structure.

If, on the contrary, the undulations of sedimentary terranes are of a great radius of curvature, we may assume that they simply express the movements of the underlying basement, which we can thus analyze in a very precise manner. Of course, in order to do this, we must not take into account the undulations of the upper beds of the cover, since they may be due to the subsidence of the sediments around buried relief features, or they may be a function of the difference in facies, as indicated in Chapter 8.

The Paris Basin is a very good example of a region whose dislocations may be attributed to mild basement tectonics. This basement crops out in a series of old masses on the periphery of the basin; but, although it is easy to study the structure of the Paleozoic basement, it is almost impossible to recognize movements of Tertiary or Mesozoic age. On the other hand, a certain number of undulations have been observed within the basin, the most important of which is the Bray anticline. However, the dips of the southwest side of the anticline are much too slight to represent a typical cover structure such as might have been produced if the cover had been subjected to horizontal compression.[2] There is little doubt (except for the possible influence of differen-

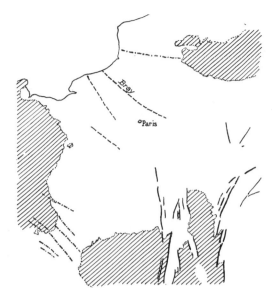

FIGURE 152

Principal structures of the Paris Basin.

tial subsidence, whose role has not yet been precisely determined) that these undulations indicate slight deformations of the basement (Fig. 152).

Morcover, these deformations are of quite diverse origins. In certain cases, for example in the Poitou folds, the directions of structures that affect the Jurassic prolong those of the Hercynian folds of the basement, which leads to the belief that these folds have continued to act with a very small amplitude. So there it is a question of a posthumous reaction of Hercynian structures; we would not understand this real significance if we were to consider them as mere dislocations of the Tertiary or Mesozoic socles. On the other hand, the Sancerrois faults, for example, evidently form a part of a group of structures of Tertiary age that border the Limagnes farther to the south, since they show no relation to the old structures of the Massif Central; they are evidently a manifestation of basement tectonics that may be considered, in terms of age, as a consequence of the Alpine orogenesis.

The detailed correlation of numerous well logs obtained in the Paris Basin establishes a series of undulations, studied especially at the horizon of the Upper Cretaceous. Contrary to the working hypotheses used by the early authors, these undulations do not form continuous lines of anticlines and synclines, but form bulges and irregular hollows whose amplitude is generally from 100 to 200 m, but much greater in the case of Bray. Must we consider these undulations as posthumous folds conforming to the old plan of the Hercynian structures, or as expressing new Alpine dislocations? Gravity measurements have shown that they correspond to important anomalies, which are disproportionate to the visible undulations, indicating that the Hercynian basement, which initially was compensated isostatically only in a very regional manner, has progressively yielded until it finally reached a local compensation; that is, the light zones have risen and vice versa, while deforming the sedimentary cover. Moreover, it is not at all impossible that the Alpine movements have played a role if only to release the movements of readjustment, perhaps by the appearance of fissures.

Even for structures of such slight amplitude as those of the Paris Basin, we see that several interpretations are possible for deformations of the basement. For this reason, it will be useful to examine how the problem appears from a mechanical point of view.

A homogeneous mass, to which it is impossible to assimilate the nonstratified basement except in a first approximation, may react either through homogeneous deformation or through the action of breaks when subjected to exterior forces.

A homogeneous deformation may be recognized by certain details of structure that were studied in Chapter 4; it may be expressed by a general schistosity, stretching or boudinage of beds or veins, ptygmatic folds, and so forth. But these characteristics are really clear only for an already very important deformation, corresponding to a flattening of two-thirds or at least one-half, to make a definite estimate. The frequency with which this amount of deformation has been surpassed leads us to suspect that even more often masses of very great dimensions have undergone homogeneous deformations involving smaller strain. Such deformations are almost impossible to recognize, but the possibility of their existence must always be kept in mind.

Very often, instead of remaining distributed in a regular manner, the deformation affects certain parts of the mass, either because the latter is not perfectly homogeneous or simply because a first deformation diminishes later resistance, in which case certain parts will be very deeply deformed before neighboring zones are affected.

The deformed zones included between the intact parts should theoretically form belts of constant thickness (Chaps. 4 and 5). But in reality, things are not so clear-cut, and we have to deal with greatly deformed zones between masses whose deformation, too slight to be recognized by study of their structure, is, however, very far from being negligible. The result is that the greatly deformed zones do not constitute continuous belts, but may thin out and relay each other in a quite capricious manner. Such is the case, in particular, for the zones of mylonite that may extend into the heart of a granitic mass.

The strong deformation of a belt of limited thickness that has been pushed to an extreme constitutes a transition between continuous deformation and actual rupture along a surface of discontinuity. Moreover, there are often several surfaces of discontinuity, or several faults, close together, along which a certain thickness of strata, or remnants torn from the margins, may be crushed or very highly deformed.

It is not necessary to enter into the structural detail of these abnormalities, since mechanics furnishes very precise indications on the relations between

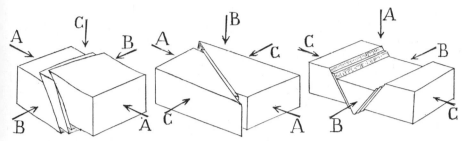

FIGURE 153. *The three essential types of rupture of the earth's crust. A always indicates the strongest of the principal pressures, and C the weakest. At each point, the vertical pressure is the result of the weight of the overlying rocks.*

their directions and those of the stresses, that result immediately from the laws of rupture, as illustrated by the Mohr diagram. By restricting ourselves to the case in which the principal directions of stress are respectively horizontal and vertical, it is possible to distinguish three essential cases (Fig. 153). If the earth's crust is subjected to horizontal compression, such that the horizontal pressures are superior to the vertical pressure determined by the weight of the overlying terranes (not only along a horizontal direction of maximum pressure, but also in the perpendicular direction), breaks will appear that are inclined to the horizontal at an angle of 45° or slightly less. These breaks will behave like reverse or overthrust faults. The intermediate pressure may exceed the minimum vertical pressure by an exceedingly small amount; this is the case if no extension is possible in this direction. The basement will be divided into a series of slices thrust over one another. The distribution of the forces is never so regular that these breaks are parallel to each other, and the scales often present an amygdaloid form in plane. In general, it is to be observed that all breaks that appear are inclined in the same direction.

Such overthrust faults produce an uplift of the surface that should react against gravity and thus absorb work. As in the case of cover folds, it can be shown that gravity should tend to reduce the value of the uplift of the surface and spread it over the greatest possible area. We should thus expect that the overthrust faults, especially for structures of great dimensions, would be closer to the horizontal than Mohr's simple theory of rupture would have had us assume.

The second case to be distinguished is that in which, the horizontal pressure along one direction still being greater than the vertical pressure, the horizontal pressure at right angles is less. There then appear vertical transverse faults making an angle of 45° or a little less with the direction of maximum pressure, which produce a horizontal reaction that at times may continue along a great length. In general, such faults appear only along one of two theoretically possible symmetrical directions.

Such transverse faults are difficult to recognize; they have often been misunderstood and doubtless still are, and yet they are probably quite common. We have already cited the Villefort fault. A much more remarkable example is to be found in the "Great Glen Fault" of Scotland (Fig. 154), which presents, according to Kennedy,[3] a horizontal displacement of 105 km, calculated with the assumption that the Strontian and Foyers granites are parts of a single massif. The movement was probably later than the Middle Devonian and earlier than the Upper Carboniferous, but the fault was active after the Jurassic and still constitutes a line of seismic activity.

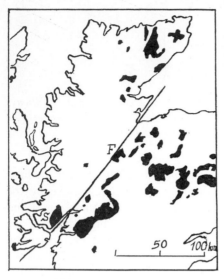

FIGURE 154

The Great Glen Fault. (S = Strontian, F = Foyers, granitic masses shown in black.)

The third case is that in which the horizontal pressure acting within the earth's crust is less than the vertical pressure; that is, it is an extension effort that is superposed upon the hydrostatic distribution of the pressures that would result from the weight of the strata alone. We shall assume that along a horizontal direction at right angles the pressure is also, by however small an amount, less than the vertical pressure (If it were not, we would be duplicating the preceding case). Moreover, owing to the slight elastic deformation that precedes the rupture, it is sufficient that no deformation is possible along this third direction. The breaks that appear then are inclined at a little more than 45° and act like normal faults. In contrast to the compression faults that remain isolated or all act in the same direction, these extension faults often group together to determine troughs between two faults with opposite dips; moreover, each of the faults may break down into series of parallel faults that are more or less close together and which have the same dip.

Frequently, trenches of great dimensions, bounded in this manner by normal faults, are the seat of a particular sedimentation that continues during the course of the movement and which does not take place outside the trench; the best example in Europe is the Rhine graben, occupied by the Alsatian plain. It is known that the Oligocene (continental) sediments there attain great depth. In particular, they contain thick beds of salt with several beds of potassium salts (Fig. 155).

The Limagne and Bresse are both examples of subsidence troughs occupied by a great thickness of Oligocene deposits. Moreover, the faults are of unequal magnitude. The faults west of Limagne have throws much greater (1000 m)

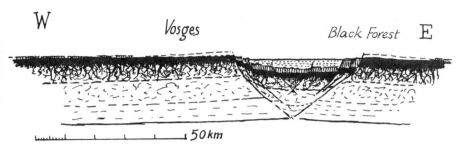

FIGURE 155. *Section of the Rhine graben, showing how the crust is affected.*

than those to the east; the faults located east of Bresse are larger than those to the west. The Oligocene basins of Alès and of Marseille are of the same type.

Doubtless the most natural way to interpret the parallelism of faults that mark the edges of such a trench is to assume that their inclination is such that they intersect toward the base of the earth's crust, which was subjected to extension. Under these conditions, isostatic equilibrium requires an uplift of the edges of the trench, which compensates, to a certain extent, for the subsidence of the trench.

Care must also be taken that the dip of the faults in depth is not necessarily identical with the dips that can be measured on the surface in the sedimentary cover. In fact in a series of competent beds separated by plastic beds, the faults determined by a change of level in the basement have a tendency to tilt and to approach the vertical.

The system of trenches occupied by the African Great Lakes (African Rift Valley) and the Red Sea is by far the most important structure of this type; their interpretation as the result of a distention has for a long time been accepted by numerous authors (Fig. 156).

However, the inverse hypothesis of a compression that should have forced a wedge of the earth's crust downward has been proposed by Wayland and retained by Bullard [4] as a conclusion from his measurements of the intensity of gravity. But it should be noted that Bullard calculated the isostatic anomalies by the classic methods used in geodesy, which assume that the density of the earth's crust is uniform and that the distribution of compensating masses is a function of the height of the relief alone. A direct calculation [5] shows that the values found are in complete harmony with the hypothesis indicated above of a trough bordered by oblique stretch faults determining a subsided wedge, if we assume that the density increases with the depth and if isostatic equilibrium is realized as indicated above. Gravimetry also confirms this interpretation in the case of the Rhine graben.

The objection that seemed to result from Bullard's measurements is thus removed. We may learn from this example the prudence that must be imposed before drawing geologic conclusions from gravimetric anomalies calculated

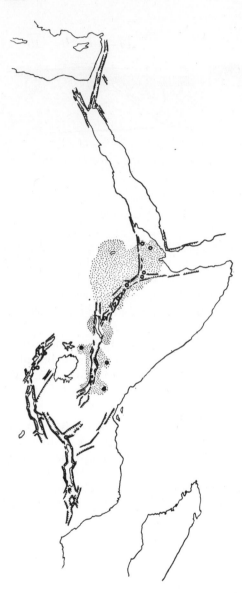

General map of the African Rift Valleys (East African Troughs). The principal volcanoes are represented by circles and the lava flows by dots.

by geodetic methods, since irregularities of structure may be produced in the earth's crust that these methods do not take into account at all.

A certain analogy exists between the subsidence troughs determined by basement stretching that we have just studied and certain abnormalities of much smaller dimensions, which result from a stretching of the cover without the participation of the basement. One of the most typical of these is the Brovès trench (Var). (See Fig. 105.) The difference of scale is such that confusion is unlikely.

In the northeastern part of the Pacific Ocean, between the Hawaiian Islands and North America, a series[6] of great parallel, rectilinear structures 3500 km long extend along the bottom. Their transverse profile seems to indicate a trough between irregularly uplifted margins, or perhaps several connected troughs whose individual width seems to be of the same order of size as that of the African or Rhenish troughs. The northernmost of these structures intersects the San Andreas fault at an angle of about 120°. Since the San Andreas fault is a line of still active movement of horizontal displacement, H. W. Menard assumes that these structures also result from horizontal slip connected with the former; their outline is much more rectilinear than that of the African trenches, thus this interpretation is favored (Fig. 194), which does not necessarily exclude an extension. This part of the Pacific is strewn with submarine volcanoes, resting on an abyssal plain, whose tops have at times been flattened ("*guyots*") by the erosion of the waves to a level that is today as much as 800 m below the surface, without making allowance for eustatic movements and subsidence.

The great coal furrow of the French Massif Central is a very curious structure that seems to correspond to two of the cases that have just been considered. The accumulation of coal-bearing sediments containing very thick beds of coal seems to indicate that this furrow acted as a subsidence trough that we may assume to be connected with extension. In places it seems quite definite that the coal deposit was bordered by marginal faults or by faults within the basin.

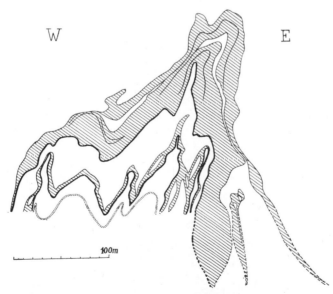

FIGURE 157. *Section across the coal-bearing bed of La Bouble (Great coal furrow of the Massif Central). [After the mine plan (300 m south of the Tollin pit); the heavy unbroken lines correspond to the parts worked.]*

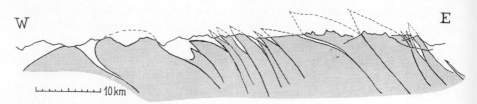

W   E

10 km

FIGURE 158. *Section of the Massif du Pelvoux. Unshaded portion indicates sedi-mentary rocks.*

But later these deposits were strongly folded into forms that appear all the more capricious the more plastically the coal behaved, producing strong disharmonies (Fig. 157). The beds must have undergone lateral compression; but the axes of the folds, as far as they can be followed, are clearly oblique to the general axis of the furrow; the compression, which tended to close the furrow, was accompanied by longitudinal slip, a displacement that is probably in part responsible for the variations in width that are recorded today. The present character of the basins of the coal furrow thus expresses the succession in time of different sorts of stresses, extension at first, then oblique compression accompanied by shearing.

We must return to the first of the three cases under consideration, the one that corresponds to compression, resulting in division of the basement into slices that were thrust upon one another. This division may go very far and may produce very complex structures of which the Pelvoux massif (Fig. 158) constitutes one of the best examples. The basement, formed of gneiss and granite, is sliced by oblique faults into irregular lentils whose mutual displacements are indicated by the presence among them of pinched remnants of the Mesozoic cover, which are often greatly crushed. The other external crystalline masses exhibit a similar structure.

In much the same way, Cretaceous and Tertiary movements have divided

50 km

FIGURE 159. *Diagrammatic map of the Pyrenees. Cross-hatching represents the Primary basement; granites are shown in black. [After Ch. Jacob.]*

the basement of the Pyrenees into a series of amygdaloid masses.[7] It is noted immediately that the structures of the basement have much less tendency to be regularly parallel than do the folds of the cover (Fig. 159).

This irregularity of the plan of the structures affecting the basement should be due in part to the heterogeneity of the latter, certain parts of which should break or crush more easily than others. Without retracing the real cases of disharmony that eventually result from the presence in the basement of relatively plastic schists, what is to be deduced from the arrangement of the structures for the mechanical properties of the different rocks?

In the Alps, the external crystalline masses, Mont Blanc, Pelvoux, and others, are for the most part highly granitized. The few zones formed of relatively slightly metamorphic schists (north of Belledonne, small outcrop of Remollon on the Durance) are much less elevated. Is there a relation between cause and effect? The elevation of the basement being connected with its thickness, in virtue of isostasy, and hence its degree of crushing, we should

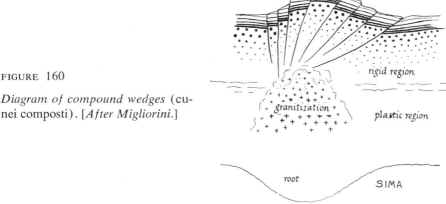

FIGURE 160

Diagram of compound wedges (cunei composti). [*After Migliorini.*]

assume that the granitized zones are less resistant and more sensitive to compression than the nongranitized zones. It must not be forgotten that granite masses, judging from the value of the corresponding gravimetric anomalies, seem to penetrate very deeply into the earth's crust in the midst of deep layers of whose nature we know but little, but which may be more resistant and at the same time heavier.

This relation, moreover, is not confirmed by the place occupied by the granites in the massifs of the north Pyrenees where it is not impossible that at great depth the area occupied by the granites or analogous rocks is notably greater than in outcrops. So the problem would require further research.

In order to explain the anticlinal wrinkles of the Apennines, which, with the exception of the very different Apuan Alps, hardly present a flexible style of real folding, but appear cut up with faults, Migliorini[8] proposed to interpret them as expressing a particular type of basement deformation in "compound wedges" (*cunei composti*). He assumed that the autochthonous sedimentary cover, which is relatively thin, and which contains few beds capable of producing a notable disharmony, passively followed the basement; the wrinkle outlined by the surface of the latter is bordered by a series of faults of varying dips that converge in depth, suggesting that a horizontal compression must have produced the uplift of the wedges limited by these faults (Fig. 160). Migliorini assumed, by analogy with what is to be observed in one of the wrinkles at Campiglia (where a granite is intrusive in the Lias), that at the moment of deformation, granitization must have been taking place at a depth of several kilometers, conferring on the basement a certain plasticity precisely in the zone toward which the faults bounding the wedges were converging. With this hypothesis, then, there would be no breaking deformation by faults, except in the upper part of the basement, whose deformation would have been more or less directed by the plastic crushing of the deep part of the basement (aided by the granitization).

It seems proper to distinguish between objective verification that shatter structures affecting the basement tend to form there a relatively narrow wrinkle which should actually correspond to the action of a system of fan faults (whose dips have only been actually observed in a very small number of cases) and the interpretation of the deep structure, very ingenious, but clearly more hypothetical.

So far, we have considered basement tectonics and cover tectonics separately, but this constitutes only a first approximation; there should evidently be mutual interactions.

Cover tectonics is for the most part provoked by deformation of the basement, even when it seems to be largely independent in detail. For example, we have seen that the Helvetic nappes result from the compression between two blocks of basement of the contents of a sedimentary syncline that has been thrust forward. Many structures of the cover are connected in an even more direct manner with the deformation of the basement. But there is also a reaction of the cover on the basement; for example, when the cover is thrust forward by compression, it may carry remnants of the basement along with it in the form of slices, at times very thin, pinched in the midst of the sedimentary terranes (Fig. 161). Quite a great number of slices or scales

FIGURE 161. *Section to the west of the Col du Bonhomme, showing a series of crystalline scales (in black), pinched in the midst of the Lias.*

(*écailles*) of this type have been found in the Alps.[9] Moreover, it may sometimes be quite a difficult matter to distinguish scales of this sort, which are of purely mechanical origin, as has just been indicated, from those that may have been formed by a superficial slip during the course of sedimentation contemporaneous with an earlier deformation (see Chap. 3).

Up to now, we have been concerned primarily with deformations of the upper part of the basement in contact with the sedimentary cover, which greatly facilitates study.

When the study of a more deeply eroded part of the basement is undertaken, the problem becomes much more difficult; if the deformed material is made up of metamorphic rocks, it produces special conditions. Scarcely any further disharmony is possible, but in such rocks the reference horizons of known initial form are few in number. However, it is essential to distinguish the successive phases of deformation, if only the recent movements, during which the mass behaved as if rigid, breaking along surfaces marked out by mylonites—more or less visible according to the rocks that they affect— from the old movements, contemporary with the metamorphism. There are reasons for believing that metamorphism could have influenced very important deformations aided by recrystallization. Moreover, if the mass had been folded before metamorphism, it might be difficult to recognize. The first phase in the study of such a region should evidently involve the search for breaks marked out by mylonites, in order to recognize the most recent movements, which have necessarily contributed to masking the earlier structures.

The study of the earlier structures usually requires certain *a priori* hypotheses whose bases should be discussed. We have already pointed out that it is generally assumed that bedding (and schistosity) were initially horizontal, as well as the zones of isometamorphism, which were superposed on a given vertical in a constant order. What is known of the schistosity of sedimentary rocks, which in general presents a quite strong dip, scarcely justifies the first hypothesis. Doubtless there may be a difference between the schistosity of deformation and the schistosity of crystallization, but it would be hard to conceive that the mechanical setup of the stresses is radically different. The hypothesis of a horizontal schistosity seems to imply a regime of horizontal distension of the earth's crust, which differs from that displayed by most dislocations. Must we admit that the periods of metamorphism were radically different from the periods of orogenesis? There would be very strong objections to that.

No one doubts that, on the whole, metamorphism is due to actions of deep origin. Does this mean that everywhere the degree of metamorphism was steadily decreasing from the bottom to the top? Could one not assume, as Lapadu-Hargue[10] suggested, that metamorphism has sometimes followed a detour, starting from more or less laccolithic injection zones? In the past few years, evidence along this line has been increased. The most striking discovery was made by F. Ellenberger,[11] who established that the augen-gneisses of the Sapey (Savoy, Vanoise Massif) should be placed at the top of the non-metamorphic Carboniferous series and that they are overlain in transgression by the Permian. This establishes the Hercynian age of the migmatization, which has been confirmed by petrographic study. Although the very intense Alpine dislocations introduce certain complications, it is possible to follow this gneiss body for some fifty kilometers, which is perhaps a unique example of metamorphism produced at very slight depth, below which a thick series was unaffected by it.

Apropos of certain tectonic syntheses of metamorphic regions, we must take into account ideas that have held sway upon the respective part of the different types of deformation. Following investigations on the Alps, in particular those of E. Argand, geologists thought, around 1920, that the normal type of deformation of the earth's crust must be analogous to the great Alpine nappes; so it was a question of finding in all masses of crystalline schists the superposition of nappes comparable to those of the Pennine Alps. The difficulty of the observations and the occasionally subjective character of their interpretation do not always permit us to assert that the proposed synthesis, influenced by such *a priori* ideas, is the only one possible. Subsequent studies in the nonmetamorphic regions having shown that the appearance of great overthrust nappes was relatively exceptional and was related to quite special mechanical conditions, it seems necessary to once again consider, from the beginning, the problem of the existence of great nappes in metamorphic series.

Notes and References

1. Destombes, J. P. and Vaysse, A., *Sur le Gothlandien de la vallée de la Pique (Haute-Garonne)*, Bull. Soc. géol. France, 5ᵉ ser., vol. 17, pp. 404–409, 1947.

2. Fallot, P., *Au sujet de la genèse des plis du Bassin de Paris,* Soc. géol. France, Comptes-rendus, pp. 20–21, Feb. 2, 1942.

3. Kennedy, W. K., The Great Glen Fault, Quart. Jour. Geol. Soc. London, vol. 102, pp. 41–76, 1946.

4. Wayland, E. J., The African Bulge, Geogr. Jour., London, vol. 75, pp. 381–383, 1930.

Bullard, C., Gravity Measurements in East Africa, Phil. Trans. Roy. Soc. London, vol. 235A, pp. 445–534, 1936.

5. Goguel, J., *La structure des fossés africains et la gravimétrie,* Annal. de Geophys., vol. 5, fasc. 2, p. 174, 1949.

————, *Gravimétrie et fossé rhénan,* Kon. Nederl. Geol.-Mijnbouwk. Gen., Verhandel., Geol. ser., vol. 18 (livre jubilaire F. A. Vening Meinesz), pp. 125–147, 1957.

6. Menard, Henry W., Deformation of the N. E. Pacific Basin and the West Coast of North America, Bull. Geol. Soc. America, vol. 66, pp. 1149–1198, 1955.

7. Jacob, Ch., *Zone axiale, versant Sud et versant Nord des Pyrénées,* Soc. géol. France (livre jubilaire), vol. 2, pp. 389–410, 1930.

8. Migliorini, C. I., *I cunei composti nell' orogenesi,* Boll. Soc. geol. Italiana, vol. 67, pp. 29–142, 1948.

9. The list of crystalline "scales" known at this time is enumerated in: Gignoux, M. and Raguin, E., *Découverte d'écailles de roches granitiques au N. W. du Col du Lautaret* (*Hautes-Alpes*), Bull. Soc. géol. France, 5e ser., vol. 2, pp. 513–526, 1932.

10. Lapadu-Hargue, P., *Les massifs de la Margeride et du Mont Lozère et leurs bordures,* Bull. Carte géol. France, vol. 46, no. 222 (thesis). The author's position was more clearly expressed at the time of his oral defense of his thesis.

11. Ellenberger, F., *Migmatites d'age permien dans la zone houillère briançonnaise* (*Alpes occidentales*), Soc. géol. France, Comptes-rendus, pp. 64–67, 1954. (See also Comptes-rendus de la Soc. géol. France, 1954, p. 448 and p. 498.)

CHAPTER FIFTEEN

Different Types of Alpine Structures. The Root Idea

Role of nappes and roots in a paleogeographic synthesis—Sub-Alpine folds and corresponding overthrusts—Helvetic nappes, relations with movements of the basement—Embrunais nappe—Sub-Briançonnais north of Pelvoux—Briançonnais; overthrust of the Carboniferous and deformation of its cover—Metamorphic Pennine nappes; independence of *schistes lustrés* in relation to the basement—Prealps—Nappes in the Himalayas—Franco-Belgian Carboniferous basin—Caledonian overthrusts in Scotland —Nappes of the south slope of the Montagne Noire.

THE STUDY of the Alps, since the long past epoch during which Horace Bénédict de Saussure established the existence there of rock deformation, has played a fundamental role in the development of tectonics. But inversely, in the knowledge of the Alps the progress of stratigraphy has played a no less essential role than the understanding of very complex deformations. It may be said that, in the present state of synthesis, it is essentially the comparisons of facies that lead to the definition and classification of units whose limits are evidently imposed by tectonics.

For more than half a century, the investigation of an Alpine synthesis has been dominated by the concept of the nappe, associated with the complementary concept of the root.

In an earlier phase, for an example of which we may take the studies of Charles Lory,[1] geologists were preoccupied with distinguishing a series of zones in the Alps, separated in a more or less conventional manner by faults; in each zone, it was possible to unravel the stratigraphy, which differed from one zone to another.

The notions of nappe and root have provided, for these stratigraphic comparisons, a much more flexible framework, which has made it possible to explain multiple peculiarities. To a stratigrapher, the Alps seem to have been carved by erosion into a pile of nappes, each of which is tied to a root, located to the south or east, which corresponds, considerably reduced, to the emplacement where the deposition of the sediments that now constitute the nappe originally took place. One of the best examples of this role of the conception of nappes in stratigraphy is furnished by the maps that accompany Jean Boussac's Mémoire[2] on the Alpine Nummulitic, in which the different units have been brought back to their original places in order to make possible a paleogeographic synthesis.

Moreover, it is often found that the nappes present a quite marked continuity in the direction of the line of the mountain chain, since each of the basins is characterized by sediments of determined character, having originally had the form of a furrow parallel to the future mountain chain.

The framework thus set up and completed by grouping the elementary units into successive assemblages sometimes assumes an overly dogmatic form, as if the units and groupings thus defined had an absolute significance comparable to that which the naturalist attaches to species and genera that enable him to classify living forms.

The description of the grouping would be outside the framework of this treatise. If, in the present chapter, we review the principal types of Alpine structures it is essentially in order to analyze their present form and the movements from which they result. We shall postpone, to Chap. 17, the study of their mutual relations and the place that they occupy in the mountain chain as a whole.

Certain examples of Alpine structures have been cited in the foregoing chapters. If it seems necessary to return to most of them, it is because their complexity is such that we could not be satisfied with a purely geometric, or even a purely kinematic, analysis; even in the simplest cases, it is necessary to clarify the mechanical aspect of the deformation and, in particular, the role of gravity. As we proceed, we shall be led to discuss the concept of "root" the full meaning of which is at times difficult to state precisely.

The sub-Alpine, or Jura, type of folds, which result from the wrinkling of a sedimentary cover on a basement that does not participate in the movement, have been sufficiently studied above. If only by way of comparison, it is well to examine what plays the role of a root when a fold is transformed into an overthrust.

The only difference between the mass slip of the cover, more or less folded on itself, and an overthrust is that, in the second case, a part of the sedimentary cover is caught under the overthrust. So we should logically consider the root as constituting the part of the normal series situated immediately behind the overridden remnants. A first difficulty is due to the fact that

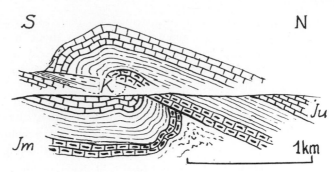

FIGURE 162. *The overthrust of Caussols (Alpes-Maritimes). Section along the right bank of the Loup, completed from the region situated immediately behind. (See Fig. 83.) The Jurassic series has slipped on the Trias; the overthrust is limited by a free synclinal hinge, which defines the position of the roots. (K = Cretaceous; Ju = Upper Jurassic; Jm = Middle Jurassic.)*

nothing in the structure of the normal series can indicate this limit; in the absence of a deep erosion section that exposes the overridden series, we have no means of fixing the position of the root.

If such a section exists, several cases may appear; if the overridden series ends in a free synclinal hinge, which is especially the case if the overthrust was made on the surface of the ground (Fig. 162), the position of the root seems quite definite. But it is not the same if the overthrust is the result of shearing in the midst of the strata, a shearing that may be free or may be accompanied by synclinal or anticlinal folds. The overridden series may then thin out into a series of remnants whose limit is ill-defined, in which case it is hardly possible to speak of a well-determined root.

This idea does not recover its full value except at the ends of an overthrust; it is very important to examine the manner in which such a structure ends, longitudinally. Except for a secondary complication (or complete erosion), the overthrust generally passes into an anticline that is either sym-

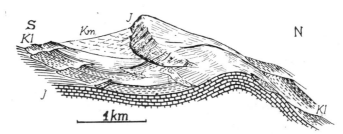

FIGURE 163. *Rooting of the overthrust at Thorenc (Alpes-Maritimes). The anticline, situated in the foreground to the right, is prolonged in the background by an overthrust series, the Jurassic resting on the Middle Cretaceous of the syncline. (Km = Middle Cretaceous; Kl = Lower Cretaceous; J = Jurassic.)*

metrical or slightly overturned, is affected by a strong axial plunge, and rapidly disappears. With a suitable level of erosion it is possible to see at the same time the anticlinal hinge and the synclinal hinge without their common limb being broken (Fig. 163). It is often said that the overthrust "takes root." Such observations are important in that they establish the connection between the overthrust series and the overridden series and make it possible to reject certain hypotheses implying the presence of fragments of nappes of distant origin. But such a rooting does not establish the position of the actual root in the zone where the overthrust has developed.

We have just considered the case in which the cover may slip freely on its basement (Fig. 164); structures that affect it, symmetrical folds or overthrusts, after all, express only irregularities in the movement of slipping; their localization may be determined by variations of facies, such as the passage of thick Dauphinois facies to the Provencal facies by a thinning, followed by a development of calcareous series at the latitude of Castellane for the southern sub-Alpine chains, or by the braking force of an accumulation of detrital Tertiary formations.

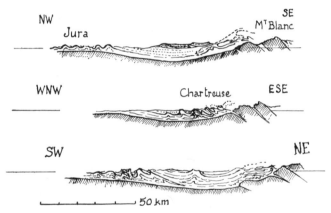

FIGURE 164. *Three overall sections across the sub-Alpine zone: (1) from Mont Blanc to the Jura, (2) across the Grande-Chartreuse, and (3) from the Massif du Mercantour (Argenters) to the environs of Castellane. Vertical scale exaggerated. The cover was able to slip and fold freely; the localization of the folds results especially from the variations of lithologic composition of the series (thinning of the Tertiary in the Jura, passage to the Provencal facies at Castellane).*

But when a certain volume of covering terranes lies between two basement elements and is compressed between them, the deformations cannot simply come into juxtaposition while keeping a moderate intensity. Although already folded, a relatively narrow belt should continue to deform. If these deformations continued in place along a given vertical, the material would be carried to a great height, and considerable work would be done against gravity. In-

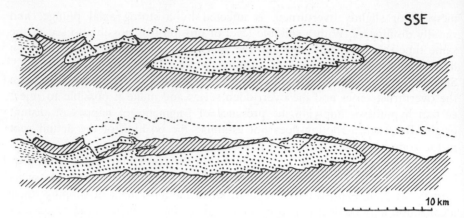

FIGURE 165. *Section of the Glarus Alps (Switzerland). Above. The old interpretation of two facing recumbent folds ("double fold"). Below. The hypothesis of a single nappe. This interpretation, by analogy with the structure of the Carboniferous basin in the north of France, proposed by Marcel Bertrand, marked an important stage in the comprehension of the Alps.*

stead of that, the mass spreads over a quite considerable breadth, such that its thickness never attains more than a moderate figure. That is, instead of accumulating in height, the portion of the cover under consideration, driven from the interval separating the two blocks of the basement between which it is compressed, spreads over a quite considerable width.

The deformation of the basement, expressed by the compression of two wedges against each other, corresponds to a thickening that should, in view of isostasy, be expressed by a quite notable uplift. The result in the mass is that a slope forms that still further favors this spreading and lets it develop on one side only, toward the exterior of the mountain chain. Isolated fragments may even slide along this slope, losing their continuity with the principal mass of the nappe.

The nappe is formed by a stratified mass, that is, one that will always tend

FIGURE 166. *A zone of roots of Helvetic nappes. End of the Aar Massif in the region of Loetschberg. [After Lugeon.] The crystalline mass is broken into multiple wedges between which the sedimentary material has been crushed and carried away; only Lias and Trias (in black) can be seen here; Jurassic and Cretaceous have been carried away and form nappes, properly so-called.*

FIGURE 167. *Section of mass of Helvetic nappes on the right bank of the Rhône (Lugeon). The ruled area represents the crystalline basement, here hidden under the carapace of the nappes. The different stratigraphic horizons are indicated by broken lines (heavy dashes for the Upper Jurassic). Dotted lines indicate Flysch and upper units in which the nappes are hooded.*

to deform by folding; so the beds in the tilted mass outline a series of folds of flexible character. Certain competent beds retain their continuity over considerable areas; however, the reversed sides of the folds are often stretched or replaced by faults. Certain plastic beds greatly facilitate the movement and may cause disharmonies or very important slips.

Better than any explanation, the examples presented in Figures 165–168 will give an idea of the complexity that such dislocations may attain in *Helvetic nappes.* In Switzerland, we are led to distinguish several superposed nappes that seem to proceed from furrows between the successive crystalline masses. For example, the Morcles nappe is formed by the sedimentary cover that was initially caught between the Mont Blanc Massif and the Aiguilles Rouges Massif, and was subsequently driven out by the drawing together of these two massifs, which are now separated by only the narrow Chamonix syncline (occupied by Lias and very crushed Trias).

FIGURE 168. *Section across the valley of the Reuss (eastern Switzerland). [After Albert Heim.] Here the nappes are represented essentially by their plunging heads.*

These superposed nappes in the Valais (Morcles, Diablerets, and Wildhorn) formed successively, beginning with the most interior and at the same time most elevated, except the Morcles nappe, which seems the oldest. But naturally the first nappes were in turn deformed at the same time that the inferior nappes were being formed; thus, peculiar complications may have originated. Remnants of upper nappes may have been isolated from their roots and may later have moved by slipping above the moving series of lower nappes and the crystalline masses that originated them, slipping at each stage

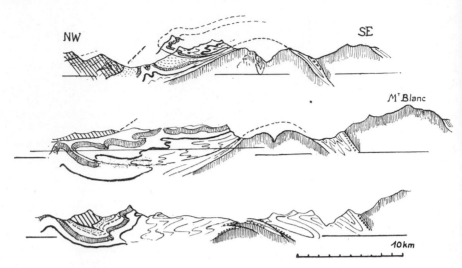

FIGURE 169. *Three sections across the Morcles nappe and its southern prolongation. Oblique ruling: upper units (Prealps, Klippes). Dots: Tertiary; gray:
Urgonian; black line: Upper Jurassic; crystalline rocks indicated by vertical
rulings. Above, classic section through Champéry and the Dents du Midi.
The nappe is separated from the autochthon by a Tertiary syncline. In the
middle, through Mont Blanc and the right bank of the Arve. It is not possible to follow the syncline that might separate the nappe from the
autochthon. On the eastern edge, the nappe does not rest on rocks per-
ceptibly younger than itself. Below, in the Mégève region (south of the
Arve) the folds of the Lias and the scales of the crystalline basement have
a local character. There is only one series of folds of the cover and no
nappe can be distinguished from the autochthon.*

with the aid of the inclination of the surface on which they were resting. The
thicker the mass under consideration, and the greater the number of
superposed nappes, the easier such movements were.

According to its mode of formation, the root of a Helvetic nappe is to be
sought in a sedimentary syncline lying between crystalline massifs. However,
gliding tectonics suggests that a nappe could originate, not in a syncline, but
in the cover of an anticlinal mass from which it had separated by slipping and
thus causing a tectonic denudation. Collet and Paréjas were able to follow the
elements of the Morcles nappe and connect it with the Chamonix syncline
between Mont-Blanc and the Aiguilles Rouges, in which only Lias and Trias
are found today, which are, moreover, divided into slices and refolded. On
its north side, the ancestral sedimentary basin was already separated from
the basin in which the material of the sub-Alpine mountain chains (of very
similar facies) was being formed. The two basins were separated by a zone
tending to emergence, which corresponds to the present Aiguilles Rouges

Massif. The corresponding sedimentary series, characterized by its lacunas and preserved at least in some places, evidently separates the nappe and the autochthonous foreland; this is all the more important, since near Champéry, the frontal folds of the nappe approach very close to autochthonous anticlines of very similar facies. But the Tertiary syncline that separates them continues along the left bank of the Rhône for a great length, furnishing a geometric argument for separating the nappe from the autochthon, in addition to the stratigraphic argument already mentioned. Farther to the south, however, things are not so clear, and it becomes difficult to separate the nappe from the autochthon[3] (Fig. 169).

The stratigraphic argument disappears, the southern part of the massif of the Aiguilles Rouges apparently not having played the role of shoal in the Mesozoic. In the valley of the Arve, the only syncline that may be assumed to mark the limit of the nappe and the autochthon, between the Cluses fold and that of Arâche, is buried beneath the level of the valley, and it is impossible to say how far it may continue. Farther back, where erosion again reaches what might be the base of the nappe, only a shearing surface separates different members of the Jurassic, and it must have been produced in depth. Nothing permits us to distinguish such a shearing from those that must affect the substratum of the sub-Alpine chains in the Bauges or in the Chartreuse. There is no longer any inversion of the nappe over an anticlinal zone (as there is in the Valais) extending to the following syncline, but a simple shearing in depth, the character of which it is difficult to affirm, in the heart of a series that is somewhat thrust forward in its mass and in which a series of folds of the cover have their origin. This example shows that it is impossible to make a clear-cut distinction between Helvetic nappes and sub-Alpine folds. It also shows how the rooting of the Helvetic nappes may be obscured.

The Embrunais nappe is typical of still another type of structure. Essentially, it is formed of an enormous mass of flysch mainly with Helminthoides of Upper Cretaceous age resting by overthrusting either on another Tertiary rock (to the north, it rests on the Dormillouse sandstone) or on Oxfordian marls that seem to have been partially released by erosion before the epoch of the overthrust, since they support in place transgressive Eocene (Figs. 94 and 127).

Associated with the flysch of the Embrunais nappe are Mesozoic terranes that form either thin slices marking out the base of the nappe or voluminous masses that are more or less folded upon themselves and are completely severed from any connections. A very precise stratigraphic analysis[4] has revealed that the facies of the Mesozoic vary quite strikingly from one of these folds to the next, although they are very different from those of the autochthon; these Mesozoic sediments must have been deposited in a moving zone tending to differentiate into ridges and furrows. On both sides of the

Durance and the Ubaye, these differences of facies make it possible to establish a correspondence between scales (*écailles*) that are hardly anything else than folds.

Where were these Mesozoic strata deposited? They must certainly have been deposited beyond the zone in which autochthonous Oxfordian marls are found, that is, somewhere toward the east or east of northeast. But on this side, everything is hidden by units in which the Mesozoic presents entirely different facies, so it is not possible to say whether some remnants of it have remained in place. Nor is it possible to say where the Paleozoic basement is now located, on which these strata were deposited over a width that could scarcely be less than 10 or 20 km.

This impossibility of arriving at any conclusion in the matter of roots unfortunately is not peculiar to the Ubaye-Embrunais nappe. But its essential characteristic is the manner of passive entrainment of Mesozoic units into a mass of flysch whose place of deposition we do not know exactly (it must be far away because the upper Cretaceous is known under a quite different facies of pelagic limestones in the Briançonnais) nor what was its width.

It is hard to believe that its emplacement is entirely the result of a thrust. There must also have been a favorable slope in order to facilitate its slipping. To assume that a thrust transmitted as far as the front would require a thickness of flysch far in excess of that preserved on the ridges; thus, the hypothesis according to which gravity played the essential role in emplacement seems far more probable. However, this implies nothing concerning the origin of the nappe, which may have been due, to a greater or lesser degree, to a deep thrust that drove the sedimentary material upward before it slid down a slope. The attempt has been made to distinguish in this mass various sorts of flysch from basins (or from parts of basins) that were distinct and tectonically superposed, but their relations remain somewhat hypothetical.

To the north of the Pelvoux massif, Mesozoic strata, in which certain facies are similar, in some respects, to those of the Embrunais nappe, exhibit a quite different tectonic character.[5] They are divided into a series of scales presenting a quasi-isoclinal behavior, which are inclined 30°–45° toward the east; that is, toward the interior of the mountain chain (Fig. 170). These scales, however, present quite numerous and often very complex folds, certain parts of which are overturned. The disharmony due to certain terranes, for example, the Oxfordian marls in the "Pas-du-Roc" nappe, could have brought about the separation of the stratigraphic series into two scales that were initially superposed but which have become separated, as in the "diverticulations" described by M. Lugeon, which today occupy entirely different positions. Elsewhere, juxtaposed scales present the same terranes with differences of facies that show deposition in different zones, without indicating anything of their original distances.

Owing to their inclination, which is, in general, quite steep, the various scales each crop out for only a short distance, and we know nothing either of the volume carried away by erosion or of the manner in which they terminate at depth. They were apparently wrenched from the substratum on which they were deposited, but we do not know either where this substratum was or what has become of it. The complexity of the mutual relations of the sub-Briançonnais scales is better understood if we accept the idea that, as in the case of diverticulations (p. 171), there was at first a gravity slip of successive slices, whose mutual positions may have been inverted. But for this to have been the case, the slope must have been the opposite of what we presently observe. The subsequent rotation of this entire zone must have been related to the movement of the enormous mass of the Briançonnais Carboniferous that rests on this system of scales and which must have contributed to deforming them. But it is difficult to imagine the Carboniferous mass climbing a 30° slope, since this would require a considerable amount of work. Would it not be more probable to conceive of the involvement in depth of their basement at the same time that a lateral compression was being produced? The Mesozoic scales would then have been crushed against one another, almost without undergoing a change in elevation. The work against gravity put into operation by such a suction of the basement in depth would be much less, considering the slight discrepancy between the densities of the different sorts of rocks, than that to be implied by deformations of the surface.

The Alpine structures considered up to now consist only of strata of the Mesozoic cover, either because the basement did not participate in their formation, as in the sub-Alpine mountain chains, or because its reaction is very different in the Helvetic nappes, or, finally, because its behavior is unknown, as in the ultra-Dauphinois and sub-Briançonnais units. Now we are going to study a series of structures in which the participation of the terranes of the basement becomes very important, since they constitute the cores of the Pennine nappes. The case of the Briançonnais, passing laterally

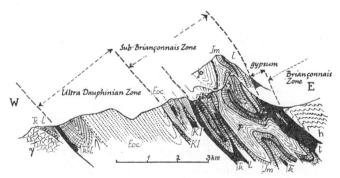

FIGURE 170. *Section of the right bank of the Arc.* [*After Barbier.*] (γ = granite; h = Carboniferous; Jm = Dogger; jc = Callovian; jo = Oxfordian; Kl = Lower Cretaceous, accompanied by Upper Eocene. Not the very complex involutions of in certain scales.

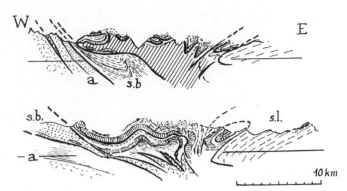

FIGURE 171. *Two ensemble sections of the Briançonnais. Above. In the region of Briançon (see Fig. 98), where the essential phenomenon is the crushing and overthrusting of the Carboniferous mass, whose covering is folded or sliced. Below. In the region of Guillestre, where the presence of the Carboniferous is not established; the Mesozoic cover is sheared off into strongly folded nappes (see Fig. 92). In both cases there are to be observed, toward the east, folds and local overthrusts that seem to date a late phase.*

to the nappe of the Grand-Saint-Bernard, however, is somewhat special because the Paleozoic basement is only represented in it by the Carboniferous, whose stratigraphic composition, with alternation of sandstones and shales, approaches that of a flysch and should therefore possess on the whole considerable plasticity. It is possible that certain masses of compact sandstone or intrusions of eruptive rocks behave locally like rigid cores, but on the other hand, the beds of coal permit a very easy mutual displacement of their walls (Fig. 171).

Actually, the essential phenomenon in the Briançonnais is the overthrusting of the Carboniferous mass, which rests on the more external units and which is crushed upon itself with probably a great increase in thickness (which is expressed by the abundance of vertically tilted beds). It has not been possible up to now either to reconstruct the detail of the deformations typical of the Carboniferous, or to state precisely the nature of its original substratum, or the connections that it may have preserved with the latter. Perhaps a more detailed study and an industrial exploitation of coal would cast some light on the first point, but the second will remain in the domain of hypothesis.

What is best known and easiest to study in the Briançonnais is the behavior of the Mesozoic cover of the Carboniferous, which is made up of a series of easily distinguished members. On the actual mass of the Carboniferous, whose upper surface was contracting, this cover is generally folded into erect folds, more or less acute, which remain intimately connected with the Carboniferous, which may rise quite high in the anticlines. In places, however, the cover (or at least its calcareous part, excluding the basal Triassic) has acquired a certain independence and has formed local overthrusts that differ but little from those found in the sub-Alpine mountain chains; however, just as the Carboniferous penetrates into erect anticlines, it forms an anticline at the origin of these local overthrusts, the most important of which are those of Termier's third scale and those of Pierre Eyrautz (Fig. 98).[6]

On the frontal edge of the overthrust Carboniferous, its Mesozoic cover overflows quite markedly and overrides the lower units alone or with the interposition of minute Carboniferous chips. This arrangement can be explained if we accept the idea of a sort of rolling of the plastic Carboniferous mass into which the more rigid cover had probably not been carried. In the "Mountains between Briançon and Vallouise" this cover forms the second scale of Pierre Termier.

However, certain remnants of Briançonnais strata, doubtless torn from the front of the second scale, have been held back, and, at least in its frontal part, the Carboniferous has succeeded in overriding them. For these discontinuous scales of quite complex character we may reserve the denomination of first scale, created by Termier in a somewhat different sense.

The Carboniferous disappears at some distance to the south of Briançon, either because it was not reached by erosion or because it always had a lesser thickness there than farther to the north. However, the Briançonnais zone continues, but is reduced to what in the north constituted the cover of the Carboniferous, and which is here divided into a series of scales, or rather elementary nappes, some of which have an amplitude of more than 10 km (Fig. 92).[7] We must not exclude the possibility that the tectonic style imposed on the cover by the behavior of the Carboniferous toward the south, where this terrane no longer existed, had spread by continuity into the Mesozoic cover torn from a different substratum. However, in the valleys of the Guil and the Ubaye there arises the problem of the nature and the initial position of the substratum of the Trias (or of the Permian), and of its subsequent tectonic behavior. Must we assume that it, like the Carboniferous of Briançon, underwent a simultaneous mass overthrusting and a horizontal contraction? If the contraction is beyond doubt, is it not more probable to assume that it is the result of the involvement of a rigid basement at depth? Here we encounter the same problem of the deep structure of the mountain chain that was posed apropos of the roots of the sub-Briançonnais nappes.

Before leaving the Briançonnais, we must point out the existence of relatively late movements (in any case later than the mass overthrusting), which canted the eastern part of the zone toward the east with some local overthrusts; conjointly with the overthrusting toward the west, particularly visible in the western frontal region, these late movements determine a fan character that we must analyze in order to determine the genesis of the present structure in successive phases.

In the other Pennine nappes, the participation of the basement becomes even more important and sometimes even involves crystalline terranes, but at the same time there appears a very marked metamorphism. This calls for a complete re-examination of all the ideas relative to the plasticity of the various kinds of rocks. We have seen that, if the deformation is slow, the change of form of the crystals by recrystallization is one of the most important methods of deformation. Placed in a chemical environment, and at a temperature such that its matter may recrystallize, any rock should behave as if relatively plastic if the deformations are sufficiently slow. We have no reason to doubt that such was the case for the Pennine nappes. So the ideas concerning the respective roles of the rigid and brittle basement and the plastic cover, acquired by observation of the external crystalline masses (Gothard, Mont-Blanc, Pelvoux) and their cover, are inapplicable here. Without excluding the possibility that the Alpine deformations may have been accompanied, at times, by some paragenesis of minerals, the mass of crystalline rocks was, on the whole, at a temperature and in a chemical environment (defined by the nature of the impregnating fluid) that did not permit their recrystallization.

The problem posed by the study of the crystalline cores of the Pennine nappes is entirely different. In these cores we should not look for fractures or a division of the mass into wedges. On the contrary, the mass behaved as if plastic and at times was greatly stretched. In our almost total ignorance of the relative values of the thresholds of plasticity in such conditions, for the different sorts of rocks, it becomes very difficult to introduce mechanical considerations. Moreover, depending on conditions of temperature, depth, and so on, this threshold could vary greatly for a given rock.

Geometric study of these folds is rendered difficult by the uncertainty of the stratigraphy. Only the facies corresponding to very aberrant overall chemical compositions remain quite recognizable after metamorphism. Such is the case, in particular, for different members of the Triassic—purely siliceous quartzites, very pure masses of limestone, sulphates in formations with gypsum or anhydrite. Beginning with this reference horizon, the crystalline cores may be placed in the Paleozoic, whether they are metamorphic Permo-Carboniferous (of ordinary chemical composition corresponding to the shale-sandstone facies), which at times contains recognizable conglomerates, or crystalline rocks, or older metamorphics, this case being probably more frequent than had at first been thought.

On the other hand, we attribute an age from Jurassic to Paleogene to a complex of metamorphic calc-schists (*schistes lustrés*) whose different facies we still do not know how to coordinate well. The presence of basic rocks (greenstones) in the midst of these *schistes lustrés* further complicates their study.

The interpretation that E. Argand has given of the immense masses thus constituted is a model of geometric and kinematic analysis (Fig. 172). The digging of the Simplon tunnel (Fig. 128) revealed, beyond doubt, that gneiss and *schistes lustrés* (often separated by a strip of Trias) alternate to form a series of great recumbent folds with gneiss cores. Argand extended

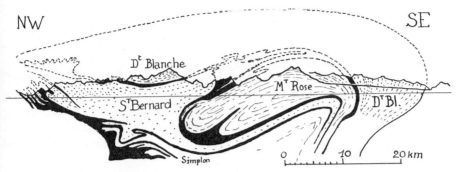

FIGURE 172. *The classic section of the Pennine nappes.* [*After Argand.*] *The Mesozoic envelope (*Trias and *schistes lustrés*) is shown in black. (It is now accepted that the nappe of Monte Rosa and that of Saint-Bernard constitute a single unit, the Mischabel nappe.)*

this concept to all the Pennine Alps, boldly increasing the scale of what had been observed in the Simplon. As a working hypothesis, he accepted the cylindrical character of the gneiss anticlines parallel to the general elongation of the Alpine mountain chain; he took advantage of the very marked lowering of the axis to the west of the Simplon to determine the perpendicular cross sections of these cylindrical folds to a height of a dozen kilometers and gave what is now considered to be a classic section. He completed this geometric synthesis by making a kinematic analysis, showing that the mutual involutions could enable us to recognize the order in which the nappes were formed and their successive movements. Figure 128 reproduces, in effect, the structure of the Helvetic nappes and shows the axial depression between Mont-Blanc and the Gothard.

However, certain questions still remain unanswered. The hypothesis of an almost cylindrical form of the folds evidently constitutes only a first approximation; the fact that the general direction of the Alpine mountain chain makes a complete turn beyond the French frontier enables us to assume that in the crucial region of the change of direction the form of the folds may change abruptly according to their direction. The phenomenon of folding has appeared to us, from the mechanical point of view, as a consequence of stratification; the material of the Pennine nappes certainly did not present any analogous mechanical property, so we might expect a very rapid variation in the form of the folds according to their direction.

Heretofore we have seen covering terranes manifest a broad independence, break off from the basement, and pile up in a compact system of slices; *a priori,* there is no reason why the structure in the Pennine should not have been formed in the same way. Before the nappes acquired their full development, their sedimentary covers may very well have undergone a series of transports such that what was originally the cover of one of these units overlapped the cover of other units. It is essentially by comparison of facies in the more external, nonmetamorphic zones that it is possible to recognize such complications. The obliteration of facies in the series of *schistes lustrés* prevents the application of such a method except for the most external nappe of the Grand-Saint-Bernard-Briançonnais, the cover of which escaped metamorphism totally or partially. We have seen how it behaves in the Briançonnais itself. Ellenberger has shown the very complicated conditions, in which scales are often overturned, that characterize the Mesozoic cover farther north, in the Vanoise. In addition, he has shown[8] that this cover is recognizable as far as the neighborhood of the next Pennine core, which constitutes the Grand Paradis Massif.

The *schistes lustrés* that rest on the Vanoise Massif and on the cover belong to cover elements of more distant origin, which were carried into an overthrust before the last folding of the cores; this is the "*schistes lustrés* nappe" of Termier, Raguin, Hermann, and other authors.

On the periphery of the Ambin Massif (Fig. 173), there has also been identified a Triassic and Liassic cover, which was overridden by the *schistes lustrés* nappe and which contains remnants of greenstone with some Triassic gypsum brought in at its base. These *schistes lustrés* no doubt originally constituted the cover of one of the Pennine cores, though it has not yet been possible to establish which one, unless they came from the synclines that separated the cores.

The problem of roots that this origin presents is comparable to those that we brought up apropos of other tectonic units constituted essentially of cover terranes. But the interpretation of the Pennine nappes poses another root problem, that of the deep structure of Paleozoic cores.

The very meaning of the word "root" is completely different here from that which we gave it in the study of nappes or overthrusts formed by the Mesozoic cover terrains. These structures are made possible by the mechanical independence of a plastic cover in relation to a rigid basement. No similarities exist between the two types of structure. Except for the Briançonnais Carboniferous, it is impossible to imagine a more rigid basement from which the

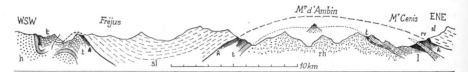

FIGURE 173. *Section across the Ambin Massif, from Mont-Cenis to Fréjus. On the metamorphic Permo-Carboniferous (rh) are remnants of the autochthonous Triassic cover; other remnants transported over a more or less great length, with stretching of their base; and finally the* schistes lustrés *nappe (sl), with transported greenstones (rv) and Triassic gypsum at its base, which rests, at Fréjus, on the Carboniferous (h) and the Briançonnais; thus the* schistes lustrés *do not constitute the sedimentary cover of the metamorphic Permo-Carboniferous.*

crystalline cores might have been sheared. On the contrary, inasmuch as the long-term plasticity of these cores seems to be due to the possibility of recrystallization, it can scarcely do otherwise than increase in depth.

There is no doubt that the formation of Pennine nappes results, on the whole, from lateral compression, but it is difficult to evaluate the magnitude of the compression. Since we do not know the initial thickness of the material of the cores, we cannot deduce the compression from their present volume. Nor can we develop their present shape, which may result from considerable stretching. So it is very difficult to state precisely the initial position of the material that constitutes them.

Diagrams by Argand (Fig. 204), which we should perhaps not look upon as a well defined system but rather as a simple suggestion, have frequently been reproduced. These diagrams show the different Pennine cores as being attached by a thin vertical peduncle, which constitutes their root, to a deep zone along which a southern segment of the earth's crust would have passed over the prolongation of a northern segment; it would seem, then, that the Pennine nappes would have been torn, in a way scraped, from the surface of a deep basement.

As we have already seen, nothing demands that we assume the existence of such a basement. Gravimetry leads us rather to assume that long-term plasticity (without any relation to instantaneous rigidity) becomes very strong from a depth of 30–40 km. The theory of isostasy hardly enables us to understand the passage of one basement over the other. Since we cannot escape the notion of a lateral compression, evidently under the effect of a deep cause, it is natural to assume that this compression is also produced at depth, whence the notion of a crushing together through the whole thickness of the earth's crust (Fig. 203). Isostatic equilibrium requires that the thickening that results from this crushing manifests itself, for the most part, by subsidence of the crushed material and to a lesser degree by uplift of the surface.

In such a concept, what becomes of the idea of roots? It is evident that this term can only be applied to the synclines that separate the anticlinal cores. In the general movement of crushing, which we try to visualize, these synclines should have been stretched and thinned. Since movement of subsidence toward the bottom is much more pronounced than the uplift of the surface, these synclines probably descend to quite a great depth, thus giving the impression of having been drawn downward.

These synclines may even descend to a depth where the intensity of the recrystallization has been such that they can no longer be lithologically distinguished from the anticlinal cores. According to this hypothesis, the synclinal hinges, which alone enable us to define the roots, were probably eliminated by metamorphism, which may have fused them into a granitic mass.

We must now turn back to mention a type of structure to which allusion has already frequently been made. The Prealps, both in Switzerland and in Haute-

Savoy, and the Klippes, of much less area, which prolong them at both ends, are formed of remnants of overthrusts resting on autochthonous sub-Alpine folds or on Helvetic nappes (Fig. 93); we have seen that the boundary between these two zones is seldom very clear-cut. Leaving out of consideration the often very intense later folds, it is possible to distinguish a series of superposed units on the basis of their facies and their geometric relations. These units may not all be superposed on a given vertical. Some of the units may even be stretched; for example, the internal and external Prealps, located on the internal and the external edges of the belt, are remnants of a single unit, which is not only hidden in its median part by higher units but is also stretched and practically eliminated.

Ever since the exotic character of the Prealps was proved by M. Lugeon, attempts have been made to identify the roots of the various units that constitute them, using the analogy of the facies and the order of superposition as a basis for identification. Despite numerous discussions, no clear-cut solution of the problem has been found and perhaps it does not admit any.

The facies of the lower unit (internal and external Prealps) suggest a close relation with the Helvetic nappes; and it may be that the lower unit represents an outlier of one of the highest nappes (ultra-Helvetic). The higher units exhibit similarities with the facies encountered in the diverse nappes or scales that are rooted in a more internal position. But these units are, in general, poorly represented or are absent in transverse sections of the Prealps; thus, terms of comparison must be sought in other, widely separated transverse sections. The persistence of the facies along a given line parallel to the mountain chain being quite uncertain, no definitive conclusion can be drawn from such comparisons.

In the classic concept of thirty years ago, the superposed remnants that constitute the Prealps were considered as the erosional remnants of a system of superposed recumbent folds. Attempts were made to graphically reconstruct their form on overall cross sections of the Alps, using dotted-lines to trace the configuration of portions of the folds removed by erosion. In this concept it was necessary to locate the roots of each of the recumbent folds, the only problem being to establish the correct correspondence between roots and overthrust remnants.

About 1940, M. Lugeon showed that recumbent folds were produced by gravity rather than by lateral compression, the remnants slipping on a favorable slope, all connections being broken with their eventual roots. This idea was immediately accepted and the special case of the Prealps constitutes the finest example in support of the theory of "gliding tectonics," because it is one of the few in which lateral compression certainly plays no direct role.

Theoretically, it is conceivable that the sedimentary cover would begin to slip on a slope following a simple upwarping of the basement. However, we find no such simple upwarping of the basement anywhere in the Alps. Since the basement is always divided by multiple fractures into scales that are thrust upon one another, the cover could not remain unaffected by this movement; it was then also divided into more or less overthrust scales. This division must have played an essential role in bringing it into the position from which it could slip by gravity.

The complex structure of the Prealps leads us to assume that emplacement occurred in several phases. The highest unit having flowed freely, the zone on which it came to rest was uplifted in turn. Owing to the lateral compression that it was undergoing and, in part, to its weight, its sedimentary cover began to slip all the more easily, since the upper unit that it was supporting constituted an overload. This phenomenon may have been reproduced several times, perhaps without pause between successive phases; numerous complications were produced in the details.

We have seen that the lower units of the Prealps (external and internal) are hardly to be distinguished from the highest units of the Helvetic nappes. We have also shown how the Helvetic nappes were formed as a result of compression of the sedimentary material between two blocks of the crystalline basement and its subsequent spreading under the action of their own weight. For these "ultra-Helvetic" units, the spreading becomes such that it passes more or less progressively to sliding on the slope.

The concept of emplacement by gravity completely modifies the approach to the problem of the roots of the Prealps. It is almost a platitude to say that it is useless to search in the places where originally there were terranes that we know have slipped some tens of kilometers. A few revealing remnants could no doubt have remained in the region of origin, which might be enough to permit a comparison of facies, but not necessarily so. It is altogether possible that in the zone of origin of such units, we might observe nothing more than a crystalline mass without any sedimentary cover, if it too had not been masked by another overthrust.

In the hypothesis of emplacement by gravity, there is no reason to insist that the superposed units must succeed each other in the order of their regions of origin (to avoid the word "roots"). We have pointed out above (p. 171) the diverticulations described by Lugeon, in which a series of scales are superposed in the inverse order of their original arrangement. Inversions of much greater range may have been produced, and nothing prevents us from imagining that a unit might have started on its way only after having been passed by the main part of the sliding mass and that it might come to rest on units that are actually of a more internal origin.

If we wish to present our hypotheses concretely, by tracing stippled lines in the aerial part of our sections, these lines will represent only in small part the strata carried away by erosion. Essentially, they indicate diagrammatically the trajectories followed by the different remnants, inasmuch as the configuration of the terrain has been profoundly modified since the movement. Obviously there is nothing to prevent these trajectories from crossing if the movements take place successively.

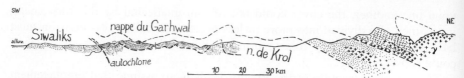

FIGURE 174. *Section of the Himalayas in the region of the Ganges, "a preliminary attempt," by J. B. Auden. The autochthon contains Paleogene resting on Precambrian; the Krol nappe is formed of beds going from Carboniferous to Tertiary; the Garhwahl nappe consists of schists and gneisses. The roots probably disappeared in a metamorphic zone.*

No other mountain chain has shown such a variety of structures as those that have been observed in the Alps; the foregoing discussion gives only a very incomplete idea of their nature.

However, important overthrusts have been described in a certain number of other mountain chains. In the Himalayas, in the neighborhood of the valley of the Ganges, J. B. Auden[9] has shown the existence of overthrusts represented by synclinal remnants isolated by erosion (Fig. 174). The terranes involved seem to belong to the Mesozoic and to the Lower Tertiary, but they are quite metamorphic. The roots seem to be lost in a granitized zone.

The geologists who accompanied the recent expeditions to Mount Everest and to Makalu[10] brought back a sketch of a transverse section of the mountain chain between the plain of the Ganges and the culminating points that mark the border of Tibet. Hereafter, we shall follow Bordet and Latreille (French expedition to the Makalu), whose section was drawn a little more to the east than Lombard's. Their section includes a transverse anticline whose axis is followed by the valley of the Arun (a river that drains a part of Tibet across the culminating crest), which enabled them to estimate the amplitude of the overthrusts (Fig. 175).

On the edge of the Quaternary plain of the Ganges, the Siwalik series, continuous the whole length of the Himalayas, is formed of folded or tilted

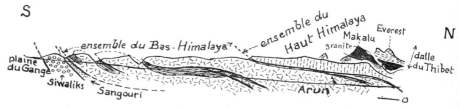

FIGURE 175. *Structural diagram of the Himalayas following the valley of the Arun (After Bordet and Latreille). Vertical scale doubled. The gneisses of the mass of the High Himalayas are thicker than they appear in this section, along the transverse anticline that follows the valley of the Arun and lifts the foreground in relation to the midground. Total length of the section = 140 km.*

Miocene and Pliocene, perhaps even some Pleistocene. The Sangouri series, probably formed of metamorphosed Mesozoic rocks, crops out over only a slight width. Farther west it seems to correspond to the Navakot nappes and might be an equivalent of the Krol nappe of the above section insofar as it is possible to attempt a correlation at a distance of a thousand kilometers.

To the north of this series, up to the Tibetan border, there are nothing but deeply metamorphic terranes. Bordet and Latreille distinguish two lithologically different masses, the Low Himalayas and the High Himalayas. The first, which is composed of an enormous thickness of gneiss, is surrounded by a quite uniform series of mica schists, quartzites (with cipollini), phyllites and calcashists, forms several superposed nappes whose mutual overlaps are at times visible for 40 km. The gneisses are probably Precambrian, and the series that overlaps them might be Paleozoic. This assemblage is overlapped by that of the High Himalayas, the visible amplitude of the overthrust attaining some 50 km in the valley of the Arun. It includes garnet gneiss and black gneiss above which the granite lentil of the Makalu is situated, the thickness of which varies from 100 to 5000 m. According to Hagen, toward the west this granite probably passed into Mustang granite, which metamorphosed the Upper Cretaceous. According to Bordet and Latreille, this granite was probably intercalated in the midst of a continuous series—perhaps, to be sure, sided by an abnormal contact—whereas, according to Lombard, it constitutes the base of another unit, the Tibet flagstone. Be this as it may, on this granite the Mount Everest series includes dark gneisses, then mica schists, and phyllites and passes progressively into fossiliferous beds that are developed in Tibet (and so could not be studied by the recent expeditions) where Permo-Carboniferous, a classic Triassic and Jurassic, Cretaceous and Eocene are known to exist.

It is presently impossible to establish the epoch of the metamorphism that affects the base of the series of the High Himalayas or that of the Low Himalayas. It may very well have been contemporaneous with the emplacement of these enormous masses or immediately subsequent to it. If, in the overall mass, the Himalayas are formed of a piling up of very great nappes, it is to be noted that nothing indicates the existence of a root zone; on the contrary, the highest unit of this pile is the "Tibetan flagstone," which extends very far to the north and is affected only by structures of little importance.

All observers are agreed in stressing the importance of the very recent movements that produced depressions now being filled (such as the plain of Katmandu) or the importance of the cutting off of inclined terraces. But the erosion of the valley of the Arun cuts through nearly 15,000 m of gneiss, which should have taken considerable time. Great overthrusts of Alpine age have been described in Timor by Brouwer.

Movements of Paleozoic age have also furnished examples of overthrusts. One of the best known, owing to mining operations, is in the Franco-Belgian Carboniferous basin—a complex of structures that may be grouped under the

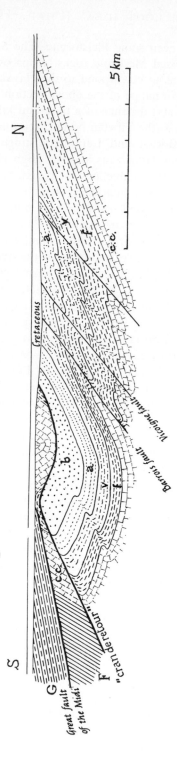

FIGURE 176. Section of the Nord Carboniferous basin at Crespin. [After Bourroz, Ann. Soc. Géol. Nord, t. LXX, 1950, pl. G.] G: Gedinnian; F: Famenian; cc: Carboniferous limestone; f, v, a, b: Westphalian (divisions of Flines, Vicoigne, Anzin, and Bruay). Note the overthrust of the Westphalian syncline by the great Midi fault. There exists locally a scale of overturned and folded strata, limited by the "cran de retour."

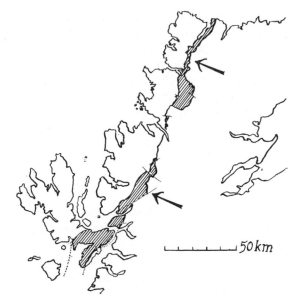

FIGURE 177

Map of northwestern Scotland, indicating the outcrop of the "Moine thrust" (the shadings indicate the crush zones).

50 km

designation of "midi fault" (Fig. 176). On the productive Carboniferous syncline, which is affected by a certain number of folds and is extensively overturned on its southern limb, an assemblage containing the Silurian and marine Devonian that constitute in short the border of the Ardenne Massif comes to rest on a surface of slightly inclined abnormal contact. There is no indication as to how far this surface of abnormal contact may be prolonged; it might possibly be the outcrop of a fracture affecting the mass of the earth's crust. In any event, there is nothing to suggest that this structure is limited to a cover presenting any independence in relation to a basement.

This structure may be compared to the "Moine thrust," an overthrust that causes a complex of Precambrian gneiss (Figs. 177 and 178) to rest on the

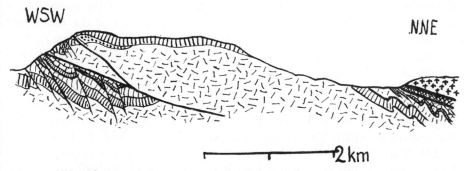

WSW   NNE

2 km

FIGURE 178. *Characteristic section of the "Moine thrust." The Cambrian (cross-hatched) in a series of slices is pinched between the Torridonian (Precambrian) on which it rests, and the overriding Precambrian "Moine schists" (crosses).*

Precambrian and Cambrian basement that constitutes the northwest coast of Scotland; the surface, or rather the zone of abnormal contact, crops out for a distance of 200 km, the visible amplitude of the movement approaching 20 km. Under the principal overthrust surface (Moine thrust), which plunges slightly toward the east-southeast, a multitude of secondary surfaces and, in places, some folds affect both the Precambrian gneisses and schists and the Cambrian; the latter is sometimes divided into multiple, imbricated slices. The movement is of late Caledonian age, and it seems here, too, mark the outcrop of a major fracture of the earth's crust.[11]

The structure described by B. Gèze[12] on the south slope of the Montagne Noire is of a very different type and, up to now, is unique in the whole of the Hercynian mountain chains. To the north of the metamorphic axis and in the western part of the south slope, the Paleozoic terranes outline a series of more or less broken folds that are tilted toward the south in the north and toward the north in the south for a distance of some 70 km and a width of nearly 15 km, whereas the local folds, which are quite numerous and well marked, affect overturned series, as established by the study of the perisynclinal and perianticlinal termini (Fig. 179). Moreover, an intermediate synclinal fold has led to the division of these overturned terrains into two units: (1) the Pardailhan nappe, which includes beds from the base of the Cambrian to the Ordovician, and (2) the Faugères nappe, which includes strata from the Ordovician to the Dinantian.

Moreover, at its eastern end, the Dinantian of the Faugères nappe is overlain, around Cabrières, by a series of Devonian slices, some normal, the others overturned, the superposition taking place along a surface of discontinuity, often producing a basal planing. So the style of these scales is fundamentally different from that of the Pardailhan and Faugères nappes, characterized by the existence of an overturned series, not stretched.

Gèze considers these nappes as having come from the south, the root zone having been hidden by the transgression of the Mesozoic and Tertiary, and the normal flanks having been eroded. As for the fronts of the nappes, they have been eliminated by erosion subsequent to the action of the faults that ascended the axial zone; the principal argument in favor of southern roots is the behavior of the Silurian-Devonian synclinal fold that separates the two nappes and which opens toward the north at Berlou.

Harrison[13] compared the overturned series of the Pardailhan and Faugères nappes with certain anticlines that he had observed in Persia; he thought they might come from the axial zone from which they were probably detached at the time of its uplift. Taking up Harrison's brief suggestion, L. U. de Sitter and R. Trümpy, using the observations of Gèze as a basis, have proposed an entirely different interpretation,[14] namely, that the nappes probably came from the north and originally constituted the cover of the axial zone. The nappes, then, were probably moved into place by mechanical flow, to be compared with gliding tectonics; this would explain the development of the exceptionally well-preserved overturned limbs. The two nappes, which comprise different

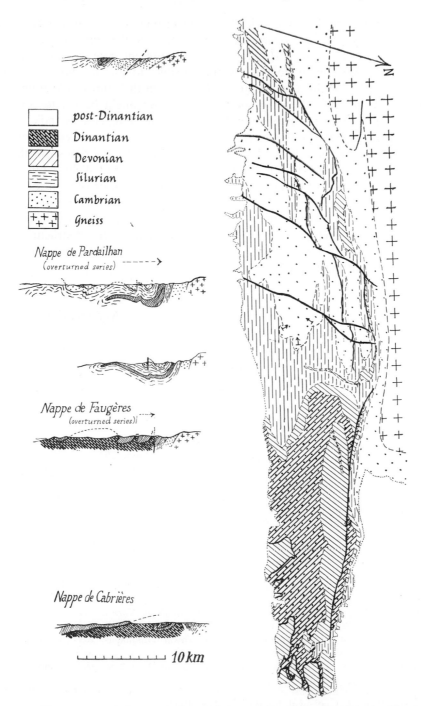

post-Dinantian
Dinantian
Devonian
Silurian
Cambrian
Gneiss

Nappe de Pardailhan
(overturned series)

Nappe de Faugères
(overturned series)

Nappe de Cabrières

10 km

FIGURE 179. *Nappes of the south slope of the Montagne Noire (Gèze). The folds and faults indicated on the geologic map affect an overturned mass, constituted by the overturned limbs of large nappes.*

members of the stratigraphic series, could correspond to the cover of the same zone, twice detached and overturned, somewhat like the "diverticulations" of M. Lugeon (p. 172, Fig. 131). In view of the present state of knowledge regarding this question, it does not seem possible, to me, to choose between these two interpretations, which are both based on the same observations.

Following the hypothesis of southern roots, we might be led to consider the flexible style of the nappes of Pardailhan and Faugères as indicating a deformation that had probably been produced at great depth, corresponding to the existence of normal limbs. On the contrary, the Cabrières overthrusts were probably produced later, after notable erosion and at slight depth.

The lacunas that we observe, caused either by erosion or subsequent transgressions, prevent us from formally establishing the exact nature of the tectonic deformations; we are thus compelled to introduce other arguments and to seek the laws that govern the grouping of different sorts of structures and their relations with other geologic phenomena. The study of these laws will be the object of the following chapters.

Notes and References

1. Lory, Ch., *Description géologique du Dauphiné,* Grenoble, 1860–1864.

2. Boussac, Jean, *Etudes stratigraphiques sur le Nummulitique Alpin,* Mém. Carte géol. France, Paris, 1912.

3. Goguel, Jean, *Le passage de la nappe de Morcles aux plis subalpins,* Bull. Soc. géol. France, 6ᵉ ser, vol. 1, pp. 439–451, 1951.

———, *La zone radicale de la nappe de Morcles,* Bull. Carte géol. France, vol. 52, No. 241, 1954. Comptes-rendus des Collaborateurs pour 1953.

4. Schneegans, D., *La géologie des nappes de l'Ubaye-Embrunais entre la Durance et l'Ubaye,* Mém. Carte géol. France (and thesis), 339 pp., Paris, 1938.

5. Barbier, R., *Les zones ultra-dauphinoises et sub-briançonnaises entre l'Arc et l'Isère,* Mém. Carte géol. France, Paris, 1948.

6. Termier, Pierre, *Les montagnes entre Briançon et Vallouise,* ibid., Mém. Carte géol. France, 182 pp., Paris, 1903.

Goguel, J., Acad. Sci. Paris, Comptes-rendus, vol. 209, pp. 632, 693, 765, and 836, 1939.

———, *Tectonique de la chaîne de Montbrison (feuille de Briançon au 1/50,000),* Comptes-rendus des Collaborateurs pour 1939, Bull. Carte géol. France, vol. 42, no. 203, pp. 187–201, Paris, 1940.

7. Goguel, J., *La racine de la nappe de Guil et l'éventail briançonnais,* Bull. Soc. géol. France, 5ᵉ ser., vol. 20, pp. 289–296, 1950.

8. Ellenberger, F., *Le Crétacé supérior briançonnais au Nord de l'Arc et la nappe des Schistes Lustrés,* ibid., Comptes-rendus, pp. 10–12, Jan. 22, 1951.

9. Auden, J. B., The Structure of the Garhwal Himalayas, Records Geol. Surv. India, vol. 71, pp. 407–433, plate 37, 1937.

10. Lombard, A., *La tectonique du Népal oriental,* Bull. Soc. géol. France, 6ᵉ ser., vol. 3, pp. 321–327, 1953.

———, *Presentation d'un profil géologique du Mont Everest a la Plaine du Gange,* Bull. Soc. Belge de Geol., vol. 62, pp. 123–129, 1953.

Bordet, P., and Latreille, M., *La géologie de l'Himalaya de l'Arun,* Bull. Soc. géol. France, 6ᵉ ser., vol. 5, pp. 529–542, 1955.

Hagen, T., *Uber die räumliche Vertilung der Intrusionen im Nepal-Himalaya,* Schweiz. Miner.- u. Petrogr. Mitt., vol. 34, pp. 300–308, 1954.

11. In a study that is important from the point of view of the history of experiments on scale models, H. M. Cadell (*Experimental Researches in Mountain Building,* Trans. Roy. Soc. Edinburgh, vol. 35, p. 337, 1890) has tried to show that the flat faults of the Moine thrust group could be the superficial manifestation of a fold of flexible behavior. In depth, such a fold constitutes, according to the author, the normal modality of deformations of the earth's crust. We have seen that, on the contrary, folding is characteristic of stratified rocks; a fold of the amplitude that this hypothesis would assume will, however, be hard to conceive from the point of view of isostatic equilibrium. We cite this hypothesis, which is now abandoned, for historical purposes only.

12. Gèze, B., *Etude géologique de la Montagne Noire et des Cévennes méridionales,* Mém. Soc. géol. France, new ser., vol. 29, Mém. No. 62, fasc. 1–3, 215 pp., Paris, 1949.

13. Harrison, J. V., Comptes-rendus, Soc. géol. France, p. 370, 1950.

14. Gèze, B., de Sitter, L. U., and Trümpy, R., *Sur le sens de déversement des nappes de la Montagne Noire,* Bull. Soc. géol. France, 6ᵉ ser., vol. 2, pp. 491–535, 1952.

CHAPTER SIXTEEN

General Tectonics. Isostasy

Relation between deformation and relief—Overall conception of an orogenic structure; geophysical data—Gravimetry, principle of isostasy; reestablishment of equilibrium in Scandinavia; hypotheses used by geodesists (Pratt, Airy, Vening Meinesz); hypothesis of inverse roots; their geologic applications—Usefulness in prospecting—Condition of equilibrium furnished by isostasy—Interpretation of residual anomalies.

WE HAVE just shown how to recognize, by as detailed observation as possible, the deformations that we propose to study. By comparing such observations, we should obtain an overall view of tectonics and of its connection with the constitution of the earth's crust and with other phenomena, such as volcanism. And finally we may hope to form an idea about the origin of the deformations, something which up to now has escaped us.

Moreover, attempts to compare such results have not been delayed until detailed tectonic studies were available. Very often the attempts at synthesis have preceded any detailed study, either because the mountainous relief was considered as a sufficient proof of recent movements or because some isolated stratigraphic observations provide some indication of the age of the movements but no complete elucidation of the geometry of the deformations. As the indication of the age and nature of the movements became clearer, successive syntheses were built up, often on the ruins of the preceding ones. Since Eduard Suess dared, for the first time, to consider the face of the earth as a whole, our information on regions then little known has increased, but no one has risked modernizing his work; the boldest have limited themselves to the study of whole continents, as did Argand in his famous *Tectonique de l'Asie.*

We are not going to undertake such a synthesis here; besides, the necessary elements would be lacking in large part if we attempted to distinguish in a precise manner the different movements according to their age in order to set up a correlation table of the truly simultaneous deformations.

We shall limit ourselves here to presenting the results of regional studies concerned with the relations between the different types of tectonic deformations that are associated in an orogenic structure and between the latter and the characteristics of sedimentation, of metamorphism, the localization of granites and mineralization, volcanoes, foci of earthquakes, and so forth.

The concept to be formed finally of an orogenic structure should of course be integrated within a hypothesis on the structure of the earth, which should furnish us an explanation regarding the genesis of the deformations. But such hypotheses are still weak and under discussion, and we shall attempt to present the results acquired in any case without depending too much on any arbitrary element that may be included in the proposed hypotheses.

It is quite evident that such hypotheses should not only take geologic observations into account but should also consider all geophysical data. Of these data, the most accurate are those that concern isostasy. Since these data very often enter into the considerations of regional geology, we shall briefly point out what we can and what we cannot expect from isostasy.

According to Newton's law, the force exerted upon a body at the surface of the earth (that is, its weight) is the resultant of the attractions that it is subjected to by all parts of the earth and of centrifugal force. If masses are equal, nearby material plays a more important role than that more distant; if we compaare the intensity of gravity and the direction of the vertical at two neighboring points, the difference is due in great part to the action of the nearest material, the action of all that is more distant being essentially uniform. Thus, we may hope to obtain some indication of the distribution of masses beneath the surface of the earth.

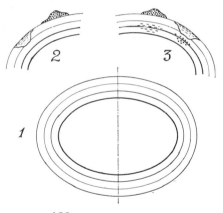

FIGURE 180

Diagram of successive approximations in the interpretation of the field of gravity of the earth: (1) distribution of masses for a fluid mass in rotation, showing concentric layers; (2) relief simply superposed on such a distribution; (3) the relief is compensated by deviations of density in depth.

Moreover, it has been shown that even a complete knowledge of the field of gravity would not enable us to make a complete determination of the distribution of masses in depth, but would furnish only certain indications.

If we take into consideration the centrifugal force due to diurnal rotation, the field of gravity around the earth is very close to that which would be produced by a fluid mass in equilibrium formed of layers whose densities would gradually decrease from the center to the surface. In such a mass, the forces

are reduced at every point to a hydrostatic pressure that does not tend to produce any deformation. Of course the field of gravity would be exactly the same
for a solid globe with the same distribution of densities; the forces might still
be hydrostatic at every point, but residual tensions might also exist within the
solid (Fig. 180).

In order to take account of relief (including relief in ocean depths), it is
possible to calculate separately the effect of each of its parts and to readily
determine the deviation from the vertical and the intensity of gravity at a
given point. Starting with the globe formed of homogeneous concentric layers
that we considered as a first approximation, if we imagine that the mountains
are placed on its surface and that the oceans are hollowed out of the latter the
values thus calculated are much farther removed from those that are actually
measured than if no account had been taken of the relief. Since the effect of
relief cannot be doubted, it must be compensated for; the compensating masses
that the mathematician has been led to consider have no autonomous existence; physically, they correspond to variations of density, which therefore is
not constant at a given depth as it would be in a fluid globe in equilibrium.
The density is greater than normal beneath an ocean and is less under elevated
regions. By performing detailed calculations for a series of hypotheses we
realize that these compensating variations of density must lie at depths of less
than 100 km.

The mere consideration of the field of gravity could not enable us to state
precisely this distribution of densities. Airy introduced the working hypothesis of isostasy, which consists of setting up as a postulate what appears as an
approximate consequence of the compensation of densities; on a surface of
constant depth, greater than those at which the inequalities of density are situated, the pressure is the same under an ocean, a continent or a chain of mountains, exactly as the case would be in an entirely fluid globe. It may be the
same at any greater depth.

From this postulate, certain consequences immediately result. We know
that various types of transformations of the surface may greatly modify the
pressure that is exerted in depth; erosion diminishes it. We also know that
erosion has at times carried away several thousand meters of rock. Sedimentation tends to increase this pressure, and there again it may be a question of
thousands of meters of rock. The formation of an ice cap, such as those that
presently exist in Greenland and in the Antarctic, also produces an increase of
pressure.

Thus, if isostatic equilibrium, that is, equality of pressures at a given depth,
is now present, it is because it constantly tends to re-establish itself. To do that,
as soon as the pressures cease to be equal, the material deforms in depth; it
is naturally driven from the points where the pressure is strongest toward those
where the pressure is weakest at equal depth. Such a deformation is of exactly the same type as that of a liquid on which a series of less dense bodies
might float, and which might eventually be able to support overloads. We

should not be too quick to conclude from this that the earth's matter is actually liquid; on the contrary, the propagation of seismic waves shows that it behaves as a solid up to 3000 km in depth. But the forces to which the matter reacts as a solid are exerted only during periods of about one second (or a day for the tides). This is not incompatible with a long-term deformation under the action of forces acting permanently. We may gather an idea of the speed at which this deformation is produced from the example of Scandinavia, which has tended to rise since the melting of the Quaternary ice. Certain deposits in this ice contain periodical beds or varves, which suggests that they may have been formed about 12,000 years ago; isostatic equilibrium must have been established, at least partially, during glaciation, and had probably been expressed by a regional subsidence. Today it tends to re-establish itself, but so slowly that after 10,000 years a quarter of the readjustment still remains to be made. The bottom of the Gulf of Bothnia is being uplifted at the rate of 1 m per century; an uplift of from 50 to 60 m would still be needed to bring about isostatic equilibrium. In 10,000 years the displacement has been around 200 m. On the shores of the Baltic it has uplifted old beaches whose ages are indicated by the mollusk faunas, which have changed every time the opening or closing of the Danish straits has transformed the Baltic into a sea or a lake. The molluscs are found in this order: *Yoldia* (sea), *Ancylus* (lake), *Littorina* (sea), then *Limnaea* (brackish-water fauna), and finally *Mya arenaria* (marine). Such a slow readjustment seems to indicate a very high viscosity of the deep matter in harmony with its behavior under influences of slight duration. But on the scale of geologic time, this readjustment seems very rapid. As a first approximation, in the study of the transformations of the earth's crust, there are grounds for considering that isostatic equilibrium is achieved at every moment.

The foregoing qualitative indications have been made definite by a certain number of hypotheses, incompatible however, that have a quantitative character. In order to properly understand their significance, we must remember the purpose of the geodesists who proposed them. Their final objective is to determine the form of the geoid (surface of mean sea level). A relation exists between this geoid form and the intensity of gravity at every point on its surface, which makes it possible, at least theoretically, to calculate it. Before making this rather laborious calculation, it is convenient to imagine that we are displacing certain masses; each one of these fictitious displacements simultaneously modifies the form of the geoid and the intensity of gravity, but by amounts that are relatively easy to calculate. So we substitute for the true geoid a corrected, fictitious geoid, or cogeoid differing by known quantities, a surface to which it is possible to relate the measurements of the intensity of gravity. The form of the cogeoid is all that remains to be calculated. The form of the cogeoid is easier to calculate than that of a true geoid because it is possible to arrange it so that all the masses are interior to its surface and so that it is less irregular. One method consists of eliminating the topography and the masses that compensate it. To do this, we mentally divide the relief into a series of vertical prisms bounded by radial planes and concentric cylinders. We then calculate the effect of each of these prisms and of the compensation corresponding to the point where the measurement was made. These calculations, which are very long, are made possible with the aid of tables. If the hypothesis used corresponded to reality, the corrected values of gravity would be the same as on a globe formed of homogeneous concentric layers. At least an effort is made to choose a hypothesis such that the deviations (anomalies) on the whole may be as small as possible.

Since the calculations must not introduce errors approaching the magnitude of the errors of measurement, the geodesists are obliged to define very precisely the arrangement they use to represent the distribution of masses by which the compensation is made. Geologists must not let themselves be deceived by this apparent precision.

We shall rapidly review a series of these hypotheses. In Helmert's hypothesis, the compensating masses (which are added algebraically to the masses of homogeneous concentric layers) are assumed to be concentrated at a constant depth (20 km for instance). Pratt and Hayford assume, in their hypothesis, that the compensating masses are distributed uniformly between what is called the "depth of compensation" (for example, 113 km) and the surface. Evidently these are calculation devices that cannot claim to represent reality.

Other arrangements are based on more or less probable hypotheses for the constitution of the earth's crust. According to Airy's hypothesis, two media of different densities are separated by a surface situated at a depth such that in each elementary prism the mass per unit of section above a fixed depth is the same. The light upper medium is then thinner beneath the oceans, thicker under the mountains ("roots" of the mountain chains). This arrangement was suggested so as to identify the upper light medium with the sial (silico-aluminous rocks) and the deep heavy medium with the sima (ferromagnesian rocks). In terms of this hypothesis, each elementary prism is in isostatic equilibrium; the compensation is local.

The hypothesis of Vening Meinesz takes into account the mechanical bounds that should exist between the neighboring parts of the earth's crust. The relationship is satisfied by the analogy with an elastic plaque floating on a liquid, which under definite load sinks over a certain area defined by the "radius of regionality."

To each superficial mass, positive or negative, there correspond compensating masses that are spread over a larger area and whose depths are chosen once and for all according to the variant used. It is also possible to consider other hypotheses. Although it has not actually been used in the calculation of isostatic corrections, since the necessary tables have not been set up, let us cite R. A. Daly's hypothesis[1] of the anti-roots (French, *racines inverses*). Above the deep magma, the earth's crust is assumed to be formed of two layers, one lighter and the other heavier, representing respectively a granitic layer (sial) and a crystallized basic layer (sima), the magma corresponding to the molten sima. We have thus two parameters; the indetermination that results may be removed by defining the temperature of the earth's crust as a function of the geothermal gradient; use has been made of the mean content of radioactive elements, which are generators of heat, in basic and acid rocks. This hypothesis has been studied only in the case of a local compensation, but it might be combined with a certain degree of regionality.

Whichever hypothesis is chosen, it must be made precise by choosing the values of the parameters upon which it depends: thickness of the earth's crust for zero altitude, density differences, degree of regionality, and so forth. The only means of making this choice consists of making the calculations for a series of values of the parameters and calculating the mean (or the quadratic mean) of the remaining anomalies, that is, of the differences between the corrected values and those calculated for the theoretic globe in the given arrangement. It is also possible to choose the value of the parameter such that there is no correlation between the station altitude and the value of the anomaly (Heiskanen). Experience has shown that by either of these methods we obtain a rather rough determination of the first parameter, but that it is very difficult to obtain a second parameter, the minimum of the mean of the anomalies not being sufficiently marked. For the same reason, no significant differences are found between the minima of the anomalies corresponding to the different hypotheses; thus, it is not possible to choose between them in a clear-cut manner. For this reason, gravimetry offers nothing regarding the general structure of the earth's crust. On the other hand, it can provide very useful clues concerning particular structures (see Chap. 7 and Chap. 19). Within the framework of a given hypothesis, it may simply specify the value of one of the parameters upon which it depends. This parameter often expresses a thickness of the earth's crust, but we must never lose sight of the fact that it is a question of a fictitious thickness corresponding to a given hypothesis. It is possible to show that the same observations may lead to the adoption of a "thickness of the earth's crust" approximately one half less with Airy's hypothesis than with Pratt's, and possibly only a third or a quarter if the Vening Meinesz hypothesis is used. However, we are going to indicate some applications of the different diagrammatic hypotheses that may be of some aid in understanding how certain geologic phenomena[2] appear to the eyes of the geophysicist.

Let us suppose that the structure of the earth conforms to the Airy hypothesis, and let us consider a basin in which sediments are accumulating for which we assume a density equal to 2, for purposes of discussion (Fig. 181). If we assume, as is usually done, that the density of the deep magma is 3.4, calculation shows that re-establishment of the equilibrium requires a displacement downward of 2/3,4, or about six-tenths of the thickness of the deposits formed; their apparent thickness will be only four-tenths of their real thickness.

If we assumed the basin to be completely submerged, we would find a subsidence of only 42 percent of the thickness of the deposits, the depth of the basin diminishing by 58 percent of this real thickness. We see that it would be going much too far to say, as is sometimes done, that isostasy explains subsidence, that is, a sinking that permits the accumulation of a great thickness of sediments deposited at shallow depths (for example, 2500 to 4000 m of Carboniferous deposited near the level of the sea in the Franco-Belgian basin). The subsidence must have been brought about by an active cause. The conclusion would be even clearer if we took into consideration the mutual influences between contiguous compartments as expressed by the regionality in the Vening Meinesz sense.

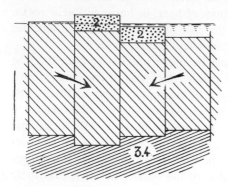

FIGURE 181

Effect of an accumulation of sediments. Left. On a continent (the arrow indicates the sense of the evolution); Right. In an ocean, in accordance with Airy's hypothesis. The sinking is only a fraction of the thickness of the sediments.

In order to interpret the regional anomalies, to which we shall have occasion to return (Chap. 19), this author formulated a hypothesis designed to represent the main lines of an orogenic deformation that would correspond to a buckling of the elastic earth's crust under the action of lateral compression while sinking into the magma upon which it floats (Fig. 182). This buckling was probably maintained in depth in spite of the hydrostatic thrust that it underwent from the denser magma, owing to the mechanical solidarity between adjacent compartments of the earth's crust, which is expressed by the regional character of the compensation. This quite suggestive hypothesis has been somewhat modified and has been taken up again under various forms by a certain number of writers who, more recently, have attempted to specify the details of the formation of mountain chains.

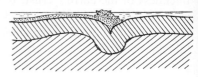

FIGURE 182

Hypothesis of buckling of the earth's crust. [After Vening Meinesz.] The figure indicates the possible behavior of a sedimentary cover, crushed by buckling.

The principle argument that seems to have urged R. A. Daly to formulate the hypothesis of anti-roots is the possibility of explaining a vertical movement in the absence of any superficial change as being due to a decrease or an increase in temperature that would result in the crystallization or the fusion of a certain thickness of the sima, which would in turn produce subsidence or uplift of the surface respectively.

It is generally thought that the formation of a mountain chain is the result of a thickening of the sial by lateral compression; however, only a part of the thickening corresponds to an uplifting of the surface, the other constituting a "root." Daly remarks that if the deformed mass has conserved its temperature it should heat up again in order to re-establish the geothermic temperature corresponding to thermal equilibrium. From this reheating (which should be slow), an ascensional movement will probably produce a considerable elevation of the old erosion surfaces, as is to be noted in the Alps.

These few examples show the sort of suggestion that may be expected from the hypotheses considered by geophysicists. But from the gravimetric point of view, none of these hypotheses can be imposed. We might conceive of a multitude of others, combining the foregoing, or introducing still other factors. The utilization that is made of them in geodetic calculations requires that each of these hypotheses define completely the distribution of densities in depth as a function of the surface relief, but it is not necessary that this distribution conform to reality. Thus, geophysicists cannot make allowance for the differences of geologic structure or for the infinitely variable nature of structural complications. The actual distribution of densities is certainly much more complex and irregular.

For the geologist or the prospector who is trying to establish these structural complications on the basis of gravity anomalies, the calculation of isostatic corrections often provides a convenient approximation of the regional anomaly; in this way, we assign a value, accepted in a more or less conventional manner, that is supposed to represent the variations of attraction by all the deep or distant zones. This regional anomaly can show only slow variations of a relatively regular nature. If we subtract it from measured values, we obtain a residual anomaly, which is generally small in magnitude, but of rapid variation, which should result from the action of shallow geologic complications, about which it may furnish interesting indications (see Chap. 7, p. 93).

Let us keep in mind, too, that whatever hypothesis we may propose to explain the structure of the earth's crust, the parameters upon which it depends should take account of measurements of gravity. This condition imposes upon us, in particular, a maximum thickness of the crust, which could not in any case surpass 100 km and which would generally be less than 50 km. At a lesser depth than this, the material yields in the long run, and hydrostatic equilibrium is set up. This is what is expressed by the term "asthenosphere," defined by Barrel.

But the essential result of studies relative to isostasy is that they have made it possible to state a law, at least an approximate one, which subsequent measurements seem to verify in the great majority of cases and which defines the level at which any division of the earth's crust will become established relative to sea level. Whatever transformations the earth's crust may have undergone, isostasy determines (as a function of composition) the height above sea level, approximately for a block 20 km square, very exactly for a block 100 km square. Their positions are probably the same as if they were floating on a dense, deep magma behaving in the long run like a liquid, in which the pressure has the same value everywhere at the same depth. This equilibrium, which is established in about a few tens of thousands of years, may be considered as almost instantaneous on the scale of geologic transformations.

When measurements bring to light an extensive isostatic anomaly, several interpretations are possible. It may be a question of a zone in the process of resuming an equilibrium that had been disturbed, as is the case with regions covered in the Quaternary by large glaciers. It may also happen that isostatic equilibrium is in fact established, but according to modalities very different from the hypotheses used for the calculation. But if an anomaly of constant sign occupies a large area in all directions, it must be assumed that it actually indicates a digression from isostatic equilibrium. Even at depths far greater than the accepted thickness of the earth's crust, nonhydrostatic forces must exist; thus, we cannot affirm that the densities are uniform at a given depth. The question of knowing what relation may exist between zones of isostatic disequilibrium and zones of tectonic processes presently active remains an open one.

These disequilibriums are, however, of relatively little importance, as is indicated by the size of the anomalies; the latter rarely attain 100 milligals. In certain zones, a few anomalies surpass 200 milligals. A horizontal layer 10 m thick, of density 2.38, produces an attraction of 1 milligal. So the greatest anomalies correspond to a deviation of 1000 or 2000 m from the height corresponding to equilibrium.

Aside from these exceptional cases, it is isostasy and isostasy alone that determines the height at which a division of the earth's crust of determined structure establishes itself in relation to sea level. If this division rises or sinks, its vertical movement necessarily expresses a change of structure which modifies the conditions under which isostasy applies. But isostasy teaches us nothing regarding the nature of this structure, concerning which there is no reason for thinking that it is in conformity with any of the arrangements used by the geodesists.

A fortiori, isostasy furnishes us no indication of the nature of the changes in depth responsible for variations in height that we often observe in the absence of any superficial change capable of explaining them.[3] Isostasy is a state of equilibrium that is valid during periods of calm and, to a certain extent, during the course of crises that disturb the earth's crust. We must always keep in mind the indications that it furnishes us when we are attempting to reconstruct tectonic phenomena. But we must not expect too much from it; that is, we cannot expect to obtain either precise information on the structure of the earth's crust or the explanation for transformations of the crust,

Notes and References

1. Goguel, J., *Réflections sur l'isostasie. L'hypothèse des racines inverses,* Annales de Géophys., vol 3, fasc. 3, pp. 229–248, 1947.

2. Regarding the importance of isostasy from a geological point of view, see: Daly, R. A., *Strength and Structure of the Earth,* New York (Prentice-Hall), 1940.

3. Certain objections formulated especially in America are directed not at all at its principle, such as it has just been stated, but at the considerations by which Bowie thought he could explain tectonic deformations on the basis of isostasy (see reference 27 in Chapter 22).

CHAPTER SEVENTEEN

Overall Considerations on Orogenic Deformations Echeloning In Time and Distribution in Space

Inaccuracy of the determination of the age of a movement—Historical; notion of discontinuous tectonic phases—Critique of this concept; continuity of the tectonic deformation—Information furnished by stratigraphy on the preliminary phases of deformation—Definition of tectonic units by their stratigraphic characters; limitations of this method—Notion of geosyncline; impossibility of accurate statement of content of this concept—Relation between nature of deposits and depth—Contemporaneous deformations, furrows and cordilleras—Flysch and molasse—Speed and duration of movements; their order of succession—Rapid and spasmodic action of faults—Distribution of deformations in the Alpine mountain chain; deformation of the basement—Tectonics of the basement in the Pyrenees—Absence of tectonics of autonomous cover in Hercynian orogenesis—Evolution or permanence of the conditions of tectonic deformation?

WE HAVE seen in Chapter 3 how it is possible, through relation to the chronological scale furnished by paleontologic stratigraphy, to determine the epoch in which a given deformation took place. The observation of a discordance, even one beyond discussion, always leaves a certain indetermination corresponding to the interval of time that passed between the deposition of the most recent of the preserved beds older than the movement and that of the first transgressive bed. Analysis of the sedimentary series deposited in the vicinity of the structural complications often permits a much finer chronological determination, but some doubt always exists concerning the exact nature of the movements that provoked any given discharge of conglomerates into a sedimentary basin.

In one way or another, the exact determination of the age of a movement is, in general, possible only in a few privileged places, which are often very far removed from one another. In between, for lack of transgressive terranes of suitable age, the age of movements can be determined in only a very inaccurate manner (for example, post-Cretaceous, pre-Miocene). So, wherever precise determinations are possible, a record is often made, at a given point, of the repetition of successive movements whose effects are very difficult to distinguish wherever conditions do not lend themselves to an exact chronology of the movements. We can only try to extend the distinction of the successive phases, established wherever possible, by basing our findings on the continuity of the structures, their differences of style, and their direction.

At first sight, this last criterion seems to be very convenient to use. But we know of numerous examples of exactly contemporaneous folds whose arrangement is quite complex and, in particular, presents varied directions, with the result that their directions cannot be reliably used to distinguish successive phases of deformation; in fact, such utilization has involved numerous grave errors. From the point of view of the general history of the earth, it is very important to investigate how the periods of deformation that have engendered successive mountain chains are spaced.

Elie de Beaumont[1] was the first to show clearly that the "tilting of beds took place in various mountain systems at very different epochs," and he sought to fix these epochs. The stratigraphic scale then in use was based on the idea of sudden changes of the fauna which led him to place the "revolutions" responsible for the "mountain systems" at the boundaries between the stratigraphic "divisions." Through his study of discordances, Elie de Beaumont had recognized four systems at the time of the presentation of his memoir, but this number had risen to 9 at the time of printing and was to rise progressively to 12, 17, 21, 32 and 95. Moreover, Elie de Beaumont did not believe that this series "has ended and that the mineral crust of the terrestrial globe has lost the property of wrinkling successively in different directions."

Unfortunately, the direction of successive wrinkles was later to occupy him more than the exact determination of their ages. We are familiar with the extremes to which he was led in his consideration of the "pentagonal network," according to which these directions were supposed to be arranged. But the idea of "revolutions" located at the boundaries between the stratigraphic stages seems to have persisted more or less unconsciously in the mind of many a geologist.

Rollin T. Chamberlin[2] expresses this point of view very well: "The current divisions into periods which represent the general judgment of geologists as to what are natural divisions, and which are based on various considerations, largely stratigraphic and paleontologic, are in fair accord with the divisions that would be made if diastrophism were chosen as the primary basis of division." When the doctrine of successive creations was rejected by paleontologists and it became evident that the evolution of the living world was a continuous process, migrations or invasions of a fauna only being able to give locally an impression of sudden change, stratigraphers flattered themselves in thinking that they could find in orogenic deformations a justification for divisions between the periods or eras into which the continuity of geologic time had been conventionally divided. From all the evidence that was a *petitio principio,* a fallacy; we have no right to assume, *a priori,* that movements are simultaneous in distant regions. Tectonic movements may have established maritime or continental connections and thus made possible migrations of a fauna, but we cannot see what direct influence they could have had on evolution.

Be that as it may, numerous studies have been devoted to a census of tectonic movements in all parts of the world. Following the example of Elie de Beaumont, various authors have striven, in general, to synchronize the movements observed in different regions and to give names to the phases thus identified, whose individuality is thus affirmed.

As documentary evidence, there have been assembled, in the accompanying table, the "tectonic phases" accepted in the most recent studies, principally those of Stille,[3] modified on certain points by Kober.[4] We are adding the list of Precambrian movements given by Holmes.[5] It should be noted, however, that Stille, in a more recent study,[6] seems to have abandoned naming all tectonic phases. He now seems to be satisfied with indicating them on a chronological graph, which may suggest that some doubt exists as to their actual individuality.

Correlation Between the Tectonic Phases, Principally Precambrian (Ages in Millions of Years).
[After A. Holmes.]

America		Europe	
Circumpacific	1–70	Alpine	20–70
Recent Appalachian	200–230	Hercynian	200–250
Old Appalachian	350	Caledonian	300–320
Lake Superior	550	Charnian	600
Killarnian (Lake Superior)	750	Carelian	850
Laurentian	1050	Svécofénnien	1050
Great Bear Lake, Black Hills, South Dakota	1350	(Western Australia)	1250
Old Black Hills	1600	White Sea	1600
Manitoba	1750		

This table is an attempt at correlation of the major phases of Precambrian history. However, it is rendered somewhat unreliable by the inaccuracy that still exists in many age determinations based on radioactivity. It is by no means as detailed as are Stille's analyses. It seems questionable whether the introduction of the special names given in this table, which will be added to the already weighty list of stratigraphic nomenclature, is really justified.[7]

	Tectonic Phases		Stratigraphic Age		Observations
			Prior to:	Posterior to:	
New Alpine	Vailac (Pasadenian)		Quarternary	Upper Pliocene	
	Rhodanian		Plaisancian	Pontian	
	Attic		Pontian	Sarmatian	
	Styric { new		Tortonian	Helvetian	
	{ old		Helvetian	Burdigalian	
Middle Alpine	Savic		Aquitanian	Upper Oligocene	
	Helvetic		Middle Oligocene	Lower Oligocene	Kober, 1933. Not accepted by
	Pyrenean		Ludian	Eocene (sic)	Stille, 1924. In fact, post-Bartonian
Old Alpine	Laramian		Paleocene	Senonian	
	Sub-Hercynian		Senonian	Turonian	
	Austrian		Cenomanian	Lower Cretaceous	
	New Cimmerian		Tithonian	Upper Jurassic	
	subdi- { Hils		Upper Valanginian	Wealdian	Subdivided in Germany by
	vided { Osterwald		Upper Portlandian	Purbeckian	Dahlgrün 1921; Stille, 1940.
	into { Deister		Portlandian	Kimmeridgian	
	Agassizian		Malm	Callovian	The pre-Callovian phase of the
	Old Cimmerian		Rhetian	Triassic	northern slope of the Caucasus is not mentioned.
?	Labinian		Carnian	Ladinian	Name proposed by Stille in a letter to Kobayashi (Jour. Fac.
New Variscan	Pfalzian		Triassic	Thuringian	Sci. Tokyo, sect. 2, vol. 5, pt. 7,
	preliminary phase		Thuringian	Saxonian	May 17, 1941, p. 258). Later
	Saalian		Saxonian	Autonian	on, Kobayashi introduced quite a series of Triassic phases:
Middle Variscan	Asturian		Stephanian	Westphalian	Akiyoshi (Ladinian); Omine
	Erzgebirge phase		Moscovian	Namurian	(pre-Carnian); Momonoki (pre-Middle Carnian); Utatsu (pre-
	Sudetian		Namurian	Visean	Norian); Sakuradani (Middle
	Breto- { Selkian		Visean	Tournaisian	Norian); Toyogadake (pre-Liassic); and two "late Triassic"
	nian { Nassauan		Tournaisian	Gattendorfia zone	phases, Weiyang and Nenhsing (Geotectonics of the Japa-
	{ Marsic		Wocklumeria zone	Upper Devonian	nese Islands, vol. 2, Meguro
Old Variscan	Middle Devonian		M. to U. Devonian	Lower M. Devonian	Book Co., Tokyo, 1948).
	Lower Devonian		Upper Coblentzian	Lower Coblentzian	
New Caledonian	Irlandian		Gedinian	Lower Gedinian	
	Ardennian		Lower Devonian	Downtonian	
			Downtonian	Ludlowian	
Old Caledonian	Taconic		Llandoverian	Ordovician	
	Sardian		Silurian	Cambrian	Stille, 1935.
	Salairian		Upper Cambrian		

To appreciate the significance of identified tectonic phases, we should not lose sight of the difficulties raised by a stratigraphic parallelism at a great distance and the inaccuracy of most stage limits; if there has been a tectonic deformation, it is conventional to place the limit between the two stages, at the level of the corresponding discordance. The fact that a discordance in relation to the stratigraphic scale has been located in different regions in the same manner by no means implies a real synchronism. In fact, the number of identified phases is so great that, within a rough approximation of stratigraphic determinations, any movement whatever can almost always be placed in one of them. Many writers have striven to relate the deformations that they are studying to one of the already known phases, rather than to seek an independent age determination that might have involved a complex stratigraphic discussion.

Despite these attitudes, which may have given the mistaken impression that the principal phases occurred in quite varied regions, the study of new regions has resulted in the discovery of tectonic movements of undetermined age. The introduction of numerous phases following studies in Japan by Kobayashi is a very characteristic example of them; in the present state of research, it is not at all impossible that tectonic activity is an approximately continuous process, affecting in turn the most diverse regions of the earth. So it is important not to dismiss, *a priori,* by the language we use, a given hypothesis which might deserve being more carefully considered than it has been up to the present.

However, we should mention a suggestion made by P. Fallot.[8] According to Fallot, movements of the cover resulting essentially from gravity slips were probably produced very slowly and consequently gave the impression of multiple phases or of continuous movements, whereas movements of the basement, from which they originate, were probably produced by discontinuous movements; however, the latter point remains hypothetical.

It is certain, however, that a thorough study of a limited region does not confirm the hypothesis of discontinuous tectonic phases. The detailed analysis of deformations, which permits the study of contemporary sediments, gives rather the impression of an almost continuous deformation. This does not mean that the rate of deformation was constant; there could have been paroxysms, but a detailed analysis multiplies their number; what appeared as a first approximation to be a single phase may thus be divided into a series of jolts which doubtless represent only relative maxima between which the movements never ceased.

As emphasized by J. Gilluly,[7] apropos of the particularly typical example of Tertiary movements in California, the number of discordances varies when we pass from the axis of an anticline to the adjacent syncline, in which the sedimentation may have been continuous throughout the duration of the movements. Depending on the depth of the erosion, we could be led to different conclusions concerning the number of movements. Wegmann[7] emphasized that the appearance of discordances at a point during the course of orogenic movements depended in part on the rate of sedimentation or on the rate of erosion.

We have seen what difficulties are involved in making a direct determination of the age of a fold. For a group of parallel folds, this would usually be possible only at a few isolated points, for example at the external edge, in contact with the adjacent sedimentary basin. It is probable that these folds formed successively, beginning with the most internal, which may be considerably older than the external folds, whose age alone has been determined. The frequency with which conglomerates (which attest to the tectonic activity in a more interior zone) are tilted furnishes a direct proof of this progressive migration of the deformation. Nor can we exclude the possibility that in certain cases such deformations began at a point, to be prolonged longitudinally.

Thus, the analysis of the echelonning in time of movements that have produced an orogenic structure cannot be reduced to the identification of the phases that are represented in it. The employment of the names proposed to designate these phases should be avoided (except in a very vague and general sense), because it would imply a misleading simplification of the problem by the two notions of a rigorous synchronism between distinct regions and a discontinuity of the tectonic process. The problem should be studied independently of these unproved hypotheses. Each of its successive movements should be related to the stratigraphic scale with the greatest possible precision, without losing sight of the continuity of the tectonic phenomenon, both in time and in space.

We have seen in Chapter 3 that the study of the nature of sediments could in certain cases enable us to recognize certain movements of the bottom of the basin of sedimentation. This method has enabled us to recognize, with respect to various folded ranges, that a series of embryonic movements took place long before the intense tectonic deformations that were to occur. For this reason, it is necessary to study with great care the nature of the sediments that constitute a folded region.

But before showing how it is possible to deduce indications upon the embryonic movements and upon a phase to some extent preparatory to the tectonic deformations properly so called, we must try to indicate to what extent we can distinguish different tectonic units on the basis of the distribution of stratigraphic facies.

This classical procedure is based on the hypothesis that the constancy of stratigraphic characteristics in a given area indicates that the area reacted as a single block to the changes of depth prior to folding, which permits us to assume that the area must have behaved in the same manner when folding took place. This hypothesis may seem rather dubious, but certain favorable conditions nevertheless permit its utilization, at least as a first approximation, as a guide in disentangling a region still insufficiently explored. In the Alps, the facies seem to have varied quite rapidly along a transversal. The width of each facies zone, already slight in relation to its length, has apparently been further reduced by lateral contraction due to folding. Finally, as we saw in Chapter 3, the facies zones succeeded one another at the time of deposition in a well-determined order, which sometimes enables us to reconstruct the initial mutual positions of the units that they serve to define.

However, we must not go too far along this route, attempting to find all along a mountain chain the same zones, characterized at once by the same stratigraphic series and by tectonic dislocations of the same age and same style. It is remarkable that zones of facies are often aligned parallel to the axis of a mountain chain and thus react subsequently in a uniform manner to the tectonic deformations because an embryonic deformation, premonitory to the tectonic deformation properly so-called, has determined uniform conditions of depth. But this relation cannot be set up as a general law. Many other factors intervene at the moment of deposition in the distribution of facies zones. Quite accurate surveys have often shown that the isopic lines are in reality oblique relative to the tectonic complications.

It is quite possible that the succession of facies zones may vary considerably along the various transversals in a mountain chain such as the Alps.

The concordance between the zone characterized by a certain facies and the zone in which later structures of the same type are produced may also be due, not to the parallelism of the movements that have determined the conditions of depth favorable to the facies in question with those that produced the structures, but to the fact that the rocks, once deposited, reacted to stresses under conditions that depend on their mechanical properties and hence on their facies. This factor plays a role especially in cover tectonics, where the structures often result from remote deformations of the basement, in which case the distribution of the facies expresses the tendency toward uplift or toward sinking at the very point where deposition took place. The section of the Sub-Alpine mountain chains situated to the south of the Drôme shows a particularly clear example of such a relation. Owing to bathymetric conditions that prevailed in the Lower Cretaceous, the Urgonian facies (massive, very thick limestones) is lacking in the Vocontian Trench. This facies is replaced by somewhat marly limestones, which are bedded and not very thick. During folding of the cover in the Miocene, this region reacted quite differently than did the plateaus of Vercors and Ventoux, which were affected by some long flexures or rectilinear faults. In this region, sharp anticlines, which are quite dislocated, and which may be tilted in any direction, separate broad synclinal areas. The fact that this type of deformation is allied with the mechanical properties of a stratigraphic series deprived of the rigid Urgonian flagstone is proved by the reappearance of this same mode of deformation in a small region, the Gigondas massif, in which the Urgonian was removed by erosion in the Oligocene.[9]

Let us return to the analysis of the conditions prevailing in the zone that was to fold subsequently, as indicated by the nature of the deposits. As early as 1857, James Hall observed that in the folded Appalachian chain the various stages of the Paleozoic are at least ten times thicker than in the nonfolded Mississippi basin that succeeds it to the west.[10] For the zone of thick sedimentation, later folded, Dana created the word "geosynclinal," which was eagerly accepted. According to Hall, the exceptional thickness of the sediments was the actual cause of their later folding, through some unspecified process. However, no other writer seems to have accepted Hall's theory. Emile Haug[11] introduced the notion of the bathyal character of geosynclinal deposits and emphasized a sort of compensation between the movements of the sea (transgressions or regressions) in the geosynclines and on continental areas.

From the beginning, Hall and Dana defined geosynclines as originating on the border of a continent into which the mountain chain originating in the geosyncline was later to be incorporated. Haug, on the other hand, held the opinion that a geosyncline always lies between two continental masses.

The notion of the geosyncline, which coordinates the characteristics of sedimentation, the displacements of seas, folding, and, as we shall see later, various eruptive manifestations, appears as one of the great laws, if not *the* great law governing the evolution of the earth's crust. Unfortunately, as soon as we delve into the details of the relations among these different phenomena, they become so inexplicably vague that we wonder if it is possible at all to formulate a significant law to express the relation between the nature of deposits and later folds, which is implied in the very concept of geosynclines. Since it is impossible to condense the sought-after relation into a single formula with a single meaning, it seems we should resume the study of the problem from the beginning and analyze, without any preconceived idea, the nature of the sediments, which we might deduce from the conditions of deposition and the movements of the bottom. We could then seek the relation that should exist between the movements that may be qualified as embryonic and the later tectonic movements. Although the methods of study may often be different, there is no means of establishing a clear-cut division between embryonic movements and principal movements. So, let us examine the different kinds of phenomena that the geosynclinal concept endeavors to relate.

We might first ask whether a basin whose sediments present geosynclinal characteristics is always folded. It must be observed that if it is folded, the mere inspection of the outcrops makes it possible to indicate the great thickness of the beds. On the contrary, in a nonfolded region, the outcrops due to the hollowing out of the valleys, for example, make it possible to evaluate the thickness of the beds only where it is slight. When a great thickness of beds has accumulated, only the most recent are visible, and often there are no surface indications from which we might estimate this thickness. When measuring the thickness of beds at the edge of a basin, where erosion enables us to study them, we often arrive at a figure much too low for the thickness of the series at the center of the basin.

In fact, the study by well logs of great sedimentary basins in the search for oil has often shown the existence of a great thickness of beds, considerably thicker than it would have been possible to assume after study of the outcrops. One of the most typical regions in this regard is the coast of the Gulf of Mexico (U.S.A.), where the accumulation of sediments, uninterrupted since the Jurassic, continues very rapidly with the alluvial deposits of the Mississippi.

Though some authors employ the word "geosyncline" to designate these nonfolded basins with thick sediments there is rather a tendency to use for them the more objective term of "subsidence," [12] which simply expresses the sinking of the bottom, correlative of the accumulation of sediments without implying subsequent folding. But we must not balk at this difference of designation, which expresses no essential difference in the nature of the sediments, and we must remember that we know of numerous present-day basins in which sediments have accumulated to a great thickness, but which have not undergone folding.

In addition, tectonically deformed zones exist that do not affect an area of subsident sedimentation. One of the clearest examples is furnished by the Pyrenees, whose central part has received from the Trias to the Lower Cretaceous only a thin accumulation of sediments in which numerous lacunae exist, amounting altogether to a very long period of time. In like manner, the folds of Provence affect an area a part of which corresponds to the shallow facies of the periphery of the Maures Massif. So the bond between the subsidence zone and the deformation zone is much looser than was formerly assumed.

What is the exact significance of the accumulation of a great thickness of sediments? The few indications obtained regarding the rate of sedimentation by recent oceanographic research (the collection of samples of sediments and the determination of their age by radioactivity) show that deep deposits, organic muds, and, above all, red clay are deposited very slowly (around a tenth of a millimeter per century for red clay). On the other hand, terrigenous deposits, which in general do not attain a very great depth, may be accumulated much more rapidly as a function of the material supplied by the continents. So it is in the neighborhood of the coasts, for example at a relatively shallow depth, that we should expect to find the greatest rate of sedimentation.

Counter to the American writers, who insisted on the characteristically shallow depth of geosynclinal sediments, Suess often sustained the pelagic character of sediments in the folded regions as opposed to the gaps or brackish intercalations of tranquil regions.

Haug interpreted a great number of sediments considered as typically geosynclinal—in particular, shales, marls, and more or less compact limestones—as having been deposited between 80 and 900 m, and he created for this zone the term "bathyal," accepting an essentially terigenous sedimentation. Oceanographic research has not entirely confirmed this concept, and it is probable that in most cases the terrigenous sediments were deposited at a depth far less than 900 m. However the Snellius expedition in Indonesia pointed out terrigenous sediments at a much greater depth. Either because submarine slides had taken place, or in the absence of a littoral platform, these sediments had been deposited directly in a deep trench close to the coast. Recent research by Ewing has shown the importance of "turbidity currents" made heavy by the terrigenous materials that they hold in suspension and which, through the canyons that cut into the edge of the continental plateau, may attain great depths and fill the ocean bottoms to a uniform level; the geologic consequences of this oceanographic discovery are still far from having been exhausted.

Be that as it may, the thickness of the deposits is incompatible with the simple filling of a pre-existent depression. The bottom of the basin, and this is the essential part of the notion of subsidence, must have sunk gradually, in step with the sedimentation, such that the depth of the sea varies very little. In Chapter 16, we studied a factor often invoked to explain this sinking, that is, isostatic compensation, and we saw that it explains only a small part of the sinking, around 40 percent of the thickness of the sediments. In order for the depth to remain constant, an active phenomenon of deep origin must determine a subsidence of the bottom of the basin; this is one of the manifestations of tectonic deformations, or at least of their embryonic phase.

This active sinking movement has not necessarily been regular and continuous. In fact, we must take into account, in calculating the movement of the bottom of the basin, the progressive settling of the sediments (other than the gravels and sands), which are deposited as mud saturated with water. The water is eliminated gradually under the pressure of subsequent sediments. The slowness of the filtration of the water through masses that are not very permeable slows the settling, which is probably distributed over a very long period, and thus gives the impression of a continuous sinking movement favorable to the accumulation of an uninterrupted series of sediments. The stopping of the active sinking movement of the basin does not involve an interruption of sedimentation. Such an interruption would imply a true uplift movement of the bottom.

The mechanics of sedimentation tend to maintain constancy of depth in the zone of deposition. Owing to the turbulence of the waves, deposits have little tendency to form or maintain themselves on a shallow bottom; inversely, the subsidence of a zone in which terrigenous elements are held in suspension calls for sedimentation, since the waters beyond a certain depth are calm enough to permit the fine elements to be deposited. Thus, we believe that the depth of the sea varies relatively little in the zone of transport of terrigenous elements, even if the thicknesses of the deposited sediments vary greatly from one point to another. To appreciate the significance of the present continental platforms, it is evidently necessary to take into consideration that they were fashioned, in part, during periods of the Quaternary, when the sea was lower than today, owing to the development of glaciers.

The same regulatory action was probably in effect in the case of continental sedimentation. Depressions, whether or not they are occupied by lakes, naturally call for sedimentation, which, on the other hand, avoids high points.

It may even be asked if, essentially, continental platforms are not due to the accumulation of terrigenous sediments. The submarine geophysical studies of Ewing and his collaborators have shown that the continental shelf along the Atlantic coast of North America is formed of relatively recent sediments,

FIGURE 183

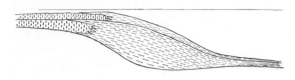

Variations of thickness of the Barremian and the Bedoulian, of the Vercors at the Vocontian Trench and their relations with the depth of the deposit.

but little consolidated, whose thickness gradually increases seaward and in whose constitution the crystalline basement does not intervene.

As M. Gignoux has shown, when we compare the thicknesses of certain Mesozoic stages of the Dauphiné, we find a distribution comparable to what present conditions of deposition suggest (Fig. 183). In the Lower Cretaceous, for example, we find the following succession: (1) a zone of calcareous formations, improperly called reefs, but characterized, in any event, by an accumulation of the debris of organisms that lived at a rather slight depth; (2) a zone of terrigenous marly-calcareous sediments, some of which contain chert, indicating the abundance of sponges; the thickness of this zone is enormous (1500 m for the Barremian alone, to the north of Die); (3) a zone of much reduced thickness (some tens of meters), which includes marly limestones that contain ammonites, which probably indicate deeper deposition (Vocontian Trench). It must be concluded that if the embryonic movements produced a furrow, it was not entirely filled by the sediments, most of which accumulated on its margins. The complexity of the history of this region is further indicated by the slides of sediments that took place in the Cretaceous, determining characteristic bed contortions (Chap. 7, p. 000). They indicate a slope of the bottom that may be due either to conditions of sedimentation on the edge of the continental talus, or to an unequal sinking of the bottom.

In the interpretation of tectonic movements, we should attach almost the same importance to the production of a depressed furrow if conditions have not let it be filled by sediments, as if the sediments had converted it into a subsident trench or a geosyncline, depending on which word may be preferred.

Thus, we cannot limit ourselves to the notion of geosynclinal sedimentation, and we must examine much closer the movements of the bottom that determine the nature of the deposits. In the Alps, these movements seldom produced a thick accumulation of sediments. On the contrary, when we replace the different units in the relative situations corresponding to their deposition, we reconstruct a series of cordilleras, or geanticlines (this term, created for a very different situation by Dana, is to be avoided), that is, zones characterized by numerous lacunae and signs of emergence. Certain stages may be represented therein by breccias, which often do not seem to result from the transport of elements by the ordinary agents of erosion, but rather from a reworking of the earlier sediments after collapse or destruction by the action of waves working on newly risen islands. The cordilleras were affected on numerous occasions by movements of uplift affecting a relatively slight width. They were separated by furrows that tended, on the contrary, to sink and in which fine, thick, monotonous sediments accumulated; for this reason, we should not speak of an Alpine geosyncline but of a multitude of elementary furrows whose evolutions are often quite different. Moreover, furrows and cordilleras have not always maintained the same position. In the Briançonnais and the Vanoise, what was formerly a furrow in which thick sediments were deposited from the Carboniferous through to the Triassic, took on the characteristics of a cordillera from the Jurassic on, while the adjacent region of the Grand Paradis, which lacks Carboniferous deposits and which contains a greatly reduced Triassic, seems to have been the site of deposition (from the Jurassic to the Tertiary) of the thick sedimentary series that produced the *schistes lustrés*. The region of the Grand Paradis is often considered as the typical "Alpine geosyncline."

However we must not think of furrows and cordilleras as outlining a series of parallel belts. Cordilleras probably consisted rather of archipelagic lines that succeeded each other at quite variable intervals. It may be admitted that during a given epoch the arrangement of these islands must have shown a certain elongation in the direction of what was to become the folded mountain chain, but it is impossible to say to what degree. Certain furrows could, at least in their central part, receive only a relatively small amount of sediments. We must by no means reject the possibility that the direction of some of the furrows may have initially been quite different from that of the later mountain chain. Such is the case for the Vocontian Trench in particular. This trench was especially active in the Upper Jurassic and Lower Cretaceous; it extended in a NW-SE direction to the south of the present valley of the Drôme. It is interesting to note that the trough has been only slightly deformed by subsequent folding.

To sum up, what we must retain of this analysis is the notion of a bottom in movement long before the period of the most active movements, with a differentation between zones tending to rise and others tending to sink. However, these zones do not remain absolutely fixed in the course of time; thus, a certain evolution may be established.

Sedimentation assumes very special characteristics during the phase of the most active folding because of the relief developed under the influence of erosion. In Chapter 3, we indicated the characteristics of the corresponding flysch. Sedimentary basins are constantly being deformed as a result of folding, such that a given mountain chain may exhibit a whole series of flysch deposits of different ages and variable extensions. On the whole, the zone of deposition, subdivided by numerous cordilleras, tends to be displaced toward the exterior of the mountain chain.

It is possible to pass progressively from "flysch" to "molasse," more homogeneous complexes of sediments that are often interrupted by torrential or deltaic conglomerates, with a notable proportion of fresh water deposits. On the whole, molasse deposits are post-tectonic sediments; the phenomena of subsidence plays a subordinate role in their deposition, or more exactly, they are localized within a certain number of basins bordered by faults. The fact that these basins sink seems to indicate a relaxation phase in the earth's crust rather than one of active compression. We know, moreover, that a resumption of active movements in the western Alps deeply affected the molasse toward the end of the Miocene and, in particular, produced the main part of the folds of the Jura.

The chronology of embryonic movements, registered by sediments that can be dated, is easier to establish than that of intense deformations, which can be studied only indirectly. There is every reason to believe that adjacent structures were formed successively, the earth's crust yielding first at the least resistant point and then, after consolidation and thickening, at adjacent points, and so on; all the indirect evidence that we possess confirms the mechanical reasoning. Thickening due to deformation results in an uplifting of the surface, which produces either the slides of gliding tectonics or simply a tilting of the structures toward the depressed region, that is, toward the exterior of the mountain chain, which is still too often interpreted by speaking of a thrust direction (*sens de poussée*), an expression that has no meaning from the mechanical point of view. The thrust is a pressure that is transmitted from place to place. At each point, at any given moment, the action is equal and opposite to the reaction, if we ignore the forces of inertia, which are negligible for all slow movements.

A single zone of intumescence, originating in the central part of the mountain chain, is hardly sufficient to explain all the complications. Just as embryonic movements involved the uplift of several cordilleras, tectonic movements may have produced the uplift of irregularly arranged massifs, thus complicating the action of slides; Lugeon has shown that the Aiguilles Rouges massif of Chamonix had already begun to rise while the Tertiary flysch of the Chamonix syncline was being deposited, since a slice of granite from its southeast side, which had become very precipitous, slipped and came to rest in the midst of the flysch. Later, however, the Aiguilles Rouges massif offered no obstacle to the gliding of the Prealps; it must have already been much smoothed by erosion by the time an active tectonic movement caused the Mont Blanc massif to rise up and crush the Chamonix syncline, whose contents were driven forward to form the Morcles nappe. The projection that the Aiguilles Rouges massif could still produce was not an obstacle to this development; at most, this massif was an abutment preventing an overall slip. At the same time that the great recumbent fold of the Morcles nappe was forming, the structure of the Prealps, which had earlier slipped to its emplacement, was being pushed farther forward.

Another quite characteristic example of the relations between two structures of the basement is furnished by the Mercantour Massif and the Barot Dome, which are situated a little farther to the south (see Fig. 101). Certain variations of facies show, as early as the Mesozoic, at least a relative tendency toward uplift in the Barot Dome. However, when the active movements of the Mercantour caused the slip of the cover, the slip took place without obstacle at the emplacement of the Barot Dome; at most, the folds in the Middle Triassic strata indicate a certain local resistance.[13] It was not until later that the Barot Dome was uplifted; thus, its entire Mesozoic cover was carried away by erosion after perhaps having undergone minor local folding.

What can be said concerning the rate at which these movements took place? We know that a slow plastic deformation may often be produced under the action of a force less than that required to produce the same deformation in a shorter time. However, we do not think that the force required diminishes indefinitely as the deformation becomes slower. These mechanical considerations involve a presumption in favor of rather slow movements, which would probably have been barely perpectible to a spectator, but whose duration was not unlimited. During the span of a geologic period, a whole series of successive structural events may have occurred. It is possible to estimate the duration of these deformations only by comparison with the duration of phenomena with which we are familiar, such as erosion and sedimentation. When a given tectonic deformation produced a relief feature, the feature thus produced was probably attacked by erosion at the moment of its uplift, but it has certainly not been gradually leveled by it; in order to understand this, it is sufficient to verify that today relief features that border Miocene basins still stand far above the maximum level attained by the deposits (for example, the Grande Chartreuse, opposite the Chambaran plateau, or the mountains from Digne to Castellane, along the Valensole conglomerates).

In the Bas-Dauphiné the most external anticlines were buried under the Miocene sediments, which have not undergone deformation, owing to their resistance, whereas for more internal structures, the movement continued, involving the Miocene (Fig. 184). It has been determined that the erosion is scarcely any deeper on the elevated ridges, on which it has acted during the whole period of the folding, than it is on the anticlines, protected by a covering of Miocene.

Moreover, it is possible to indicate the relative proportion of erosion that took place during and after the movements by the corresponding proportion of alluviation; tilted conglomerates exist along all the mountain chains, but

FIGURE 184. *Section across the Grande Chartreuse massif, showing (left) the anticlines buried under the Miocene of the Bas-Dauphiné, and (right) the folds, more or less broken, prosterior to the Miocene.*

the post-tectonic alluvium in many cases plays the most important role. Besides, the tilted conglomerates may have been deposited, not during the movements, but between two successive phases of deformation.

In like manner, when the erosion has been sufficient to diminish the mechanical resistance of an anticlinal zone to the point of inducing its rupture, it is, in general, because a phase of quite prolonged repose separated two periods of tectonic activity (Middle Cretaceous to Upper Eocene, in Provence; Upper Eocene to Miocene in the southern sub-Alpine mountain chains).

In certain cases, it is possible to establish that an overthrust was directly produced on the surface of the ground (vicinity of Digne and of Castellane, certain points of the Jura). It is then quite evident that the overriding mass must have culminated in an escarpment, which erosion or landslips were able to wear away, but which they did not destroy, since they essentially still exist.

Folds caused by the overall displacement of a cover slipping on its base, such as those of the Jura or of the southern sub-Alpine mountain chains, pose a small chronologic problem. In what order did the different parallel structures originate? In general, we do not have data that enable us to answer this question directly. Basing our reasoning on mechanics, we can say that the first structure produced was the one that required the least mechanical work. But the one that comes immediately after, in the order of increasing work, may as well be on one side as on the other. If the emplacement of the folds is determined by a resistant abutment, for example a basin with thick detrital sedimentation, the folds will form at first at the point of contact, then progressively toward the interior; but the opposite case may also appear, for example if the emplacement is determined by a diminution of the mechanical resistance, due to a change of facies. This seems to be the case for the Jura, where it may be assumed that the thickness of the Tertiary sediments prevented folding of the cover at the emplacement of the Swiss Plain. So the folds must have been formed successively from the interior toward the exterior, an order of succession that is doubtless as frequent as the opposite case. It is also possible that the successively outlined folds were simultaneously accentuated during the course of a final phase that could have established equilibrium, or at least the regular echelonning of heights. So the question posed does not admit of a general answer.

On the whole, we do have reasons for thinking that, if plastic deformations of rocks (including easily deformed rocks, which lubricate certain overthrust surfaces) are slow in relation to the scale of time imposed by the duration of our lives, to the extent that it would perhaps be difficult to recognize them if they were produced now, they are however relatively rapid in relation to other geologic phenomena, such as erosion and sedimentation. When a tectonic deformation occupies a relatively long geologic period, it does so rather by the successive action of adjacent deformations than by the very gradual progress of a given deformation.

On the other hand, there are many reasons for thinking the movement of a true fault took place rapidly, through jolts capable of producing seismic shocks. Both the mechanical considerations relative to friction and the result of upheavals due to earthquakes lead us to this notion of very brief jolts, often of small amplitude. Must we then oppose the notion of "shock tectonics," produced rapidly, by faults, to the concept of "flow tectonics," very slow and produced by plastic deformation? [14] Folds and faults are associated much too closely, concurring in the building of the same structures, to permit us to be able to attach great weight to this distinction. Transverse faults, on both sides of which the folds often have very different forms, illustrate this quite clearly.

It must be admitted, we think, that slow plastic deformation has progressively placed the faults under tension and that they have thus been able to act through a sudden jolt when this tension surpassed a certain limit. According to Benioff,[15] the action of aftershocks in the hours or days following an earthquake is probably an expression of the elasticoviscous adaptation of the rocks to the new state of constraint. The tension, thus relaxed, begins to build up again, until a new shock takes place. The elasticity of the terrane must have been sufficient to permit correspondence between the progressive movement of plastic deformation and the discontinuous movement of the faults, whose very numerous shocks are almost the equivalent of a continuous movement on the scale of geologic time.

The predominance of either supple folds or brittle faults constitutes a characteristic that has great influence on the tectonic style of a region. How are these two arrangements going to be distributed in a tectonic structure? *A priori,* we should expect to find a predominance of faults in deformed zones near the surface, where the pressures to which the rocks were subjected were too weak for the rocks to behave plastically. On the other hand, we should expect folding to be the dominant mode of deformation at depth. But this general notion should be very seriously qualified; in particular, we cannot establish a depth of flow beyond which the rocks would necessarily behave as if plastic, but above which they would behave as if brittle. Not only would such a limit be extremely different according to the rocks, but it would probably depend, for a given rock, on the speed of deformation and on the prevailing physicochemical conditions. For all sedimentary rocks (except perhaps certain sandstones), we have observed plastic deformations that may have been produced very close to the surface, sometimes beneath hardly more than about 100 m of cover, but which no doubt took place quite slowly. On the contrary, in the prolongation of a fault acting with a sudden jolt, rocks will break down to a depth at which they might easily deform plastically if they had the time. So the notion of a predominance of faults in superficial zones has only a statistical value and involves numerous exceptions, as much in one direction as in the other. In any event, it is impossible to establish, even for a given rock, a limit of depth separating the zone of fragile behavior from that of plastic behavior. It used to be thought that strongly folded zones are, in principle, lacking in faults. A survey of very detailed maps shows, on the contrary, the existence of numerous faults, often with slight displacements, which constitute insignificant details in relation to the folds (which had led the first cartographers to disregard them).

Just as on the time scale of geologic phenomena the multiple jolts that constitute the action of faults appear as only trifling details, in the continuous development of tectonic deformations their brittle style is often only an imperceptible detail in the general deformation of the masses that make up the earth's crust.

The geographic distribution of tectonic structures appears under multiple aspects. During a given epoch, the deformation in general affects a belt of a certain width, presenting therein, moreover, quite varied modalities. The deformation of a given belt often continues for quite a long time. The history of such a zone, which evidently forms an entity, cannot be separated from various phenomena that generally accompany deformations, such as metamorphism, formation of granites, eventually volcanism, and, for the more recent movement that may be considered as unfinished, earthquakes. For the moment, we shall postpone consideration of the study of movements of much less importance that may be produced outside the belts of intense deformation.

In the overall study of tectonically deformed zones, at least of the more recent, it is impossible to ignore the fact that they almost always correspond to mountain chains. Deeply eroded plateau regions exist that have undergone no folding, in some cases since a very remote epoch (for example, the Colorado plateau, where the Cambrian is horizontal). But the zones of recent deformations always correspond to mountain chains, or sometimes to garlands of islands rising far above the bottom of the surrounding seas. This relation is so constant that it is easy to confuse, in words, the notion of a zone of recent tectonic deformation and that of a recent mountain chain or orogenic structure.

In fact the relation is not as simple as it seems at first sight. The study of the evolution of the relief of many recent mountain chains, the Alps in particular, shows that their present elevation is due in great part to a relatively recent overall uplift, which, in any event, clearly took place after the end of the tectonic deformations, properly so called.

We have seen, in the previous chapter, that the elevation of a given division of the earth's crust is the direct expression of its constitution, through the action of isostasy. Thus the relations that have just been very briefly stated indicate that the deformed regions present a much greater thickness of relatively light terranes than do the surrounding zones. This is an essential part of our concept of an orogenic structure.

The overall uplift that follows tectonic deformation is difficult to interpret. Since it does not correspond to any change near the surface, it must result from a deep transformation. Daly has attributed the latter to the re-establishment of a normal thermal gradient involving the fusion of a certain thickness of originally crystalline rocks at the base of the earth's crust; to account for the uplift of at least 1000 m recorded in the Alps, the fusion of at least 10,000 m of rock would have had to occur, and the uplift seems to be much greater for other mountain chains (Andes, Himalayas). This is only a hypothesis, which, for the moment, we are unable to verify.

We may also assume that the zone that had just been folded was not in isostatic equilibrium, but corresponded to a negative anomaly up to the moment at which its uplift re-established equilibrium. We would then be faced with the problem of determining which hypotheses concerning the nature of deep phenomena connected with tectonic deformations could explain this negative anomaly.

Be that as it may, the connection that exists between tectonic deformation and orogenesis, that is, relief, makes it quite possible to follow on the earth's surface the outline of recent zones of transformation, especially if we group all Tertiary movements under this designation. The Andes and the Rocky Mountain ranges on the one hand, the Alps and their prolongations through the Caucasus and the Taurus, the Iranian mountain chains, the Himalayas, Malaysia and the Sunda Islands, the archipelagoes of eastern Asia and New Zealand on the other hand evidently constitute the great lines of the face of the earth. We should associate with the picture that they offer us those sketched by the tracing of earlier movements.

In detail, the Tertiary movements may be of very different ages at different points. But since (when it is possible to determine in a precise manner the age of successive movements in a given region) we generally record that they have continued during a very long period, these differences of age at different points should not mask the basic unity of great orogenic masses. If, on the whole, deformation continued during a very long time, the detail shows here and there a series of localized crises, spreading from time to time or succeeding one another at the same point.

We do not intend to present here an overall description of the deformations of the earth's face, but to indicate by the aid of some examples the method that should be applied to their study. So we are going to examine, in a given sector of an orogenic structure, how the different sorts of deformations are associated with one another, using as a basis previously mentioned examples, for the most part taken from the Alpine mountain chain.

To begin with, the distribution of structures presents an extreme complication. If we wish to indicate the main belts, a genetic point of view is necessary; we have seen that numerous structures, in particular almost all those that affect the sedimentary cover, result indirectly from deeper deformations of the basement. So, through analysis of the structures of the cover, we must determine the mode of deformation of the basement.

As far as the Alps are concerned, we will be led (in the whole area of the sub-Alpine chains, most probably including the Jura) to consider structures of the basement only rarely, since the cover essentially folded upon itself, owing to a mass separation (*décollement*) far in advance of the last structures in the basement.

In the area of external crystalline massifs, we shall have to ignore the piling up of the Helvetic nappes formed by the cover and consider only the division of the basement into enormous wedges crushed against each other. The detail of the folds of the cover, however, gives us information regarding the chronology of the movements of the basement and shows us that the internal structures are generally the oldest, and that as we go toward the exterior, we find more and more recent structures. In detail, these structures seem to be brittle in comparison with the much more plastic beds of the cover, but the overall resultant of all the fractures of detail is equivalent to a plastic swelling of the mass. Naturally we do not know the exact nature of the deformation at depth, but it is not unlikely that it passes from a brittle type to a plastic type.

If we study the form in plan of these structures of the basement for the arc of the western Alps, we find that they do not form parallel belts, but relay each other mutually, the southern prolongation of each structure passing to the exterior of the following one; it may be deduced from this, since the internal structures are the oldest, that the movement along each structure progressed toward the south (Fig. 185).

FIGURE 185

Map of external crystalline massifs in the French Alps. The outcropping parts are in black; those whose form may be recognized by the behavior of the sedimentary terrains that cover them are indicated by shading.

The curved line of western Alps constitutes a very particular case, but it is very general for structures of the basement to form amygdaloid masses that are relatively short in relation to their width. Thus, the behavior of the continuous long folds, which sometimes affect the cover, should not deceive us. The deformation in well-formed cylindrical folds is by no means the normal modality of structures of the earth's crust, but is a peculiarity of deformations of the cover that is connected with its stratified nature, like the very existence of flexible folds; basement structures in general show much more irregular behavior.

In the Alps, beyond the area of the "external crystalline masses," we find an area in which the deformation of the basement becomes much deeper, since it is involved in the complex deformations of the Pennine nappes. Here again, the sedimentary cover plays an essential role in the structures that we are discussing; this role is, moreover, complex, the cover being very generally loosened and separated from the elements of the basement to which it belongs.

As for the movements of the basement, it is difficult to give an accurate description of them. We may speak of a stirring up, a sort of boiling, following which there are often to be seen superficial primitive elements sinking toward the depths. On the whole, there is no doubt that the result of these deformations was an important lateral compression, but it is difficult to estimate its value. What essentially distinguished these deformations of the basement in the Pennine area from those of the external massifs is their plastic character, which permitted a much deeper dislocation. It seems that the cause of this plasticity should be sought in the physicochemical conditions, the "climate" that prevailed at the moment of deformation, and which facilitated recrystallization of the material, expressing itself through metamorphism of the rocks, which must have made possible a change of form under the action of relatively weak stresses.

A zone of deep, plastic deformation of the basement, aided by metamorphism and passing laterally into zones of shatter deformation, probably after the end of the metamorphism of the axial zone and consequently dating from a period when the latter had resumed all its rigidity—such is the picture that we can draw in the matter of deep deformations of an orogenic structure such as the Alps. We shall see later on that it is probably necessary to complete this picture through the existence of movements of the basement perhaps connected to shattering fractures, before the paroxysm of the deformation.

To be sure, this constitutes only the skeleton of the deformation; the physiognomy of the mountain chain is furnished by the plastic veneer of the cover, which reacts in an extremely complex manner to the movements of the basement. However, this is not the place to enter into the detail of these deformations of the cover. In addition to the horizontal compression that elements of the basement may exert, an essential factor that directs or determines the movements of the cover is furnished by the mean elevation of the different elements of the basement all along the line of deformation. Setting aside eventual delay of certain isostatic readjustments, it seems that we can count on an uplift that will spread progressively from the interior toward the exterior contemporaneous with deformation. Thus, throughout the period of uplift, a slope should exist at the external border of the already deformed zone on which slips or flows may be produced. Aided by the progressive migration of the slope, these flows may continue over very long distances without a continuous slope ever having existed over this entire distance.

Of course we cannot claim that the deformation of the basement should spread symmetrically on both sides of the axial zone. On the contrary, if the mountain chain is arcuate in plan, there is a strong probability that the deformation may continue predominantly on one side, toward the exterior in most cases.

The scheme that has just been sketched cannot be applied to all mountain chains. Very often the deformation does not proceed this far, in which case there is no metamorphic zone with deep plastic deformation of the basement, but instead the latter is simply broken following a fracturing tectonic movement. The Pyrenees in the Cretaceous and in the Tertiary furnish an excellent example of this type of deformation. We have seen (Chap. 14) that the Paleozoic basement, folded, granitized and metamorphized in the Hercynian, was broken into a series of massifs of very unequal dimensions; the fractures that border them range from simple changes of level to more or less accentuated crush zones. The cover adapted itself in one way or another to the dislocations of the basement, but only rarely gave place to real overthrusts, such as that of the Pic du Bugarach.

It would be possible to cite numerous examples of still less important dislocations, coming down to a few fractures or even flexures of the basement, and it seems that we pass through a whole series of intermediaries to zones that are not deformed, properly speaking, but which have undergone more or less important changes of altitude.

In order to understand the distribution of tectonic structures on the earth's surface, we would first have to reduce each one of them, by a detailed analysis, to the corresponding deformation of the deep basement. Among these structures of the basement, we could then determine whatever correspondence might exist.

However, we should point out here a quite profound difference that seems to separate the older structures (of Paleozoic age[16]) from mountain chains of Alpine age (Tertiary or Mesozoic). In the Hercynian mountain chains, it is exceptional to find the distinction between cover tectonics and basement tectonics that has been established as so valuable, at least in certain Alpine zones. In the Armorican Massif (Brittany), there is a series of fairly regular folds, anticlines and synclines, but there is nothing to indicate that the series they affect may be considered as the disharmonic covering of a deep mass. The Armorican anticlines are occupied by Precambrian phyllites or post-tectonic granites. In the Applachians, if the folded sedimentary series passes without tectonic discontinuity to the crystalline mass of the Blue Ridge, for the more external "Valley and ridge province," it has been proposed [17] that the tectonics of the sedimentary terranes be interpreted as the result of a separation from the basement, analogous to that of the Jura. The motive force of the separation and the folding of the cover should be sought in the thrust exerted by the crystalline Blue Ridge. Later work, however, shows that the crystalline "Blue Ridge" area is made up of metamorphosed Paleozoic rocks, which rules out any comparison with the Jura.

With the exception of this very important case, the overthrusts of the Hercynian mountain chains (see above), such as those of the Franco-Belgian Carboniferous basin, or of the Caledonian mountain chain, much as the Moine thrust in Scotland, appear to be the superficial parts, eventually deformed by certain disharmonies, of deep structures affecting the whole of the earth's crust. They by no means exhibit the contrast between rigid basement and a cover that would deform upon itself. The only exception to this rule in Western Europe seems to be the Pardailhan and Faugères overthrusts on the south slope of the Montagne Noire, in which a movable mass of cover folded upon itself, perhaps in great part following gliding tectonics, and without any well characterized separation being evident at the base.

The Rocky Mountains provide many examples in which the whole Paleozoic cover behaves in a way characteristic of "cover tectonics" in relation to the Precambrian basement. The disharmony is often caused by the soft Cambrian shales. It would seem hardly conceivable that the Paleozoic sedimentary cover should have had mechanical properties different from those of the Mesozoic cover of the Alpine regions. But perhaps the difference is to be sought in the basement. For independent movements of the cover to be produced, it is not sufficient for the latter to be plastic; the basement must also be relatively rigid. If its mean resistance were of the same order as that of the cover, it would probably be carried into the movements of the latter. Such seems to have been the case in at least some of the Hercynian movements in Europe.

The abundance of granites contemporary with the deformation (in particular, where the tectonics of the cover presents the least independence in relation to that of the basement) must have been expressed by a very low value of the overall mechanical resistance of the earth's crust. Whatever may be the hypothesis considered for the formation of the granite, it must be admitted that the mass in course of granitization must have offered only a rather low mechanical resistance with regard to a slow deformation. We shall return to this question in another chapter.

The Pyrenees—if we limit ourselves to the folds of Hercynian age, visible in the old massifs, where they have been only slightly deformed by the Tertiary and Cretaceous orogenies—provide another example of folding of a sedimentary series, in which it is not possible to recognize or even to suspect a basement that did not participate in the movements. When it is possible to observe the deepest part of the folded mass, a more or less rapid passage (migmatite front) is recorded to gneisses, which are not carried into the folds of flexible character, but there is no indication of a separation of the sedimentary series in relation to the gneiss. Evidently all hypotheses are possible regarding the relations between the lower part of the Paleozic and the earlier terranes, before metamorphism reached them and forever masked these relations. Now we see the flexible folds of sedimentary terrains overlying the gneiss, and we are completely unable to state what its deformations were prior to and during metamorphism.

Nor does it seem that we can determine whether basement tectonics occurred more or less autonomously with respect to the cover in the Caledonian chain. Overthrusts like the Moine thrust in Scotland, affecting a cover of sandstone, by no means appear to indicate a separation of the cover, but seem to be prolonged in the basement with analogous characteristics.

A fortiori, the Precambrian folds show nothing that may be related to cover tectonics. Very generally, deformations are accompanied by a very dynamic metamorphism and associated with injections of eruptive rocks. In such a "climate" of recrystallization, if not even of fusion, rocks should deform easily.

If the explanation of the fact that the independent action of cover tectonics can be observed only in deformation of Tertiary age is to be sought not in the mechanical properties of the cover, but in those of the basement itself, it may be that, at least in the absence of metamorphism, the deformation of the basement has become more and more difficult in recent mountain chains. We must not reject the possibility that the general evolution of the earth is causing metamorphism and magmatic phenomena to be more and more exceptional. New research would be necessary to give a precise statement of this point of view, while taking into consideration the rather deep level that erosion may have reached in old mountain chains.

Notes and References

1. Beaumont, Elie de, *Recherches sur quelques-unes des révolutions de la surface du Globe* (read as extracts to the Academy of Sciences in Paris, June 22, 1829), Ann. Sci. Nat., 1829 and 1830.

2. Chamberlin, Rollin T., Diastrophism and the Formative Processes. VII. Periodicity of Paleozoic Orogenic Movements, Jour. Geol., vol. 23, pp. 315–345, 1914.

See also: Chamberlin, Thomas C., Diastrophism as the Ultimate Basis of Correlation, Jour. Geol., vol. 17, pp. 685–693, 1909.

3. Stille, Hans, *Grundfragen der vergleichenden Tektonik,* Berlin (Borntraeger), 1924.

4. Kober, L., *Die Orogentheorie,* Berlin, 1933.

5. Holmes, A., *Principles of Physical Geology,* London, 1946.

6. Stille, H., *Der derzeitige tektonische Erdzustand,* Preuss. Akad. Wiss., Phys.-Math. Klasse, Sitzungsber., pp. 179–219, 1935. See also graph reproduced in Glangeaud, L., *Orogenèse et petrogenèse profonde d'après les théories géophysiques nouvelles,* Revue Scient., no. 3286, vol. 85, pp. 1107–1120, 1947.

———, *Einführung in den Bau Amerikas,* Berlin (Borntraeger), 1940.

7. Very pertinent critiques of Stille's ideas can be found in: Rutten, L. M. R., Frequency and Periodicity of Orogenic Movements, Bull. Geol. Soc. America, vol. 60, pp. 1755–1770, and in Gilluly, J., Distribution of Mountain Building in Geologic Time, Bull. Geol. Soc. America, vol. 60, pp. 561–590, 1949. This last article led to a discussion of orogenesis in the Geologische Rundschau, vol. 38, no. 2, 1950, under the general title "Struktur und Zeit," with the following articles:

Gilluly, J., Distribution of Mountain Building in Geologic Time (with summary in German), pp. 89–91.

Stille, H., *Bemerkungen zu James Gilluly's "Distribution,"* pp. 91–102.

Gilluly, J., *Reply to discussion by Hans Stille,* pp. 103–107.

Stille, Hans, *Nochmals die Frage der Episodizität und Gleichzeitigkeit der orgoenen Vorgänge,* pp. 108–111.

Krejci-Graf, Karl, *Uber die Phasen der Gebirgsbildung,* pp. 112–124.

Wegmann, E. *Diskontinuität und Kontinuität in der Erdgeschichte,* pp. 125–132.

8. Fallot, Paul, *Remarques sur la tectonique de couverture dans les Alpes bergamasques et les Dolomites,* Bull. Soc. géol. France, 6ᵉ ser., vol. 20, pp. 183–195, 1950.

9. Goguel, J., *Remarques sur la tectonique du massif de Gigondas et des régions voisines,* Bull. Soc. géol. France, 5ᵉ ser., vol. 8, pp. 355–362, 1938.

10. On the development and history of the notion of geosyncline, see Glässner, M. F., and Teichert, C., Geosynclines, a Fundamental Concept in Geology, Amer. Jour. Sci., vol. 245, pp. 465–482, and pp. 571–591, 1947.

11. Haug, Emile, *Les geosynclinaux et les aires continentales, contribution à l'étude des transgressions et des régressions marines,* Bull. Soc. géol. France, 3ᵉ ser., vol. 28, pp. 617–711, 1900.

12. See especially Pruvost, P., *Sédimentation et subsidence,* Bull. Soc. géol. France (livre Jubilaire), pp. 545–564, 1930.

13. Bordet, P., *Sur l'allure des plis de couverture au S. W. du massif de l'Argentera-Mercantour,* Acad. Sci. Paris, Comptes-rendus, vol. 228, p. 408, 1949.

Goguel, J., *A propos du glissement de la couverture au S. W. du massif de l'Argentera-Mercantour,* Acad. Sci. Paris, Comptes-rendus, vol. 228, p. 698, 1949.

14. Roubault, M., *La génèse des montagnes,* Science d'Aujourd'hui, Presses Universitaires, p. 231, 1949.

15. Benioff, Hugo, Earthquakes and Rock Creep, Bull. Seismol. Soc. America, vol. 41, pp. 31–52, 1951.

16. Fallot, P., *Tectonique alpine et tectonique hercynienne,* Bull. Soc. géol. France, 5ᵉ ser., vol. 14, pp. 99–102, 1944.

17. Rodgers, John, The Folds and Faults of the Appalachian Valley and Ridge Province, Kentucky Geol. Surv., Spec. Publ. no. 1, pp. 150–166, 1953.

CHAPTER EIGHTEEN

Relations of Deformation Zones with Volcanic Rocks. Metamorphism. Granite and Mineralization

Deformation of pre-existent granites—Volcanic rocks in the geosynclines —Relation between metamorphism and deformation; dynamometamorphism or metamorphism generative of folding, plastic deformation during the course of metamorphism—Metamorphism in the Himalayas and in the Pyrenees—Origin of nebulites—Intrusive granites—Syntectonic granites —Precambrian folding and deep tectonics—Relations of mineralization with eruptive rocks—Role of fractures of rocks.

DEFORMATIONS of the earth's crust, which constitute the essential phenomenon of tectonics, may affect any rocks, including granites or metamorphic rocks. It may even be said that these rocks, which originated at a considerable depth, have some chance of being visible as outcrops only if dislocations have brought them up to an altitude where erosion can easily expose them. So at first glance, their presence may seem to be connected with the existence of tectonic movements, but under conditions that have led to errors on the part of the first observers. Some early observers noted that granites and gneiss, which are among the rocks most resistant to erosion (in the absence of weathering), often form the highest peaks. They saw in the uplift of the granite and the gneisses, pushing up and bursting the sedimentary cover, the essential fact of orogenesis. The reconstruction in time of the succession of these phenomena leads to quite different concepts. We know, for example, that the granites that constitute Mont-Blanc and the Pelvoux are of Hercynian age, if not even older. They had been completely eroded and flattened in the Mesozoic and were very probably covered by the sea, at least for a time. In the Tertiary, when they were affected by the horizontal compressions that produced the Alps, they behaved like inert material, but were particularly rigid, from which a certain number of scales were driven upward and then cleared by erosion of their sedimentary cover and attacked much more slowly than the surrounding terranes so that presently they constitute the highest points.

We have already had occasion to point out the influence that the mechanical properties of crystalline rocks (granites or gneisses) have had on their subsequent tectonic behavior. The problem that is to be considered in the present chapter is that of the genetic relations between the granites or gneisses and the tectonic movements. It is in fact evident in quite a considerable number of cases that the recrystallization and displacement of material that are expressed by metamorphism and granitization on the one hand and by tectonic deformations on the other, are consequences of the same deep disturbance, whose nature remains a puzzle to us.

We have seen that the first manifestation of tectonic movements is expressed by displacements of the bottom of the sea, producing, in particular, the furrows in which geosynclinal sedimentation accumulates. Different geologists, in particular R. A. Daly and Kossmat, have noted that basic volcanic rocks of particular types are frequently associated with these geosynclines; for these very sodic basic rocks, the term "spilitic province" has been proposed.[1] The effusive types often present the structure of "pillow lavas," indicating submarine eruptions, and they are at times associated with radiolarities. There may also be intrusion of gabbros or peridodites in the midst of the sediments.

In the zone of *schistes lustrés* of the Alps, often taken as a typical geosyncline, these basic rocks have been subsequently greatly modified by metamorphism and alteration, and they constitute accumulations of serpentine and "greenstone." (The term "ophiolites" is also used.)

But Knopf [2] has cited a whole series of examples showing that very different volcanic rocks, including even rhyolites, which are sometimes very abundant, can be associated with the sediments of geosynclines considered as typical both in Hercynian Europe and in North America. He has also shown that the maximum of volcanic activity could just as well be placed at the beginning as toward the end of the period of geosynclinal sedimentation. Moreover, volcanic rocks are not present in all geosynclines; Stille's assertion that geosynclines with abundant "pliomagmatic" eruptive rocks are the only ones to be invaded subsequently by granitic batholiths can hardly be considered as proved.

The geosynclinal notion seems to be as vague and impossible to precisely define from the point of view of magmatic processes as from the point of view of sedimentary rocks or of subsequent evolution.

The movements of the bottom of a geosyncline, which have left their traces in the nature of the sediments, constitute only a preliminary phase of the intense movements of deformation, which are the essential phenomena in the genesis of a mountain chain. Metamorphism that affects all the earlier rocks is often associated with these movements in a way we shall now try to make clear. One of the most classic examples of general metamorphism closely associated with a strong tectonic deformation is furnished by the Pennine zones of the Alps.

In spite of metamorphism a certain stratigraphy is possible, in particular, because the Triassic remains very recognizable, in general, owing to the presence of two very pure lithologic facies, quartzites and limestones, as well as lime sulphate. It is thus possible to distinguish a pre-Triassic series, presently gneissic, which certainly includes some Carboniferous, perhaps other Paleozoic sediments, and probably granites or earlier gneisses. The post-Triassic series is that of the *schistes lustrés,* often rich in calcite and injected with greenstone. Ascending from the Lias, probably as far as the Cretaceous, and perhaps into the Tertiary, this series of *schistes lustrés* is often taken as an example of a geosynclinal series of whose history the metamorphism constitutes an essential phase. We have indicated above the very complex tectonic relations among these various units. For this example, as for those furnished by other mountain chains, we must attempt an accurate check of the chronologic relations between metamorphism and deformation, as well as genetic relations. Quite varied hypotheses have been formulated.

Let us remark to begin with that at least some deformations were definitely produced after metamorphism had ceased; we often find, in fact, remnants of *schistes lustrés* resting on terranes that are much less metamorphic or non-metamorphic, or pinched with them into very complex folds. Metamorphism could not have affected these terranes in such an uneven manner if they had already been in contact.

But this conclusion must not be pushed too far. The Alpine movements continued for a very long time, and the above reasoning is valid only for their last phase. There is nothing to justify applying this conclusion to the whole deformation, nor can we say that the deformation affected a material whose metamorphism was completed. On the contrary, the fact that certain forerunner fragments (*"lambeaux avant-coureurs"*) of the nappe of the *schistes lustrés,* such as the one that constitutes Mont-Jovet in Tarentaise, are clearly less metamorphic than the principal mass of the series, seems to indicate that it was already tectonically separated before the cessation of metamorphism. For the Vanoise massif, F. Ellenberger has reached the conclusion that the Alpine metamorphism took place after the emplacement of the nappes. Petrographic criteria make it possible to distinguish this metamorphism of Hercynian or earlier date upon which it may be superposed, involving at times a retrograde metamorphism, as, for example, in the Grand Paradis massif, stud-icd by R. Michel. So there is a close relation between deformation and metamorphism that may be expressed in several ways.

Let us first recall the classic theory according to which the deepening of the geosyncline probably attained such a value that the sediments were brought to a temperature sufficient to bring about their metamorphism. A serious objection to this theory comes from the fact that very thick sedimentary series exist whose lower members descended at times to very great depths (measuring in terms of tens of thousands of meters) without any metamorphism, whereas, on the other hand, we are often led to assume that the metamorphism of certain rocks takes place at much less depth. F. Ellenberger's observations on the Vanoise formally contradict the depth-of-burial theory.

An analogous objection would be valid against the theory of dynamometamorphism, according to which the recrystallization was probably a consequence of the deformation. For example, in the Briançonnais zone, series occur that are not metamorphic, although they are very profoundly deformed; the deformation is much more apparent than in zones of altogether typical *schistes lustrés*. Metamorphism is seen to increase regularly in certain zones without the more or less advanced degree of deformation seeming to have any influence.

René Perrin[3] has proposed an exactly inverse theory, that of "metamorphism generative of folds." This assumes that metamorphism is accompanied by an increase of volume. The density of the minerals having a tendency to increase during the course of metamorphism, this increase of volume implies a notable chemical contribution. The theory does not seem applicable in the case of a simple rearrangement of the pre-existent elements, nor in that of an exchange of ions, in which the chemical contributions are compensated for by the loss of certain elements. With these reservations, the theory of R. Perrin assumes that the increase of volume connected with the metamorphism is sufficient to produce the lateral compression indicated by the folds.

We know of cases in which a chemical contribution brought about by diffusion in the impregnation fluid of the rock produces an increase of volume. One of the clearest examples is that of the hydration of anhydrite, transforming it into gypsum. In this transformation, the increase of volume produces a very marked folding of the mass, or at least a severe dislocation. But we know of no example in which the compression has been transmitted to other terranes outside the mass undergoing transformation. Mechanically, it seems that the first effect of the swelling should be to produce an uplift toward the surface and not a horizontal compression of the adjacent terrains.

The crystallization of calcite into rather elongated nodules in the midst of marls or clays is also accompanied by an increase of volume, as is indicated by the appearance of fissures in the "septaria" in the center of the nodule, following the increase of volume of the external part, which is formed last. We have shown[4] that cone-in-cone structure, which greatly resembles the results of certain traction tests, may also have been due to an increase in volume of the rock.

In these examples, the effect of an increase of volume through chemical contribution remains localized in the transformed mass, and whatever the change of scale may be, it gives us no idea of the compression imagined by R. Perrin. Moreover, the increase of pressure should displace the chemical equilibrium; thus, from the thermodynamic point of view, it does not seem that an adequate moving force can be found in metamorphism to explain the folds. So metamorphism appears as neither a simple consequence nor the cause of mechanical deformations. The relation seems to be somewhat more complex.

We have seen that among the different intimate mechanisms of deformation, one of the most important in the matter of very slow geologic deformation results from the change of form of minerals by solution and recrystallization. Laboratory experiments have shown that a chemical medium favorable to recrystallization also favored slow deformation in cases as different as gypsum in the presence of water, limestone in the presence of carbonic acid, and silica in the presence of an alkaline carbonate.

It seems that these considerations may be extended to metamorphism, since metamorphism is nothing more than the recrystallization of the various mineral elements of the rock. If the rock is subjected to oriented mechanical stresses, the growth of the crystals will be modified, and the overall form of the rock may possibly be greatly changed. During metamorphism, a rock should be able to undergo a slow but very extensive change of form, even under the action of a relatively weak oriented force. That is, its mechanical resistance to a slow deformation may be very low, but this in no way prevents the structure of the existent crystals from offering continuous resistance to considerable forces without undergoing rapid deformation. Even though the rock may have remained very solid, it could behave as if very plastic for slow geologic deformations.

This by no means requires that recrystallization be accompanied by a profound modification of the nature of the minerals present. For gneisses or Hercynian granites belonging to Pennine cores, the recrystallization that was possible at the moment of an Alpine deformation could involve only a slight change in the retrogressive-metamorphic-petrographic nature, since certain of the minerals present, having formed under analogous conditions, were almost in thermodynamic equilibrium under the conditions of temperature, pressure, and chemical environment (composition of the impregnation fluid) that prevailed. But these rocks were no less susceptible to deformation, since their crystals had the possibility of recrystallizing and should do so in order to adapt their form to the uneven stress that they were being subjected to. We are aware of the difficulty that may be involved in recognizing the traces of Alpine metamorphism, which correspond to a moderate rise of temperature superposed upon Hercynian metamorphism of higher temperature.

We do not know the distant cause of general metamorphism, but we can represent it as resulting essentially from a rise in temperature and a modification of the impregnation fluid of the rock. Instead of being composed of a more or less salty water, as by ordinary sediments (leaving out of consideration the exceptional case of an impregnation by hydrocarbons), this fluid must have been enriched in various chemical elements, both through the rise in temperature (subjected to a supercritical pressure) and as a result of chemical contributions of deep origin. We cannot leave out of consideration the fact that reactions between solids also took place through migration of ions in the crystals. But since we are sure that an aqueous phase existed in all rocks, it is probable that, with this as an intermediary, the introduction of material and the displacement of elements were much more rapid than by solid reaction and thus played a predominant role. At the same time that they were encouraging recrystallization of the minerals, or the crystallization of new minerals, prevailing conditions enormously lowered the resistance of the rocks to a slow deformation.

The oscillations of the bottom, indicated by the nature of the sediments, seem to show that even before the main tectonic phase, horizontal compressions were acting upon the earth's crust for a long time (that is, the horizontal pressure was superior to the vertical pressure, which was determined by the weight of the overlying strata). Under the action of these horizontal forces, the zones undergoing metamorphism began to deform slowly, but with a very great range.

Metamorphism, or more exactly the physicochemical climate favorable to metamorphism, seems to have played a determining role in triggering tectonic deformations through the doubtless very considerable diminution that it must have introduced in the mechanical resistance of rocks. This factor must have played an all the more important role, since, in the absence of recrystallization, the major part of the mechanical resistance of the earth's crust, taken as a whole, must be furnished by relatively deep layers.

However, we would not dare to affirm that the origin of the horizontal pressures prevailing in the earth's crust and the ascent of the metamorphism, which diminishes the resistance of the rocks and enables them to yield to these compressions, are totally independent. These are two phenomena whose origin should be sought at depth and which should be derived from a single source, from internal life of the earth upon whose nature we are only able to form still very imperfect hypotheses, such as the one based on convection currents, to which we shall have occasion to return.

In support of a connection between the rise of metamorphism and the mechanical conditions prevailing in the earth's crust, we may recall that schistosity, which constitutes one of the most constant characteristics of rocks produced by general metamorphism, indicates an anisotropism of the physical conditions at the moment of recrystallization which can be due only to the existence of an oriented stress. By analogy with nonmetamorphic rocks whose banding is connected with deformation (see p. 41), it is probable that the plane of schistosity must have been perpendicular to the strongest pressure.

Petrographers distinguish minerals whose crystallization is more or less favored by the existence of oriented forces ("stress" and "anti-stress"). Among the stress minerals, whose appearance is favored by an oriented pressure, and perhaps also by the slow deformation that results from this pressure, are to be mentioned micas, sericite, muscovite and chlorite, albite, epidote and zoisite, amphiboles, kyanite, and staurolite. The "anti-stress" minerals, that is, those that find conditions of hydrostatic pressure the most favorable to their formation, are anorthite, potassic feldspars, augite, hypersthene, olivine, andalusite, sillimanite, cordierite, and spinel. As far as I know, no one has ever been able to present a thermodynamic interpretation of the changes in stability realms of minerals through oriented pressures that can justify this classification.

It is self evident that the easy deformation of rocks during metamorphism lasts only as long as the favorable physicochemical conditions. If the temperature falls, if the composition of the impregnation fluid changes, the rocks, having become incapable of recrystallizing, become rigid again, even for very slow deformations. Thus, it is possible to explain why, after a certain epoch, the Pennine zones stopped deforming while the adjacent zones, unchanged until then, owing to their higher resistance, yielded in turn.

A certain amount of prudence is necessary before generalizing, for all mountain chains, the ideas regarding the relations between metamorphism and tectonic deformations that were suggested by the study of the Alpine Pennine zones.

The case of the Himalayas, however, seems to be analogous. If we omit the Siwaliks, which result from the deformation of post-tectonic sediments by delayed movements and which are not at all metamorphic, the essential part of the mountain chain, which topographically constitutes the southern slope, shows a stratigraphic series going from the Precambrian to the Eocene, forming large overthrust nappes (Auden, Lombard, Bordet, Latreille) affected by an often very marked metamorphism (Fig. 174). This metamorphism seems to increase toward the north in the zone of the roots of these nappes. It seems to affect also the base of the fossiliferous, sedimentary series of the north slope.

The case of the Hercynian movements in the Pyrenees is particularly instructive. Leaving the intrusive granites of Carboniferous age out of consideration for the moment, the gneisses, as E. Raguin has shown, result from a metamorphism with notable additions (migmatite) which spread to the lower part of the Ordovician shales, in which the intensity of the metamorphism diminishes rapidly. If the series had already been folded, we could have expected the metamorphism to reach much higher levels in the synclines than in the anticlines, but this does not seem to be the case. On the other hand, there is no record of gneisses having been brought into the hearts of the anticlines. The very intense folds, often indicating a quite marked disharmony, seem to respect the mass of the gneisses. Is this because the latter were already rigid and their crystallization had finished at the moment of the folding? Or, for some reason that escapes us, was the mass of gneiss crushed upon itself in the course of recrystallization while the overlying sedimentary rocks, not affected by the metamorphism, were folding upon themselves according to a mode determined by their mechanical properties?

We have been led, heretofore, to consider the deformation of rocks in course of metamorphism as produced by the general compression that determined at the same moment the overall tectonic deformation. At first sight, it may seem difficult to interpret in this manner the structure of certain gneisses that contain a heavy proportion of added material (migmatites) which give the impression of a deep intimate deformation.

In a "nebulite," [5] the micaceous beds are twisted in all directions, giving the impression of having been "remelted." This entirely anthropomorphic impression indicates that the changes of direction, the torsions (on the scale of decimeters) seem so capricious that we would be tempted to explain them as being due to eddies, such as those that originate in a body that almost lacks resistance, like a liquid. In a liquid of very slight viscosity, such as water, the eddies are essentially of dynamic origin; that is, the inertia of masses in rapid movement plays an essential role in their genesis. Even if there had actually been partial fusion of the rock, the viscosity would have remained very high, and the eddies that we observe could not have the same origin. It seems that we must accept the fact that, as a result of slight petrographic differences, the local differences of resistance were responsible for the very irregular distribution of pressures and the resultant deformations, which could have been produced by recrystallization during a very slow deformation.

So we cannot affirm that nebulites, even if they give an impression of almost total refusion, have actually passed through an almost fluid state, that is, one susceptible of rapid deformation.

The Hercynian Pyrenees include not only varied gneisses, indicating a general metamorphism, but also post-tectonic intrusive granites, also present in many other mountain chains, but which play an altogether subordinate role in the Alps. So we should now examine the role of these granites. In the Pyrenees (as are many of the granites in the Amorican massif), they are evidently later than the folding of the sedimentary formations, which they cut across in some manner. The form of the folds being determined by the different mechanical properties of the successive beds implies the continuity of the latter at the moment of the folding.

Although these granites are younger than the deformation, their genetic connection with the latter cannot be doubted, if only because a very brief interval of time (from the geologic point of view) separates the folding from their emplacement. They are, in fact, everywhere older than the formations that result from the accumulation of the products of the erosion of the mountain chain (Stephanian and Permian).

Just as magmatic rocks, injected or eruptive in subsident (geosynclinal) sedimentary formations, generally present particular petrographic characteristics, intrusive granites, immediately post-tectonic, seem to belong in a general manner to a calc-alkaline family whose principal representatives (granites, granodiorites, quartz diorites) are extremely abundant.

Since the origin of granite is so obscure, it is not possible to relate their intrusion to contemporaneous orogenic phenomena in any logical manner. The deep causes that produced them must have locally aided their ascent to relatively high levels, often in the midst of sedimentary formations that had undergone no metamorphism. There is no longer any doubt that the substance of the rocks, sedimentary or other, whose place it takes has been incorporated into the granite, but it is hardly possible to state precisely the mechanism of its crystallization and especially of the homogenization which has brought about the disappearance of every trace of variations of composition of the previous rocks. It is particularly impossible to state what the proportion was of the liquid phase and what its viscosity was at the different stages of crystallization. Considering the exterior forces that may have acted upon it, did the granite in course of formation behave as if rigid or as if plastic? Note that this question does not ask whether the granite was formed and established in place in the liquid or solid state. According to what we have seen above, a solid state is perfectly compatible with long-term plasticity, and such must have been the case for the granite during the whole period in which its constituents were crystallizing or recrystallizing. The deformations undergone by granite at the moment of its crystallization and its consolidation should give us information regarding the regional forces that were then being exerted.

Cloos has shown how we can seek to analyze the forces that were acting upon granite, either after its definitive consolidation, by analysis of the directions of joints, or at the moment of consolidation, by noting the directions of the fissures that have been mineralized or injected with aplites or other dike rocks, or earlier, by the orientation of the phenocrysts. But did this orientation take place in a first phase of the consolidation when the rest of the mass was, if not fluid, at least susceptible of easy deformation? Or, on the other hand, did these phenocrysts appear later, after the mass had solidified (in which case their orientation would express the distribution of the pressures)?

In any event, it seems that the forces established by these different methods are very similar and generally correspond to the simple emplacement of the granite rising in the midst of the other rocks. So, if tectonic forces were being exerted during emplacement, it seems that they may have had no other effect than to determine or modify the form of the granitic massif. Many granites in regular massifs seem, then, to date from a period of abatement of the forces.

The upward thrust, corresponding to the intrusion of the granitic mass, and

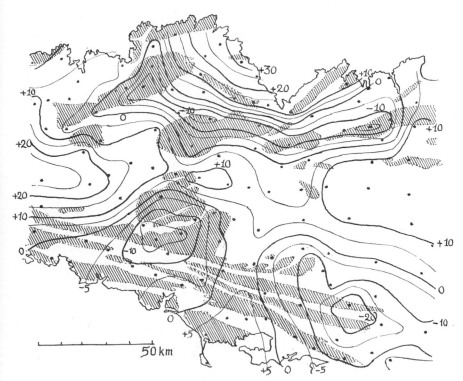

FIGURE 186. *Gravimetric map of a part of Brittany, indicating outcropping granite masses. Note that, on the whole, the granite outcrops correspond to negative anomalies. [After measurements made by R. Bollo.]*

evidenced by its structure, can be at least partially explained without introducing any unknowns. The very marked gravimetric anomalies[6] that correspond to the granitic massifs (Fig. 186) indicate a density lower than that of the surrounding formations. If we accept the notion that, in depth, the pressure was the same within the granite as on the exterior, as the result of a general plasticity, the pressure in the granite at the upper part of the massif should exceed the surrounding pressure by 24 kg/cm² for a difference of density giving an anomaly of 10 milligals, and by 48 kg/cm² for an anomaly of 20 milligals, a figure often reached. In a phase in which the granite was plastic when its density was still diminished by its high temperature, such a pressure could play a considerable role in the emplacement of a massif.

In western Europe, post-tectonic granites are best represented in the Hercynian mountain chain. Immense granitic or granodioritic batholiths exist in the Andes and in the Rocky Mountains. These are apparently of Mesozoic age (Cretaceous in Chili) and seem to have replaced the lower part of the Andean tectonic structure both in Patagonia and in Alaska.

In the Alps, post-tectonic granites are much less developed, but a certain number of them have been identified. In Bergell, one such mass cuts across the structure of the Pennine nappes; the Triassic, or the *schistes lustrés,* were metamorphosed at their contact. From all the evidence, it was emplaced before the Pennine nappes were formed.

The granite of the Adamello massif is located along a great displacement fracture, the Judicarian line, which also affects both the structure of the Austro-Alpine nappes to the north and the prolongation of the Bergamas Alps to the south, which are connected with the Dinarides and whose basement tectonics are comparable to that of the Pyrenees, with localized gliding of the cover.[7] A series of granitic piercements mark this major dislocation. The granite (Adamellite containing very abundant plagioclase) cuts across Mesozoic formations, in particular, the Triassic, which shows a perfectly clear contact metamorphism.[8] Granite dikes often cut across very clear folds, thus the post-tectonic character of these piercements cannot be doubted. However, it is possible to point out the trace of later deformations,[9] though they seem to be of moderate size and are doubtless only a reaction to the emplacement of the granite. Thus we may say, as does Marcel Bertrand, that just as every mountain chain has its flysch and its molasse, it also possesses its crystalline schists and its post-tectonic granites.

It is evident that the post-tectonic granites of a mountain chain may have been involved in the deformation of another mountain chain that had long since been formed. So it is that the granites, barely younger than the principal Hercynian phase (unless they are even older), were later involved in Alpine movements. Under the action of forces to which it was subjected at the time of reworking, granite may break more or less completely, either in a quite general manner (protogine, with fissured feldspar crystals), or along certain surfaces where the crushing may have been very intense (mylonites). In the absence of complete recrystallization, a certain metamorphism, contemporaneous with the deformation, may contribute to carrying over the traces of deformation without completely masking the previous petrographic characteristics.

However, intermediate cases between post-tectonic granites and the simple contemporary metamorphism of the deformation may also exist. In the south of Brittany, there are long belts (Fig. 186) that show a very marked linear alignment and which seem to indicate the existence of orogenic forces at the moment of their emplacement. It is conceived that the formation of a granite in the very course of a deformation ("syntectonic" or "synkinematic" granite) may have involved for the latter a structure and especially a very particular general form. Whatever the physical state of the granite may have been during its crystallization, it should have been extremely sensitive to slow deformations and have behaved tectonically like a plastic mass, as would a rock in course of metamorphism. In fact, syntectonic granites seem to form lenticular masses, apparently marking out surfaces that have taken part in the deformation, such as overriding surfaces. It is not unusual for the presence of mylonites, which could have originated only after the crystallization of the granite, to indicate movements that have continued after the consolidation, following a general direction comparable to the one that had determined the form of the masses.

The structure of these granites may be quite clearly oriented so that they resemble gneisses. But the absence of metamorphic texture, the general arrangement, the progressive attenuation or disappearance in place of the orientated structure, are sufficient, in general, to distinguish them from true gneisses. Raguin considers the granites of the Plateau de Millevaches, of Creuse, and of the Marche (west of the Massif Central) as synkinematic and, consequently, as belonging to the category just considered.

We have left out of consideration until now the Precambrian orogeny, in which the metamorphic rocks and the granitic injections play an almost exclusive role. A preliminary question presents itself. It is very difficult for us to reconstruct the level of the ground surface at the moment of folding and consequently to say at what depth the rocks that we are observing could have been situated originally. Must we think that, since the internal temperature of the earth was higher then than today, metamorphism and granitic injections occurred more frequently and rose closer to the surface and consequently played an essential role in all the tectonic deformations without exception? Or should we assume that the general conditions were analogous to what they were in the Carboniferous or the Eocene, or to what they are today, but that erosion has uniformly carried away a very great thickness of terrane on all mountain chains without exception?

It is very difficult to answer this question, since it would require a great deal more research. However, the study of the Precambrian mountain chains brings to our attention a special tectonics that has been called "deep tectonics," [10] in which metamorphism and granitic injections are associated in all deformations. However, it is very difficult to recognize the movements and even more difficult to establish their chronology. Mylonites are, in general, masked by recrystallization. Nothing certain can be said regarding the original arrangement of the different rocks. The distinction of the phases of metamorphism or of injection, characterized by different chemical behavior, may be quite arbitrary. It would be risky, in attempting to reconstruct the forms of structures, to take a position based on analogies with the folds of sedimentary beds, which are better known, since the mechanical properties are very different. In spite of all these difficulties, we have the impression of a tectonics indicating a very easy deformation of granitic masses in course of crystallization, either because the granite may actually have been injected in a fluid or pastelike form, or because the recrystallization in process may have facilitated very slow deformations.

The notion of deep tectonics seems to imply that all mountain chains, if they were eroded deeply enough, would show phenomena analogous to those exhibited by the Precambrian mountain chains. But what were the probable relations between deep tectonics and the tectonics of superficial formations? It must be recognized that very few observations enable us to define them in an objective manner; the different theories that have been proposed are mental concepts. Every theory thus necessarily implies a somewhat *a priori* idea regarding the mechanism of the emplacement of granite. We usually think of an intrusive mass as having been injected in a more or less pastelike form; perhaps it would be sufficient to change but little the terms used to adapt them to the hypothesis of an injection of hot and chemically active substances capable of encouraging recrystallization of the pre-existent rocks into granite without its ever having ceased being solid, since this recrystallization implies the possibility of slow plastic deformations under the action of small stresses.

Wegmann[11] designates the area of granitization, or of formation of migmatites by injection, as the region of infrastructure. The limit of the infrastructure and of the superstructure (whose base may be affected by a general metamorphism without additions) is, according to Wegmann, entirely independent of that of the old basement, which may involve old granites, and of the sedimentary cover, which may exhibit a geosynclinal character. The definition of infrastructure seems to be analogous to the one that A. Demay gives to the domain of deep tectonics "in the vicinity of active magma of the same orogenic period, or at least in a zone subject to its influence."

But the ideas that these two authors have regarding the style of the deformations of infrastructure or of deep tectonics seem to be quite different. Whereas A. Demay seeks, in infrastructure, flexible nappes of Alpine style and a wholly tangential tectonics, Wegmann considers the deformations of superstructure and infrastructure as completely disharmonic. Whereas the superstructure is the area of flexible folds, even of overriding nappes, the infrastructure, which is also greatly deformed, is characterized by the ascendance of masses rendered more or less fluid through their refusion. Besides, there is nothing to prevent us from imagining that, by taking some advantage of the fractures responsible for deformation of the basement of the superstructure, these injections may penetrate into them, eventually even reaching the domain of the flexible folds of the sedimentary cover. But we conceive of these injections as having arrived late at such a high level, perhaps after the abatement of the horizontal pressures; for this reason, they produce post-tectonic intrusive granites. Wegmann has shown that in certain cases the tectonic structures that had originated in a sedimentary material remain recognizable after very intense metamorphism. Such cases should be carefully distinguished from those in which an already metamorphic material, with very different mechanical properties, has undergone tectonic deformation, which would produce a very different style.

According to F. E. Suess,[12] the contrast between the regime of folds and nappes and that of granitic injections and magmatization would be even more clear-cut. The injection zones, rapidly rendered rigid by crystallization of the gneisses and granites, and hence avoided from then on by orogenic deformations, would be characterized by the absence of alignment and the irregularity of granitic injections, to whose contours the directions of the gneisses would adapt themselves; things would be even more complicated by the persistence of the phenomena of granitization during long periods. However, as E. Raguin has remarked, this interpretation seems too absolute. Chemical mobility and the ease of recrystallization, which characterize granitization, should facilitate slow deformations and determine zones of least resistance, which would invite orogenic deformation.

In German, the same word designates the mine and the mountain; the zones of old mountains are in fact the richest in metallic deposits. But the relation that exists between mineralization and orogenesis seems to be quite indirect. It may be due, in part, to the depth of erosion, which has made it possible to uncover deposits that would otherwise be inaccessible. On the other hand, the relations that may exist between mineralization and orogenic structure are also indirect. It is generally admitted that the chemical additions responsible for mineralization are related to injections of eruptive rocks, which should occupy a determined place in tectonic history. And again, the precipitations or substitutions that constitute mineralization are formed in certain preferred zones, in particular along certain fractures whose appearance is directly connected with local tectonic history.

We have indicated the very general laws that seem to govern the petrography of eruptive rocks, intrusive at the different phases of the tectonic evolution of an orogenesis. The chemical nature of the mineralization genetically connected with them depends upon their petrography; depending on the nature of the mineralizing fluids and the metals that they transport, the metals will be deposited at a greater or lesser distance from the eruptive rock in successive zones of decreasing temperature, which are designated by adding to the term thermal, the prefixes *epi, meso,* and *kata.* Although there is no reason to doubt the community of origin, the mineralizations that result are often quite late in relation to the emplacement of the eruptive rocks; they may be contemporary with a phase of consolidation which sometimes enables the mineralization to fill the fissures of the eruptive rock itself.

From the relations that we have just recalled, for the study of which we refer to special treatises,[13] there results a distribution of zones characterized by the different sorts of mineralization in relation to the elements of a tectonic edifice; but it is a question of a very general relation, at times so vague that it is difficult to discern with certainty.

However, the second of the factors considered, the localization of the zones favorable to mineralization, is strictly dependent on the tectonic deformations undergone by the rock, which often govern the finest details of the structure of the deposits. On the other hand, it is quite certain that the existence of fractures determining permeable zones is not sufficient to determine the minerali-

zation. Between the regional factor, which is determined by the nature and the distance of the intrusive eruptive rocks, and the local factor, which is due to the distribution of the fractures in the rock, there are certain intermediate factors that escape us and which determine why a given region is mineralized while another one, apparently equivalent, is not. In other words, the localization of mineralized zones in a determined region seems, to us, to be due to chance. A more precise knowledge of the tectonic history does not seem capable of removing this indetermination.

On the other hand, the structure of the deposits is largely determined by that of the network of fissures that have allowed the mineralizing solutions to pass through, whether they produced a substitution of new minerals for the constituents of the surrounding rocks or deposited minerals in the pre-existing spaces. The history of this mineralization may be very complex; once the fissures are blocked by a first deposit of minerals, others may appear, cutting off the first mineralization. We often get the impression that the movements that produced the fractures continued during the whole period of deposition.[14]

Since the localization of the deposits is controlled by the possibility of circulation of the solutions, the permeability characteristic of the different rocks must play a part; the mineralization is seen to accumulate beneath an impermeable bed (clay, for example), which is sterile. But generally when miners are able to distinguish along a vein, favorable rocks in which the mineralization

10 m

FIGURE 187. *Section of a vein at the Bell Mine, Montezuma, Colorado. T. S. Lovering, The mineral belt of the Colorado front range, in Ore Deposits as Related to Structural Features, Princeton, 1942 (p. 86). (After USGS, Prof. paper 178.) The arrows indicate the relative movement of the two walls which explains the thickening of the vein in the less inclined parts.*

thickens, as well as unfavorable rocks, this characteristic is due not so much to the permeability of the rocks as to their method of fracturing, their more or less fragile character, or, on the contrary, to their plasticity.

In an important synthesis devoted to the structural relations of mineral deposits,[15] Newhouse indicates only a very small number of examples in which the localization of the mineral is related to the folding. It seems that if lead and zinc in mineralized limestones in the Tri-State (U.S.A.) deposits, as also at Bou-Becker (eastern Morocco), are more abundant in the anticlines than in the synclines, it may be due to the fact that in the anticlines, the limestone underwent an extension that increased fissuring, whereas in the synclines, fissuring was reduced by compression.

Mineralization is almost always related to the action of fractures, which have often undergone movement and thus constitute faults. Inasmuch as this question has been of economic interest since the most remote times, efforts have been made to clarify the laws that govern the distribution of these veins. The first miners had recognized their frequent parallelism and were already attaching great importance to their direction. A more complete mechanical analysis makes it possible to establish certain relations between the network of fractures, the forces that are responsible for them, and the displacements that are produced. But in all cases, these relations do not permit us to predict the position of individual fractures, which is essentially fortuitous. The laws that we endeavour to state can be only statistical in nature.

The fracture, subsequently mineralized, may belong to two types, basically different in their mechanical origin. Some are due to shearing, which produced

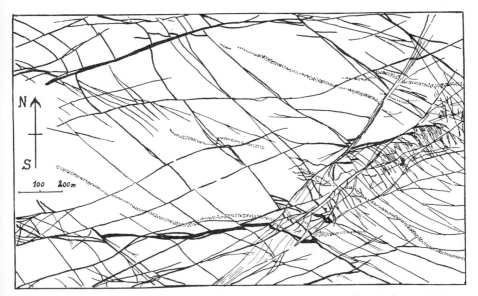

FIGURE 188. *Plan of ore veins at Butte, Montana, at a depth of almost 500 m.* [*After Reno Sales, in Lindgren.*]

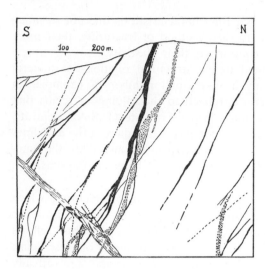

FIGURE 189

Section of the Butte region, showing the relations between veins and faults.

a relative movement of their margins. In a sufficiently rigid rock, and for sufficiently rapid movements, such faults may appear at almost any depth. According to the nature of the rocks traversed, the margins may be more or less broken; hence they lend themselves more or less to mineralization. If the fault is not perfectly planar, the two margins cannot have remained everywhere in contact; to each inflection of the direction, there corresponds, according to its

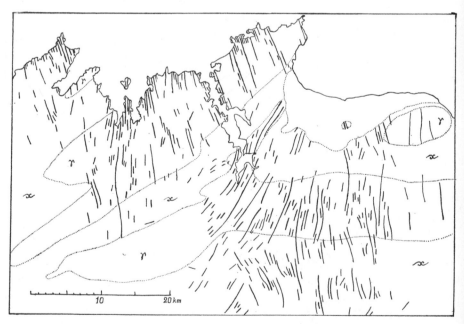

FIGURE 190. *Diabase dikes of the Cotes-du-Nord, Brittany.* (x = *schists,* γ = *granite-gneiss.*)

sense, an increase or a decrease of the open space which is expressed by a mineralization more or less rich (Fig. 187). Systems of veins, such as those in Butte, Montana, result from a complex regional deformation (Figs. 188 and 189).

A second type of fracture may appear by traction, normal to the latter. Such fractures are very rarely produced in our current experiments in the open air; but the situation at depth is quite different, inasmuch as the rock is impregnated by a fluid under pressure that immediately occupies every incipient fissure. If the pressure undergone by the rock is less than the pressure of the fluid, along a given direction, fissures will open perpendicular to this direction, and the liquid will invade them. This may be produced as well with an eruptive rock—for example, the diabase that forms a system of dykes in the Cotes-du-Nord (Fig. 190)—as with hydrothermal solutions.

In order that traction fissures may appear, the impregnation fluid must, on the one hand, have a sufficient pressure, which is produced only beyond a certain depth, and on the other hand, one of the pressures in the rock must fall below the pressure of the fluid. Since the latter increases in depth less quickly than the pressure in the solid, owing to the difference of density, the greater the depth, the less are the chances that traction fissures will appear. Traction fissures are often multiple and may be accompanied by brecciation of the surraunding rock. They may also appear on the walls of a fault directed at 45° to the surrounding rock; the accompanying section (Fig. 191) shows such traction fissures mineralized at the same time as the principal fault (*feather joints*).

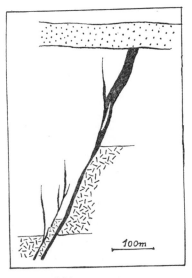

FIGURE 191

Section of San Rafael vein, at El Oro, Mexico. [After Lindgren.]

Mechanical fractures that are the sites of metallic veins may be of varied origins. It seems that it is not unusual for the emplacement of a mass of eruptive rock to have produced the forces responsible for subsequently mineralized fissures. Other fissures are due simply to the contraction of an intrusive rock on cooling. Contrary to what might have been expected, few fractures favorable to mineralization are produced during tectonic deformations. It is probable that plastic deformations play too important a role in them and that they tend to close the fractures that might have appeared, thus crushing their walls. In particular, a number of Alpine deposits appear in a definite stratigraphic layer. That is, the mineralization took place parallel to the stratification, aided by a naturally porous bed, or one that had become so through tectonic deformation. In other beds, it seems that the thrusts were too strong to permit the fissures to open, and may even have closed those that might have existed.

Naturally, the metallic deposits are more numerous in mountain chains, where eruptive rocks are best developed, but such deposits may be much younger (Jurassic zinc mineralization in the Cévennes; veins crossing the Lias in the Pelvoux). The richest deposits are related to the orogenesis or the eruptive rocks of the Precambrian.

Notes and References

1. Dewey, H., and Flett, J. S., Geol. Magaz., vol. 48, pp. 200–209, 1911.

2. Knopf, Adolph, The Geosynclinal Theory, Bull. Geol. Soc. America, vol. 47, pp. 649–670, 1948.

3. Perrin, R., *Le métamorphisme générateur de plissements,* Annales des Mines, pp. 135–170, Sept. 1934.

4. Bonte, A., Denaeyer, M., Goguel, J., *Les facteurs mécaniques dans la genèse de la structure "cone-in-cone,"* Soc. géol. France, Comptes-rendus, no. 9, pp. 182–184, May 19, 1947.

5. Raguin, E., *Géologie du Granite, Paris* (Masson), 1946. (See page 18.)

6. Goguel, J., *Mesures gravimétriques en Bretagne; interprétation géologique,* Publ. Bureau Recherches Géol. et Géophys., no. 8, pp. 30–37, Paris, 1950.
Bollo, R., and Goguel, J., *La gravimétrie de la Bretagne et la géologie,* Acad. Sci. Paris, Comptes-rendus, vol. 229, p. 1130, Nov. 28, 1949.

7. Sitter, L. U. de, and Sitter-Koomans, C. M. de, The Geology of the Bergamasc Alps, Lombardy, Italy, Leidse Geol. Mededeel., vol. 14-B, pp. 1–257, 1947.
Sitter, L. U. de, *Le style structurel nord-pyrénéen dans les Alpes bergamasques,* Bull. Soc. géol. France, 5ᵉ ser., vol. 19, pp. 617–621, 1949.

8. Bianchi, A., and Dal Piaz, G. B., *Studi geologico-petrografici sul massiccio dell' Adamello meridionale,* Padova, 1937.

9. Goguel, Jean, *Observations sur la déformation d'un calcaire métamorphique* (Adamello meridional), Bull. Soc. géol. France, 5ᵉ ser., vol. 18, pp. 441–452, 1948.

10. Demay, A., *Microtectonique et tectonique profonde,* Mém. Carte Géol. France, Paris, 1942.

11. Wegmann, C. E., *Zur Deutung der Migmatite,* Geol. Rundschau, vol. 26, no. 5, pp. 305–350, 1935.
———, *Uber einige Fragen der Tiefentektonik,* Geol. Rundschau, vol. 26, no. 6, pp. 448–451, 1935.

12. Suess, F., *Intrusionstektonik und Wandertektonik im variszisch Grundgebirge,* Berlin, 1926.

13. Raguin, E., *Géologie des Gîtes Mineraux,* 2nd ed., Paris (Masson), 1949.

14. Raguin, E., *Métalogénie hydrothermale et failles vivantes,* Bull. Soc. géol. France, 5ᵉ ser., vol. 19, pp. 415–426, 1949.

15. Newhouse, W. H. (editor), *et al., Ore Deposits as Related to Structural Features* (*a symposium*), Princeton Univ. Press, 280 pp., 1942.

CHAPTER NINETEEN

Pacific Arcs, Oceanic Trenches, Negative Anomalies of Gravity, Earthquakes, and Volcanoes

Connection of these phenomena with contemporary tectonic deformations—Distribution of altitudes and depths—Location of trenches of great depth along the arcs—Negative anomalies of gravity in relation with these arcs; their interpretation—Earthquakes; concomitant deformations; their distribution—Echelonning of deep earthquakes along inclined surfaces—Other seismic zones; Alpine mountain chain, Atlantic ridge—Deformations connected with volcanic activity—Distribution of volcanoes—Relations of volcanoes to fractures of earth's crust—Volcanoes connected with Alpine mountain chain—Possible interpretations for associated phenomena in the Pacific arcs.

THE PHENOMENA that we are going to review may seem rather disparate at first sight, but their distribution, on the contrary, suggests an incontestable relationship. They constitute manifestations of the internal evolution of the earth, which elsewhere has produced mountain chains. But whereas granitization and metamorphism, which are also connected with the genesis of mountain chains, are deep phenomena that can be studied only after prolonged erosion and so especially in old mountain chains, the phenomena considered here belong to the present, or at least to very recent times. They constitute the manifestations of the internal evolution of the earth that are

315

perceptible at the surface and which may cast a few rays of light upon present-day orogenies. First we must analyze these different phenomena separately, so that we can seek out their interrelationships and the interpretation that can be given them.

As a general rule, we have been led not to attach a very great significance to the mean altitude of different regions from the point of view of the study of the deformations that they have undergone. We know, in particular, that the Alps were carried to their present altitude by an uplift of 1500 to 2000 m in the Pliocene, long after the end of the last tectonic deformations. According to the principle of isostasy, the mean altitude of a region (calculated over some hundreds or a thousand square kilometers) depends directly on the mean density of the earth's crust taken as a whole. So it integrates the effect of all earlier deformations, magmatic phenomena, erosion, and sedimentation. Without erosion and sedimentation, which act in relation to the sea level and tend to level continents and fill depressions almost to this level, the history of the earth might be considered sufficiently complex to lead to a statistical distribution of densities and, hence, to the mean altitudes of different divisions, in accordance with the law of chance dispersion, which we have no reason to assume is symmetrical.

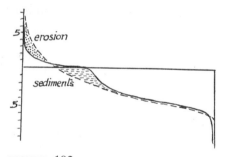

FIGURE 192

Drawing of the hypsographic curve (solid line), which gives the statistical distribution of altitudes. The broken line is a chance dispersion curve. The dotted and shaded areas show how we may consider that erosion and sedimentation have caused such a curve to pass to the hypsographic curve.

The same sort of process may have determined the depth of marine areas, except that erosion is not to be considered. As for sedimentation, it seems to be very slow in the deep parts of the oceans; its essential role has been to build up the continental shelves by accumulation of debris torn from the continents, raising them to the vicinity of the surface (or to the lower limit of the zone of turbulence).

The statistical distribution of altitudes and depths on the surface of the earth, which may be represented by the "hypsographic curve" (Fig. 192), pretty well justifies the foregoing considerations.[1] It differs essentially from a dissymmetric chance dispersion curve (which is spread farther toward the high altitudes than toward the great depths) by a reduction of altitude of the high regions corresponding to their erosion and a flattening near sea level of an expanse corresponding to the plains and the continental shelves.

But on the other hand, this dispersion curve does not seem to adequately represent the surface occupied by the very great depths, say from 6000 to

10,500 m. Since the deeper parts of present-day oceans have not all been measured by echo-soundings, such depths may be more common than this curve indicates.

This first indication regarding the special role played by very great marine depths is confirmed by their distribution. Whereas the intermediate depths, say from 3000 to 5000 m, vary in an irregular manner over the whole extent of the oceans, the very great depths form long, narrow trenches extending, at most, a few hundred kilometers, parallel to mountainous coasts or, more frequently, to more or less curved island chains (the trench then being on the convex side), which may be considered as marking the emplacement of a submarine mountain chain. The repeated discovery of trenches at great depths, as the number of soundings is increased, have always confirmed this systematic relation. So it is evident that trenches of great depth are produced by a particular mechanism, related to the genesis of mountain chains or island arcs. We shall return later on to this mechanism.

As soon as it was possible for him to measure the intensity of gravity at sea, Hecker studied one of the most typical of the deep trenches, that of the Tonga group. There he recorded a very strong negative anomaly (194 milligals after isostatic correction), which was bordered on both the east and on the west by zones of positive anomalies. This first indication has been amply checked and confirmed by the submarine measurements made with the much more accurate apparatus of Vening Meinesz, at first by Meinesz and then by other observers.

The most important results were obtained by Vening Meinesz in Indonesia. Negative anomalies on the order of 100 to 200 milligals (after isostatic correction) are grouped in a narrow belt framed by positive anomalies. This belt is parallel to the arcs and situated on their convex side, as are the trenches of great depth, but it does not coincide with these trenches. To the south of Java, and to the southwest of Sumatra, a trench 2000 to 3000 meters deep parallels the coast. Beyond this trench, a ridge emerges in a few islands. Finally, at about 300 km from the coast, there is another trench, which is more than 7000 m deep. The negative anomalies are maximum on the intermediate ridge (of course all corrections have been made to take into account the attraction of the irregularities on the bottom of the sea). The axis of the anomaly passes through the islands of Nias, Batoe, and Siberoet, to the southwest of Sumatra, and farther east, through the island of Timor, then through Tanimbar and Ceram, which constitute the most external alignment of the Sunda islands.

Measurements that were subsequently taken on a certain number of arcs and analogous trenches have amply confirmed these conclusions. In the Antilles, in particular, there is a belt of strong negative anomalies situated along the convexity of the principal alignment of the islands at a distance of some 200 km. This belt coincides, in part, with the trench situated to the north of Puerto Rico, but where this trench does not continue to the south along the arc of the

Lesser Antilles the belt of negative anomalies is more continuous; it passes through the islands of Barbados and Trinidad. Let us remember that each milligal of negative anomaly indicates a depth of 10 m below the equilibrium level; the values observed thus correspond to disequilibrium of 1000–1500 m.

The narrowness of certain belts of anomalies shows that the too light disturbing masses are certainly less than 100 km deep. So there is no direct reason for assuming that the deep zones (beyond 50 to 100 km) differ on the vertical of the belts of negative anomalies from what they are elsewhere; that is, at a constant depth, the pressure should everywhere be the same.

For the pressure to be the same here, the light rocky masses situated under the belt of negative anomalies would have to be held in depth by forces acting from neighboring zones, which are the seats of positive anomalies. Considered as a whole, the positive and negative belts would not constitute an exception to the principle of isostasy. But within the thickness of the earth's crust, important vertical forces must be acting. Under the action of these forces, there is nothing to prevent the rocks from deforming progressively and the zone of negative anomaly from rising. On Timor, Quaternary coral reefs have been found up to 1400 m in height.

In order to express this idea of a vertical pressure in the earth's crust in the neighborhood of the negative anomaly, Vening Meinesz has proposed the hypothesis of a buckling formed by the crust of light rocks (sial), driven downward in the midst of heavier rocks (sima) by a lateral compression (see Chapter 16, p. 268). It would certainly be going beyond the thought of the author to assert that this buckling results from a flexible torsion of the earth's crust as a whole, as certain diagrammatic figures suggest. The deformation of the sial could just as well have been caused by a system of faults or ruptures. A hypothesis of this sort seems to be the only way of explaining these negative belts by the intervention of horizontal compression, whose trace appears at every step in the deformed regions, without conceiving deep vertical forces which would be irreconcilable with isostasy. This being the case, it seems natural to assume that the deep trenches result from a depression of the bottom of the sea during the compression in depth of the corresponding part of the earth's crust. It is easy to understand that these trenches may either be absent or discontinuous if movements of their margins have filled them. The islands that may replace them generally show very deeply deformed rocks, as could be expected (Timor).

A first indication given by Ewing, following seismic refraction measurements taken in the spring of 1951, seems to show that the Puerto Rico trench probably involved a very great thickness of slightly consolidated sediments. The structural trench, excluding these sediments, would then be much more important than is indicated by the marine depths alone.

The displacement between deep trench and negative anomaly, such as that which exists to the south of Java and Sumatra, seems to indicate a quite marked dissymmetry in the manner of deformation of the earth's crust. *A priori,* we might have sought the reason for this dissymmetry in the upper parts of the earth's crust, the composition of which may vary considerably from an oceanic basin to the neighboring continental block. Figure 182, borrowed from Vening Meinesz, suggests that the superficial part of the continental mass (sial or sedimentary) was probably tilted into the trench, a part of which it obstructed.

But the information furnished by earthquakes suggests a very different interpretation. We know that earthquakes mark the arrival at the surface of vibrations produced by a sudden deep deformation. There are reasons for believing that the action of a fault is normally produced by a series of shocks of limited amplitudes, each of which must have produced an earthquake. The sides are placed under a progressively increasing tension until the friction limit is passed.

As early as 1868, Lyell [2] pointed out the movement of a fault visible at the surface at the time of the earthquake of 1855 in New Zealand. Examples of this sort have multiplied since. One of the best studied is that of the San Francisco earthquake in 1906, during which the San Andreas fault acted along a length of 300 km with a displacement, principally horizontal, of as much as 6 m. Many similar traces of recent movements exist in California. The greatest vertical displacement recorded at the time of an earthquake is 14 meters (Alaska, September, 1899).

However, on numerous occasions, it has been observed in Japan that the movement of a superficial fault was produced only after the destructive shock; thus it is a question not of the movement at the source of the earthquake, which must be produced in depth in a zone of resistant rocks, but of a secondary consequence of the earthquake.

Certain earthquakes may have a different origin, but these seem to constitute only a very small minority. Some very large landslips have produced shocks that have been registered by instruments (February 18, 1911: Pamir, landslip of 3 km³, from 300 to 600 m in height). Or were the landslides induced by a deep earthquake? Certain volcanic eruptions are accompanied by shocks of relatively little importance. Contrary to what has sometimes been thought, it does not seem that either the collapse of underground cavities or underground explosions play a significant role.

Direct observations are extremely fragmentary, and they provide information only on the superficial aspect of the phenomena. Earthquakes affecting deserts or oceanic zones escape direct observation.

Fortunately, the interpretation of the records of seismographic observatories now provides us with more complete information. An earthquake of a certain magnitude taking place at any point in the world may now be located to within a precision of a few tens of kilometers and to within a few hundreds of kilometers in the least favorable cases. It is also possible to determine the depth of the focus beneath the surface and establish the strength on an arbitrary scale of magnitude, from which the amount of energy released may be determined. In certain regions, such as Japan, California, Europe, even earthquakes of very small magnitude can be studied in this fashion.

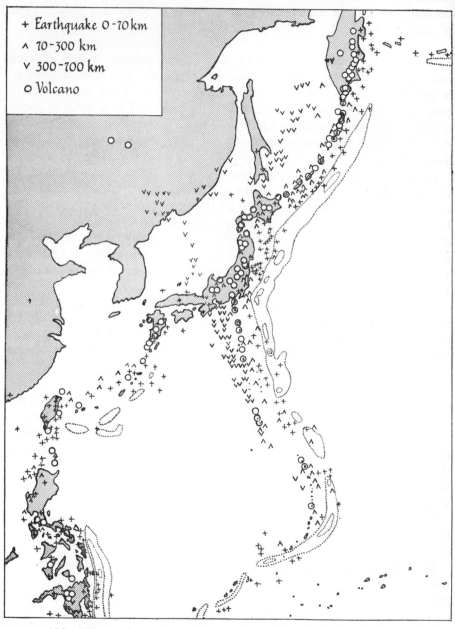

FIGURE 193. *Map of the region of Japan, indicating the location of seismic foci [after Gutenberg and Richter], volcanoes, and the trenches of great marine depths (isobaths of 8000, 9000, and 10,000 m).*

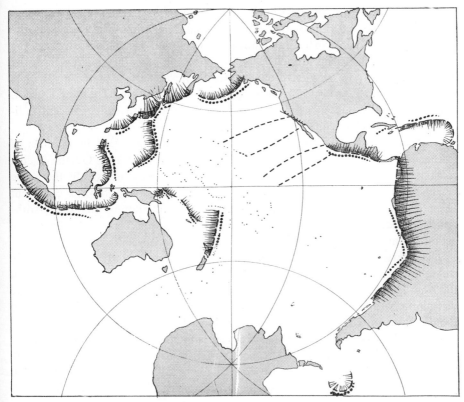

FIGURE 194. *Map of the Pacific hemisphere, showing the location of the series of earthquakes of echelonned depths (shading), marine trenches (dotted lines), and lines of fractures of the northeast Pacific (dots and dashes).*

The statistical accumulation of all such data, recorded over the past fifty years, furnishes information of essential importance on the present tectonic activity of the earth. This information has been assembled by G. Gutenberg and C. F. Richter in a fundamental work,[3] that includes a critical discussion and a description of the regional characteristics of the activity.

For a long time, seismologists have been recording the intense seismic activity on the periphery of the Pacific. The data of Gutenberg and Richter make it possible to state this notion precisely. It has been possible to estimate the mean energy released in each of the sectors of this periphery, but above all, the calculation of the depth of the focus has brought forth a very remarkable arrangement. The accompanying map indicates the location of the foci in one of the most characteristic regions. It has been ascertained that in each of the arcs that constitute the Kuril Islands, Central Japan, and the Bonin Islands, the superficial foci are situated on the edge of the deep trench off the coast (Fig. 193). The earthquakes of medium depth have their foci approximately on the vertical of the islands in a region marked by numerous volcanoes. Finally, the deep foci occupy a much more internal position. Keeping in mind the inaccuracy of the determinations, it may be said that the foci are situated near an inclined surface that would meet the surface at the inner edge of the deep trench, that is, approximately at the level of the negative anomaly of gravity, dipping toward the concavity of the arc with a slope between 25° and 45°, down to a depth of 700 km. The foci are not, however, equally numerous at all depths. A general statistical treatment indicates a somewhat indefinite minimum of about 450 km.

On the periphery of the Pacific, earthquakes are grouped in families of increasing depth, which correspond to the different island arcs. Off the Pacific coast of South America, deep trenches exist that present exactly the same arrangement, with increasingly deeper foci as we penetrate into the continent (Fig. 194). On the other hand, California shows a different character, without deep foci. There the seismicity seems to be essentially connected with the action of faults of horizontal displacement, such as the San Andreas.

The marginal arcs of the Pacific are all convex toward the completely stable and aseismic central part of the ocean, with the exception of those of the New Hebrides and New Britain, which seem to be oriented in the opposite direction, both from the point of view of the position of the deep trench and the direction in which the planes of foci slope downward.

In addition to the Pacific arcs, two very similar arcs, which constitute the Antilles and the South Antilles respectively (South Georgia, South Sandwich Islands, South Orcades), that are convex toward the Atlantic Ocean. But it does not seem that this characteristic arrangement of the foci in island arcs is to be found elsewhere. Along the Alpine mountain chain, earthquakes are, in general, relatively frequent in some places, but they do not present as clear an alignment as along the Pacific arcs. Earthquakes of intermediate depths have been located in them at some points. In Hindu-Kush, 70 shocks were recorded from the same focus (36° 5′ N lat., 70° 5′ E long.) at a depth of 230 km. A similar focus exists in Romania, in front of the elbow in the Carpathians (46° N lat., 26° 5′ E long.), around 100 to 150 km in depth; another exists in the Lipari Islands, at about 225 km in depth. Still others are located on Cyprus and Rhodes.

The only deep earthquake known to have occurred outside the Pacific peripheral zone was recorded on March 29, 1954. The epicenter was at a depth of 600 km, near Granada, Spain.

The repetition of deep earthquakes at the same point suggests a mechanism quite different from that which distributes the deep foci of arcs of the Pacific type along an inclined surface. Earthquakes with shallow foci are dispersed along the whole length of the Alpine mountain chains in a way that scarcely helps to clarify the law that would relate them to geologic deformations. Even if we assume that present deformations are only the continuation of old deformations, we must keep in mind that we are able to reconstruct them through near-surface observation only. It is very difficult to say what deformations originated at a depth of 10 or 15 km, that is, at the level where the shallowest earthquakes originate.

In order to delimit the zones where the danger of earthquakes is greatest, it is sometimes postulated that the earthquakes of the Himalayas (Assam) correspond to the action of the lines of major dislocation, along which the old metamorphic formations overthrust the Neogene beds of the Siwaliks; but this interpretation, which has not yet been proved by observation, is disputed. Moreover, the most recent movements seem to be located to the south, on the edge of the plain of the Ganges and on the upper tilted beds of the Siwaliks.

In a very anciently populated region like the western Alps, it is possible to make use of long-term macroseismic observations and, thus, to establish more reliable statistics than would result from the analysis of seismic records; but of course the depth cannot be determined. Such a study was made by J. P. Rothé,[4] who has shown that most of the foci are roughly aligned along two arcs, one of which (the Piedmont arc) runs along the border of the Alps, on the edge of the Po plain; the other (the Briançonnais arc) approximately follows the border of the internal and external zones. Other rather shallow foci, dispersed along the sub-Alpine chains, are related to certain fault subsidence zones that were active during Oligocene sedimentation.

Rothé seeks to relate these "arcs" to the root zones of the Alpine nappes. There seems, to me, to be greater reason to relate them to the most recent movements; in particular, the Piedmont arc corresponds very closely to the subsidence (oblique to the tectonic zones) that determined the depression of the Po plain. As for the foci of the Briançonnais arc, they are located near the external crystalline masses, which were broken and uplifted by the last Alpine compression on their contact with the structure of the internal nappes, which were much more anciently deformed and indurated. Naturally we cannot expect to find foci in the zones where the Mesozoic cover alone is folded upon a basement that has remained unaltered. These indications are still very vague; however, it seems that the data of seismic statistics suggest an essential difference in the nature of an Alpine mountain chain and a Pacific arc.

Earthquakes of very slight intensity and of infrequent occurrence can be observed in almost all regions, even in the most stable zones, or at least on their periphery. It seems difficult to interpret their distribution.

Seismic foci follow certain fault zones, such as the African Great Lakes or Syria (but none have been plotted along the Red Sea). We have seen above that the California earthquakes also seem to be connected with the action of recent faults. Finally, a series of foci are localized along the ridge that approximately follows the axis of the Atlantic Ocean, half way between the shores of the Old World and the New World. The soundings of the *Meteor,* in particular, showed that the relief of this ridge is extremely irregular in detail. This line of foci continues across the icy Arctic Ocean to the mouths of the Lena River. It can, at least in part, be related to the "Lomontov Ridge,"

To the south, this alignment of foci seems to be independent of the arc of the Southern Antilles. It curves toward the east, rounds the Cape of Good Hope, and extends up into the Indian Ocean as far as the entrance to the Gulf of Aden, passing halfway between the Seychelles and the Maldives. It seems that this alignment corresponds, at least in places, to a ridge (the Carlsberg ridge) on both sides of the equator. Figure 195 shows that the Atlantic ridge is marked by a certain number of volcanoes, of which the most important are

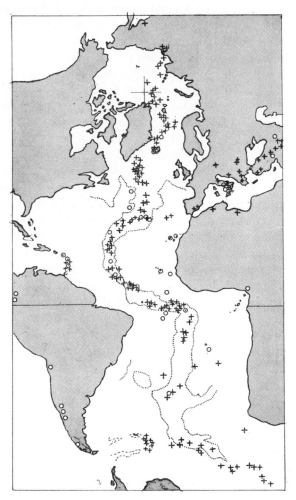

FIGURE 195. *Distribution of seismic foci (crosses) and volcanoes (circles) along the Atlantic ridge and in the Arctic Ocean. The Atlantic volcanoes correspond, in part, to submarine eruptions reported by navigators. The 4000-meter isobath (dotted lines) indicates the line of the Atlantic ridge; it has been omitted on the borders of the continents. (Conformable cylindrical projection, tangential upon the meridian 30°W.)*

those in Iceland, and also by submarine eruptions, occasionally reported by navigators, one of which Fouqué was able to observe in the Azores.

The seismic belt, which continues for a total of nearly 32,000 km, differs both from the Pacific arcs and the Alpine mountain chains; evidently, numerous hypotheses may be formed regarding its nature and origin,[5] but a few complementary data would be highly desirable to enable us to give a sure interpretation of what in any case constitutes one of the great lines of the face of the earth.

Recent studies by seismologists have made possible an approximate estimate of the energy expended in earthquakes. Gutenberg and Richter indicate, for the total annual mean, the figure of 10^{27} ergs (with a margin of error between 0.1 and 10). This order of magnitude takes on its full meaning when compared with the mechanical equivalent of the heat dissipated by conduction through the earth's crust, about 10^{28} ergs; exchanges of seismic energy are notable in comparison to the other exchanges of energy that take place in the earth.

Another essential fact is that the most important earthquakes account for the major part of this total energy. In spite of their number, the weak or medium earthquakes account for only a trivial amount of the total. Moreover, it does not seem very probable that the intensity of the strongest observed quakes may be greatly surpassed, owing to the limited resistance of the earth's crust.

This distribution of energy leads us to think that the great tectonic deformations produce strong earthquakes and that small or medium quakes correspond only to secondary readjustments. However, the possibility, and even the probability, that progressive plastic deformation could take place without causing earthquakes, must not be overlooked.

It has been shown that the earthquakes on the periphery of the Pacific alone account for 80 percent of the total energy released. Of this 80 percent, shallow, intermediate and deep earthquakes account for approximately 82, 15, and 3 percent, respectively; thus superficial seismicity remains the essential phenomenon. South America accounts for 15 percent of the world total, and the Japanese-Kamchatka zone contribute 17 percent. The Alpine mountain chains, in the broad sense (including China), contribute nine tenths of the remainder, and the earthquakes of the Arctic belt, mid-Atlantic ridge, and Indian Ocean release less than 2 percent of the total energy.

We have already alluded above to the distribution of active volcanoes. As opposed to earthquakes, which only very rarely leave indubitable traces in the stratigraphic succession, it is easy to reconstitute the action of volcanic phenomena in the past and, consequently, their variations in function from those of tectonic phenomena.

Volcanoes play an important role in building relief features, both on the continents and in the oceans, where they may form islands. But it is essentially

SW

NE

1 km

FIGURE 196. *Nested calderas of the Eboga and the Elengoum, in the Cameroon Mountains.* [*After Gèze.*]

a process in which eruptive materials accumulate in the form of lava flows and tuffs. The study of volcanism, in itself, is outside the sphere of this work, which has as its subject matter the deformations undergone by the earth's crust.

However, the activity of certain volcanoes has brought about certain deformations of the earth's crust, corresponding in particular to the collapse of the roof of magmatic reservoirs that have discharged at the surface. It is possible to interpret, in this manner, the circular fractures injected with eruptive rock that caused the "ring dykes" in the neighborhood of Oslo, during the Upper Paleozoic, or those of Mull (Scotland), which are related to Cenozoic eruptions. Van Bemmelen has described subsidence zones of Sumatra, such as that of Lake Toba, which were probably, in a way, the counterpart of neighboring eruptions.

Gèze has shown[6] that the nested cirques, which resemble calderas, in the Manengouba Mountains (Cameroons) were not formed by explosions, but rather from a circular subsidence, which it is natural to relate to the removal of eruptive rocks ejected (Fig. 196).

Injections of eruptive rocks in the thickness of the earth's crust are also related to volcanoes; for instance, the injection of magma between sedimentary strata may produce deformations of the surface of some size. Such injections may form sills or laccoliths, which erosion often enables us to observe, but which we sometimes have to assume lie beneath a volcanic region, in order to explain localized deformations of the surface.

Such a deformation was observed from July to November, 1910, on the shore of Lake Taya at the foot of the volcano Usu-San (Island of Hokkaido, Japan) when a hill 150 m high was formed after an eruption with no volcanic manifestations other than the eruption of mud. The formation of a laccolith at shallow depth seems the only possible explanation. The same phenomenon was produced at the foot of another slope of the same volcano[7] in 1944, the formations being lifted up 150 m on a diameter of 800 m in three months. But this time a little cumulo-volcano, formed of very viscous, acid lava, appeared at the summit of the dome.

We shall concern ourselves with volcanoes here essentially to seek their relations with the other phenomena of deep origin just described and, finally, with the zones of tectonic deformation. For a long time the abundance of volcanoes that make up the "circle of fire" of the Pacific has been noted.

Evidently, their distribution is related to the distribution of earthquakes, though there are great differences. In order to analyze the position of volcanoes in their relation to tectonic zones, we must give the most careful consideration to the nature of the volcanic eruptions; thus, the eruption of very fluid basalts, which typically form extensive sheets that are frequently carved into plateaus by subsequent erosion, often took place in regions where no tendency to orogenic deformation manifested itself, such as in the Siberian shield, in Deccan and in Brazil. Comparison may be made with the volcanoes of the Hawaiian Islands, also basaltic, and which seem to have built up the islands of the archipelago solely through the accumulation of their lavas without any deformation of the basement, as established by the measurements of gravity intensity made by Vening Meinesz. Moreover, the regions around the Hawaiian Islands are perfectly stable from the seismic point of view. A few little shocks in the islands themselves seem to be nothing more than reactions of the eruptions.

Owing to the basaltic nature of the lavas, this stable area of the Pacific differs from the arcs that surround the ocean, whose volcanoes emit different lavas, particularly andesites. We have already seen that these volcanoes occupy a determined position in the circle, which corresponds to the zone where the foci of the earthquakes already reach a depth of 80 to 100 km; moreover, the foci of shallow earthquakes are usually located in the ocean in front of the arc.

In certain cases, a second line of volcanoes has been observed, which is extinct or of very reduced activity, and which corresponds to the zone in which the seismic foci are now somewhat deeper (Kamchatka). The Sunda Islands present a very clear example of this arrangement. At present, the greatest tectonic activity seems to be located along the belt of negative gravity anomalies that passes through Timor, whereas the recent or active volcanoes mark the inner row of the islands, from Flores to Banda. It has even been recorded that the volcanoes of the Timor ridge, which represents a maximum of tectonic activity along the direction of the arc, are extinct (Alor) and are relayed by others situated farther back, some of which are submarine (Fig. 197). Vening Meinesz[8] observed, in the Marianna Islands, in the Antilles,

FIGURE 197

Distribution of volcanoes in eastern Indonesia. (Active volcanoes are shown in black; the circles indicate extinct volcanoes; the broken line indicates the axis of the negative anomaly. [After H. A. Brouwer, Geological Expedition to the Lesser Sunda Islands, Amsterdam, 1942, vol. 4, p. 396.]

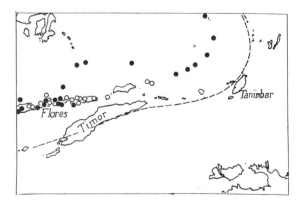

and in the eastern Sunda Islands, a third arc situated in the interior of the concavity of the tectonic arc and of the volcanic arc, which is located 300 to 350 km from the latter and separated from it by depths of 3000 to 4000 m. This third arc is marked out only by a few little isolated islands and is generally manifested only in the distribution of the marine depths.

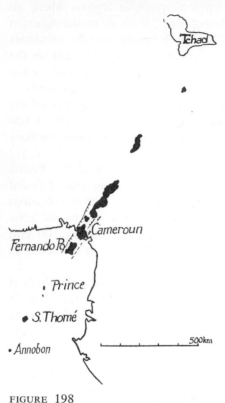

FIGURE 198

Volcanoes and volcanic islands of the Cameroons, showing their alignment, as well as the faults bordering the subsident trench.

It seems, to us, that little can be gained by reviewing the other arcs, which more or less confirm the general characteristics that have just been pointed out, but which never vary from them. We have already pointed out the alignment of volcanoes along the mid-Atlantic ridge, some of which are submarine, and which are marked by a very clear seismic activity. The volcanic activity along this ridge seems to be connected with some sort of tectonic movement as are the island arcs. Even when the volcanoes seem independent of such activity, It does not seem probable that the volcanic materials could have forced their way through the upper part of the earth's crust without taking advantage of some favorable circumstance. Actually, the volcanoes are very often grouped along a straight line, which seems to mark a deep fracture of the earth's crust. In the eruption of Laki Jokul, in Iceland (1783), the basalt visibly reached the surface through a fissure 25 km long, along which eruption centers were only progressively individualized. There it was a question of a typical plateau basalt eruption. But the alignment of distinct volcanic centers strongly suggests the existence of some sort of deep fracture; it is sufficient to consider, for example, the arrangement of the archipelago of the Hawaiian Islands.

If such a fracture exists in zones occupied by volcanoes, even when there is no other indication of deformation, there are also cases where it appears very clearly, particularly if its two margins have been active, causing it to play the role of a fault. In the system of trenches of the great African lakes, such faults can be traced for 10,000 km; and it is only in places that they are marked by volcanic structures, some of which are very important, either in terms of their extent (Ethiopia) or their altitude (Kilimanjaro). The seismic activity along these trenches is considerable, but is of relatively little importance.

The arrangement of the volcanoes in the Cameroons, including the alignment of the volcanic islands of Fernando Po, Prince's Island, St. Thomas, and Anobon, also indicates the existence of a fracture, or rather a group of parallel fractures.[9] (See Fig. 198.) Although several of these volcanoes are active, there is no indication that earthquakes occur in this region.

It frequently happens, in a zone of old volcanism, that erosion leaves only the fissures, still filled with the eruptive rock, through which the magma must have reached the surface to spread out in a sheet that has today disappeared. The diabase dikes of the Côtes-du-Nord, in France (Fig. 190) are a particularly typical example. Analogous observations have been made in certain districts of Scotland (Mull).

Although the total deformation resulting from the injection of eruptive rock is on the whole negligible, the arrangement of dikes nevertheless gives us some information on the pressure conditions that prevailed in the crust. It is obvious that the lava has not found wide open fissures to give it passage. These fissures opened only under the pressure of the lava (if the corrosion of the walls by the lava had been considerable, these walls doubtless would have not remained so perfectly parallel), which must have exceeded the pressure that existed in the terrain normal to their direction. The directions of these dikes thus indicate the arrangement, at the time of their formation, of the lines of least pressure. Moreover, the difference between the minimum pressure and the maximum pressure (which was exerted parallel to the dikes) might be very slight, and, particularly in the Cotes-du-Nord, it may be very difficult to relate the system of stresses on which we obtain information in this manner to the stresses that are otherwise manifested in tectonic deformations.

The exact position of volcanic centers associated with Paleozoic mountain chains is in general too little known for us to be able to discuss their position relative to the zones that were undergoing tectonic deformation. However, it would be very interesting to know if these relations remained constant throughout geologic time, or if they underwent a characteristic evolution.

Insofar as the Tertiary mountain chains are concerned, it was remarked above that certain types of eruption seem to be associated with the special conditions of sedimentation that prevailed prior to the formation of a mountain chain, such as the eruptions or injections of basic rocks whose alteration produced the greenstone associated with the *schistes lustrés*.

But the Alpine mountain chains are, on the whole, remarkably lacking in volcanoes, either extinct or active. The principal exception is the Caucasus and the neighboring regions. In the Caucasus, volcanic phenomena played an important role in an early geologic epoch (in particular, important volcanic formations in the Jurassic), long before the commencement of Alpine folding. The Quaternary volcanoes of the Kazbek and the Elburz are over 5000 m high, because they are situated on the highest part of the Caucasus mountain chain. But the volume of the erupted lavas is much less than that of the eruptions of Armenia. In the north of Iran, the Demavend is Pliocene or Quaternary. In all regions of Turkey there are outpourings of recent volcanic rocks, and there are two active volcanoes. The various volcanic manifestations of the Aegean Sea are prolongations of those of Asia Minor.

In western Europe, even though no volcanoes exist in the Alps, a certain relation seems to exist between the formation of the Alps and the various Tertiary volcanic regions situated at some hundreds of kilometers from their border in Auvergne and in the Eifel. If we consider the various fractures that affect the Massif Central, the Cévennes fault, the borders of the Limagnes, and the Cantal-Mont-Dore-Puys axis, as being a result of the Alpine movements, we find that it is the feature most distant from the Alps that produced the most important volcanism. These volcanoes have many characteristics in common with those of stable regions, and it is possible that the influence of Alpine orogenesis upon their genesis is relatively secondary.

Evidently the Italian volcanoes occupy a quite different place in relation to the Alpine structure; the massif of the Euganean Mountains, between Verona and Padua, is in contact with the last foothills of the Bergamasc Alps. According to certain geophysical evidence,[10] it probably constituted only a small part of a much larger massif buried under the alluvium of the Po. The island volcanoes and those on the Peninsula are closely associated with the Apennines chain. It is not beyond the realm of possibility that this difference in the situation of the volcanoes expresses a dissymmetry in the constitution of the Alpine chain at depth.

In any event, the difference between mountain chains of the Alpine type and those that constitute the Pacific arcs is very clearly emphasized by the distribution of earthquakes and volcanoes. From the point of view of relations with the internal parts of the earth, it seems to be a question of two essentially different phenomena.

The facts enumerated in this chapter, which have emphasized the originality of the Pacific area, thus lead to representing their characteristics in perhaps too systematic a manner; frequent earthquakes in the neighborhood of a slope whose intersection with the surface determines trenches of great depth and produces a buttressing of the different parts of the earth's crust, which is expressed by a zone of negative anomalies of gravity. At times recent uplifts (Timor) indicate a tendency to readjustment. A little farther back, where the seismic surface attains a depth of 80 to 100 km, a mountain chain, or an island arc, which constitutes its equivalent, frequently has volcanoes; at times there exists a second chain of extinct volcanoes. Behind the arc, there may be a continental area, an epicontinental sea, or a sea of medium depth.

We have seen how Vening Meinesz proposed to interpret the zones of negative anomaly on the basis of a horizontal compression of the earth's crust; his hypothesis would be easy to modify in order to take into account a deep oblique shearing. In particular, we might conceive of a shearing of the earth's crust, which would explain the discrepancy between negative anomaly and deep trench (Fig. 199).

Coulomb[11] has proposed a different interpretation, assuming that the shearing would be due to a stretching of the earth's crust, which the direction of the initial shock of the earthquakes would prove. The upper layers of the earth's crust probably filled the void that resulted from the stretching of the deep magma, and it is conceivable that deep trenches were created by a mechanism that the author does not seek to state precisely, in a naturally dissymmetric position, considering the dissymmetric origin of the void. It is possible to adjust the dimensions that we assume for the upper layer (sial) and for the furrow of the magma in such a way as to indicate anomalies actually observed. Coulomb suggests that the stretching of the beds at depths of 100 to 700 km was probably due to cooling, which penetrated progressively to such depths.

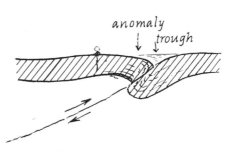

FIGURE 199

Possible interpretation of a shearing of the earth's crust in the Pacific arcs.

But this cooling is extremely slow, and we would have to assume that the state of tension probably continued for several hundreds of millions of years. The numerous known examples of isostatic readjustment, of which the history of Scandinavia in the Quaternary is only the most spectacular, have shown that matter behaves as if fluid after some tens of thousands of years. So it seems that the ruptures evidenced by deep earthquakes can only be explained as the result of a rapid building up of stresses in a few tens or hundreds of years such that plastic deformation would be too slow to cause the disappearance of the stresses. Gutenberg indicates that the viscosity deduced from the readjustments is such that the stresses would be reduced by half in some thousands of years.

Still other hypotheses could be (and have been) formulated to explain the origin of the curved strings of islands that encircle the Pacific; essentially they should take into account the mass of geophysical data that has just been briefly indicated.

With regard to the Alps or similar mountain chains, and *a fortiori,* for the structure of the mid-Atlantic ridge, the study of the distribution of earthquakes and volcanoes has brought us no analogous precise information, and there is scarcely any ground for taking into consideration the few indications gathered in the building of a hypothesis regarding the deep structure of these mountain chains. Here, of course, there is no question of the conditions of propagation of seismic waves, which may furnish information already alluded to in Chapter 7, on the structure of the earth's crust.

Notes and References

1. Goguel, Jean, *Sur l'interprétation de la courbe hypsographique,* Acad. Sci. Paris, Comptes-rendus, vol. 230, p. 219, 1950.

2. Lyell, Charles, *Principles of Geology,* 10th ed., vol. 2, pp. 82–89, 1868.

3. Gutenberg, B., and Richter, C. F., *Seismicity of the Earth,* Princeton Univ. Press, 273 pp. (of which 167 are tables), 34 figs., 1949.
Preliminary publications under the same title in Bull. Geol. Soc. America, vol. 56, pp. 603–668, 1945, and Geol. Soc. America, Spec. Paper no. 34, 1941

4. Rothé, J. P., *La seismicité des Alpes occidentales,* Ann. Strasbourg Inst. Phys. du Globe, Strasbourg, vol. 3, 1938; Clermont-Ferrand, 1944; (Conclusions); new ser., vol. 4, Strasbourg, 1948.

5. Rothé, J. P. (*Quelques aspects de la structure terrestre éclairés par la sismologie,* La Revue Scient., vol. 85, pp. 401–408, 1947) assumes that the Atlantic ridge marks the true western boundary of the Afro-European block, in part submerged. To the west, the ocean probably exhibits a structure comparable to that of the Pacific, that is, sima without a covering of acid or intermediate rocks. Continental drift, in Wegener's sense of the term, probably came into play only between America and the mid-Atlantic Ridge.
This hypothesis has been discussed and sharply criticized by Carlos Teixcra (*À propos d'une hypothèse sur la structure de l'Océan Atlantique,* Univ. Lisbonne, Bull. Musée et Lab. Min. et Géol., no. 18, 6ᵉ ser., pp. 69–79, 1950.

6. Gèze, B., *Géographie physique et géologie du Cameroun occidental,* Mém. Muséum, new ser., vol. 17, pp. 1–272, Paris, 1943. (See page 192.)

7. Minakami, T., Ishikaya, T., and Yagi, K., The 1944 Eruption of Volcano Usu in Hokkaido, Japan, Bull. Volcanol., 2nd. ser., vol. 11, pp. 45–157, Naples, 1951.

8. Vening Meinesz, F. A., A Third Arc in Many Island Arc Areas, Kon. Nederl. Akad. Wetensch., ser. B, vol. 54, no. 5, pp. 432–442, 1951.

9. Gèze, B., *Géographie physique et géologie du Cameroun occidental,* Mém. Muséum, new ser., vol. 17, Paris, 1943.

10. Morelli, Carlo, *Rilievo gravimetrico e riduzione isostatica nell' Italia nord-orientale,* Tecnica Italiana, Trieste, new ser., vol. 6, 1951.

11. Coulomb, J., *Séismes profonds et grandes anomalies négatives de la pesanteur peuvent-ils être attribués a une extension plastique?,* Ann. de Géophys., vol. 1, fasc. 3, pp. 244–255, 1945.

CHAPTER TWENTY

Mutual Relations of Successive Mountain Chains

Spread in time and space of the generative movements of a given mountain chain, revival of folded material—Examples from Haute Provence—Superposition of the Alpine range on Hercynian structures; external zone of the Alps, Pyrenees, internal Alpine zones—Juxtaposition of Hercynian and Caledonian ranges, their position on the periphery of Precambrian shields—Juxtaposition of successive Precambrian ranges—Succession of continental flexures in eastern Asia—Existence of Precambrian folds on margins of shields—Origin of continents, role of granitization—Problem of subsidence of continental blocks—Evolution of conditions of folding.

WE HAVE SEEN heretofore what a long and complex phenomenon orogenesis is, involving a preparatory phase in which the movements are recorded in the succession of sediments, followed by several phases of more or less intense deformation, finally reaching the last late movements. Not only may the movement phases succeed one another in a given region, but the movement may be propagated progressively along the mountain chain, whose age is probably not exactly the same throughout its length. Let us add that a mountain chain may present, in plan, quite notable complications.

In order to study the mutual relations of successive mountain chains, we regard as belonging to a given chain the group of deformations that were produced according to the same overall plan in the course of a period of continuous movements, or one involving only relatively subordinate phases of repose. The inevitable lack of precision in this definition is due to the fact that it is artificial and arbitrary to isolate determined groups in the overall picture of orogenic phenomena.

Even in the heart of what we consider as a single mountain chain, there may have been a revival of the deformation of material that was folded in one of the earlier tectonic phases. If the movements that take place according to a given arrangement follow one another in a determined order, there would be no reason to speak of revival. But it is possible for folds that belong to two different parts of the scheme to meet each other and to affect the same region. The example of the southern sub-Alpine mountain chains will make this possibility more easily understood (Fig. 200). Locally, it is possible to distinguish between the Pyreneo-Provencal folds and the Alpine movements, on the basis of their direction and their age. The prolongation of the Pyrenean axis probably passed to the south of the coast, and Provence was affected at the time of the first Pyrenean phase in the Cenomanian only by local up-warpings which appear especially in the distribution of the facies; the movements were then indicated by a general tipping from the south to the north until the post-Lutetian second phase, which doubtless involved a quite marked dislocation of the basement with folding of the cover. Although they were very complex and crowded, at least in the anticlinal areas, in Basse-Provence,

FIGURE 200

Relation between the folds in the cover of (a) Alpine age (solid lines) and (b) Eocene Pyrenean age (broken lines) in the southeast of France.

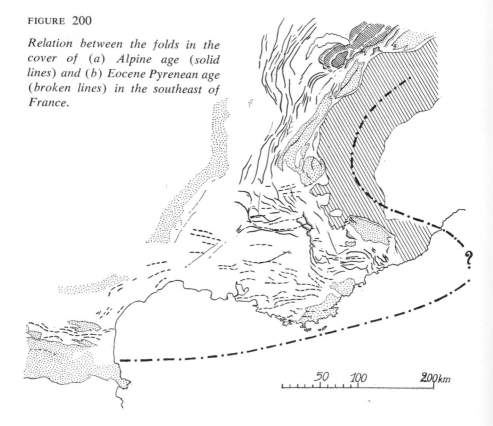

these folds were much more regular in form and more widely spaced farther north (Vaucluse, south of Drôme, and Basses-Alpes). On the whole, the structures are oriented east-west or east-northeast.

Haute-Provence was affected only by the Alpine cover movements in the Upper Miocene; these folds are, in general, directed northwest-southeast. In the region where they interfere with the first, the distinction seems easy. But if we go into detail, we find that the Alpine folds are extremely undulating. At several points these folds have exactly the same direction as the Provencal folds, distinguished only by the epoch of the movement. Contrary to what might be assumed, the direction of the tilting of these folds cannot be utilized, since it is variable, both for the movements of Eocene age and for the Miocene movements.

However, if we start with the most external Alpine folds, which were evidently formed after the deposition of the Miocene molasse, and if we penetrate into the interior of the mountain chain, we are able here and there to date the movements for which we find progressively older epochs (Oligocene movements near Castellane). Thus, the difference of age between the Alpine and Provencal movements tends to diminish.

If we consider not only the Provencal region but the mountain chain as a whole, there is no doubt that the internal zones of the Alps underwent important movements as early as the Lutetian, if not even in the Upper Cretaceous. So we cannot separate, on a chronological basis, the Alpine and Pyrenean mountain chains, which are merely two branches of the same system and must be connected in a manner as yet ill-determined. The simple fact is that, since the axis of the system is very sinuous, the successively formed folds, which originated from two different sections, again covered the same region. Moreover, we know that the sub-Alpine folds affect only the cover, which slipped along a considerable length. In the region where the Alpine and Provencal folds interfere, it is only a question of cover structures without any corresponding dislocation of the basement (we exclude here the south border of the Pelvoux). The influence of the oldest folding upon the mechanical behavior of the formations at the time of the most recent movements is thus quite easy to analyze. It can be shown that the old folds, perhaps because they had been eroded, have acted as lines of least resistance along which later structures were localized. Oblique directions, not perpendicular to the slip of the cover, have been superimposed upon these later structures, and this angle has become compensated by different sorts of structures, causing certain local complications.

But there, on the whole, it is only a question of very localized revivals. The problem of the interference of two successive mountain chains assumes its full importance when we consider two chains separated by a wide interval of time, such as the Hercynian and Alpine chains.

Whenever we can study old formations, either in the Pyrenees or in the

Alps, we ascertain that they had been affected by Hercynian folding, approximately as were the formations of the same age that can be observed outside the Alpine area, for example in the Massif Central. Such is the case for the axial zone and the various northern Pyrenean massifs, as for the external crystalline massifs of the Alps. The analogy applies in the arrangement of the Carboniferous basins, which are discordant on the metamorphic basement and folded into synclines. The directions of the Hercynian folds, where it is possible to establish them, are absolutely independent of those of the Alpine structures.

The Hercynian area extends beyond that of the Alpine folds in the north; it also extends farther to the south, in Spain and North Africa. So we are tempted to say that the Alpine folds have involved an area entirely affected by the Hercynian orogenesis; however, we cannot assert that their behavior is independent of the lines of the Hercynian structures.

The observations relative to the superposition of two tectonics are especially reliable in exterior zones; detailed analysis of their genesis shows that, throughout the Mesozoic, the Alps (including their crystalline masses) had a history that seems much closer to that of the extra-Alpine area than to the history of the internal zones. The revival of activity after the folding and metamorphism of the interior zones, which had become incapable of deformation, broke their Hercynian basement, in accordance with a tectonic of rigid blocks.

Comparison of the tectonics of the basement and of its Mesozoic cover shows that the former had been made relatively rigid by Hercynian orogenesis; however, it is difficult to distinguish the parts played by folding, metamorphism, and granitization.

The case of the Pyrenees seems to be altogether comparable to that of the external Alpine zones; Cretaceous and Tertiary tectonics affected a region whose basement had undergone a uniform Hercynian orogenesis. But it is not possible to be so affirmative in the matter of the interior Alpine zones, the detail of whose Hercynian history cannot be reconstructed. We know only that the internal Alpine Carboniferous basin (Briançonnais, Valais), owing to its thickness and its area, does not seem comparable to the lacustrine basins of the Massif Central, but resembles instead the Sarre-Lorraine basin or the Franco-Belgian basin, formed on the edge of this mountain chain.

Thus we cannot disregard the fact that, since the epoch of Hercynian folding, certain particularities distinguished the regions that were to form some of the internal Alpine zones, which evidently constitute the essential part of the Alpine range. So we may wonder whether the emplacement of the Alpine range, or certain of its features, such as the arc described by the western Alps and the displacement that separates them from the Pyrenees, were not determined by certain features of the Hercynian range.

It is not possible to review here all Tertiary mountain chains. It is sufficient to have established that they may very well have bitten deep into the area formerly affected by the Hercynian orogenesis. However, the greatest part of this area has remained unaltered by the Alpine folding.

The relations between the Paleozoic mountain chains (Caledonian and Hercynian) seem much simpler. The Caledonian folding is indicated, in places, by a lacuna or a discordance in the Hercynian area, but in the main, the two areas are juxtaposed, as may be clearly recognized in England. The Hercynian folding respected the region where the Caledonian folding is well marked, which is characterized by continental Devonian (Old Red Sandstone). On the other hand, in the south of England, on the edge of the Caledonian folds, the Hercynian folds assume importance.

To the extent that age determinations by radioactivity, or simply their mutual relations, have made it possible to recognize in the Precambrian basement masses, such as that of the Canadian shield, the remains of distinct mountain chains, it seems that they are connected to each other, the oldest occupying the center and the youngest occupying the periphery of the shields. The remains of these mountain chains are, in turn, bordered by the Hercynian and Caledonian mountain chains.

This juxtaposition of successive mountain chains might at first sight seem completed by the joining of the Alpine range to the southern part of the Hercynian area, as if the mountain chains had formed successively, each one on the border of the area affected by the preceding ones. But this concept, if it seems valid for the Hercynian and Caledonian ranges, demands broad reservations, as we have seen, insofar as it concerns the Alpine chain, since it greatly affects material folded and metamorphosed in the Hercynian epoch. The case of the Precambrian mountain chains also appears more complex.

Teilhard de Chardin[1] has described a series of flexures in circumpacific Asia that are injected with granite that formed progressively from the interior of the continent (in the Devonian) to the external part of the arc of the Japanese Islands (Miocene). The flexures that he studied are near Peking, in an area of essentially continental sediments, where the progressive development of the conglomerates makes it possible to identify a deformation that increased up to the final phase of dislocation accompanied by granitization. He shows how the progressive joining of the zones of granitized flexures around the Siberian shield was finally expressed by the enlarging of the continental area as far as the insular arcs, in which we obtain a vivid picture of the orogenic process.

However, in Asia, as in Europe, it seems that Tertiary mountain chains are entirely different from the last phase of this joining process of successive orogenies, either because they affect an area already folded at an earlier period or because they express new arrangement; the intensity of movements in them seems moreover much greater than in earlier mountain chains.

The latter, we have seen, seem to be moulded upon the shields that have long since been rigid, in which only traces of Precambrian orogeneseis are to be observed. However, we cannot simply consider these Precambrian folds as being integrated into the series of successive folds joined to one another up to the Tertiary. In fact, remnants of folded Precambrian rocks are found in the midst of the area of Hercynian structures, for example in the Massif Central or in the Appalachians. In a more general way, wherever it is possible to observe the Precambrian, it shows traces of a series of successive folds.

It is still impossible to coordinate the successive phases of Precambrian folding in the different parts of the world. All observations made in continental areas indicate only a completely folded surface and, in the Precambrian, at least the oldest phases of deformation were frequently accompanied by very advanced granitization.

The problem of the distribution of Precambrian mountain chains is closely connected with that of the origin of the differentiation between continental and oceanic areas. From the principle of isostasy, we know that, in the continental areas, the mean density of the earth's crust is less than that of the basic rocks (sima), that is, in the continental areas, the granitic rocks (sial) play an important role.

The Precambrian granitizations have thus been the agent par excellence among those responsible for the building of continents. But, inversely, the oceanic areas could not admit of such granitizations, and it is probable that their history has been completely different since the Precambrian.

The continents formed by folding and granitization of the Precambrian were not limited to the areas that constitute the present-day shields. In the folded zones attached to these shields, we find granitized Precambrian blocks as well as later marine sediments; the latter are, in a great majority of cases, of epicontinental character. They are not characteristic of true oceanic regions, but of the margins of the continental area, which was temporarily invaded by the sea before being folded and incorporated in the continent. Moreover, the corresponding sedimentary material resulted primarily from erosion of the pre-existent continents and was derived, ultimately, after a variable number of reworkings, from granitized Precambrian mountain chains.

It would be in great part hypothetical to seek to trace[2] the evolution of continental and oceanic areas since the Precambrian, inasmuch as the former is susceptible of being increased by the addition of folded and granitized zones. In addition, it would be necessary to introduce also the inverse phenomenon; we often have the impression that observable tectonic structures are incomplete and that a part of them has disappeared, replaced by a deep sea. For example, we are led to postulate a prolongation of the axial zone of the Pyrenees to the south of Provence, in the direction of the Maures, not only by reason of continuity, but in order to explain the closing of the lacustrine basins of the Upper Cretaceous. The migrations of continental faunas present an analogous problem; in order to explain them, without postulating continental drift, geologists have often proposed the hypothesis of "continental bridges" that must have disappeared without leaving any trace of their former existence in the midst of the oceans. Isostasy makes it hard to understand how a continental fragment could have subsided in this manner and requires that such a movement be the consequence of a very deep transformation of the earth's crust.

Besides, that is only one of the problems presented by the deep structure of the ocean floor which constitutes one of the greatest enigmas of geology. It would be quite presumptuous to try to formulate hypotheses that would be largely gratuitous in view of the fact that submarine geophysics is every day revealing greater possibilities and giving us the hope of obtaining positive information in a few years.

In order to keep to the continental area, it seems that we may accept the following scheme with respect to the relations between successive mountain chains. In the Precambrian the continental areas folded several times, but we are unable to reconstruct the order in which the orogenic waves broke, except in certain isolated localities.

The Paleozoic mountain chains, winding around stable areas that have become shields, manifest a tendency to join systematically, as if they marked only the successive stages of a given phenomenon progressively sweeping over a great part of the continental areas. The interval of time that separates the successive phases, for example the Caledonian and Hercynian, is much shorter than the interval separating them from the Precambrian orogeny or from the time of Alpine folding. It has been possible to maintain, with some degree of plausibility, that the Paleozoic mountain chains never reached the intensity of deformation (and consequently the altitudes) that we observe today in the Alpine mountain chains. On the other hand, they seem to have affected extensive regions as well as narrow belts. Hercynian orogenesis is manifested from Cornwall to the south of Morocco, along an actual length of 2300 km.

Even if in places the Tertiary deformations appear to be the result of this great progressive orogenic wave, the Alpine chain presents itself much more often as a structure of original plan, biting more or less into zones deformed earlier and affecting only a narrow belt with an intensity that seems to have been attained only rarely up until that time.

Whenever we make a detailed study of the relations between two successive folded mountain chains that affect a given region, the essential factor to introduce is the change in the mechanical properties of the mineral masses, determined by the older orogenesis. But on the global scale, this sort of consideration is evidently no longer sufficient. Whatever the motive phenomenon of the orogenesis may be, it must be admitted that it moved progressively, acting successively upon different belts of the surface.

From the Precambrian down to our times, the change of conditions in which orogenesis was exerted perhaps expresses a deep modification of the structure of the earth, whose solid, rigid crust must have thickened progressively; in contrast with the very extensive deformations of which this crust seemed still capable in the Paleozoic, the Alpine folds expressed the rupture of a narrow zone under the action of mechanical forces that were very superior to those in force at the time of the earlier orogenies.

On the other hand, the phenomena of metamorphism and granitic injection, connected in an almost constant manner to Precambrian folds, are considerably reduced (at least in certain zones of Paleozoic folding) and play only an occasional role in the Tertiary chains. To the extent that these phenomena are the condition for an easy plastic deformation of the rocks, the increase of the mechanical forces, with a narrower localization of the deformations, is on an equal footing with the reduction of the role of the magmatic phenomena.

A careful comparison of the conditions under which magmatic phenomena were produced, from the Precambrian to the Tertiary, and on through the Carboniferous, would be required to confirm this still very hypothetical concept of a marked change in the constitution of the earth's crust.

Notes and References

1. Teilhard de Chardin, P., *Remarques sur les flexures continentales de Chine,* Bull. Soc. géol. France, 5ᵉ ser., vol. 16, pp. 497–502, 1946.

2. Stille, Hans, *Ur- und Neuozeune,* Deutsche Akad. Wissensch., Berlin, Math.-Naturw. Kl., Abhandl., 1945–1946, no. 6, 1948.

CHAPTER TWENTY-ONE

Deformations Outside the Folded Zones

Their existence as shown by the facies and the flexures—Faults and flexures—Appearances of deformations of nontectonic origin; salt domes, sliding of sediments—Eustatic movements, influence of glaciation and climate—Isostasy, more or less local, more or less slow readjustments—Triggering of a readjustment by a tectonic dislocation—Regional vertical movements, action of faults—Transverse faults—Role of stretching.

UP TO NOW, we have been especially concerned with orogenic zones, which constitute relatively narrow belts along which tectonic deformations often attain great intensity. However, beyond these zones, traces of deformation can be observed which are often of slight intensity but whose occurrence and meaning it is important to examine.

The traces of deformation may be of different sorts. They may be recognized by the nature of the sediments. The fact that in the Bajocian and in the Rauracian (Corallian) on the east side of the Paris Basin the localization of coral reefs, situated originally on shallow bottoms, is not the same indicates a certain deformation in the interval. The variations of altitude of the rocks of a given stage, whose uniform facies indicates deposition at a constant depth, testify to later deformations. Such is the case for the Cretaceous reference horizons formed by the glauconitic beds of the Albian and of the Cenomanian in the Paris basin. Finally, the study of the morphologic evolution often enables us to recognize, in a more or less sure manner, variations of relative height. Faults, or more or less localized flexures, may produce very slightly inclined panels, involving recognizable differences of level.

However, we must not decide too rapidly in all cases upon the existence of tectonic deformations that are at all comparable in intensity to those that we studied in the orogenic zones and which seem to express the intervention of forces resulting from an evolution of the interior part of the earth.

Let us mention, as a reminder, the salt domes (Chaps. 10 and 13), which result from a re-establishment of equilibrium within the thickness of the earth's crust and which were possibly produced without any intervention of forces of deep origin, and differential subsidence, which is only an aspect of the normal evolution of sediments and, for a bed deposited horizontally, may involve folding that reflects more or less the variations of thickness or of facies of the underlying sedimentary series (Chap. 8). The consequences of this differential subsidence are well known in the oil fields of the North American Mid-Continent; the role that differential subsidence may have played in the folding of the Cretaceous of the Paris Basin has never been established, but we must not assume that it was negligible.

Most of the time, the elevations or depths that we measure, or those that we evaluate on the basis of the nature of ancient sediments or morphologic evolution, are referred to sea level as a standard. Sea level may undergo overall or eustatic variations that may be recognized in various regions, where they imply no deformation of the continents. It is quite evident that the total mass of water present on the earth cannot vary rapidly (the water brought to the surface by volcanic eruptions represents something appreciable only on the scale of geologic time). A variation of sea level may be due either to (1) the immobilization of a great quantity of water on the continents in the form of ice; (2) the melting of such glaciers, or (3) changes in the volume of the oceanic trenches, at other points on the earth. The sea-level variations that took place in the Quarternary evidently belong to the first type. These variations are no doubt still going on (the melting of the inland ice of Greenland and the Antarctic would produce another rise in sea level of several tens of meters). To the second type, we may assign the geologic transgressions that Haug has shown to be correlatives of folding (accompanied by marine regressions) in the geosynclines, that is, in the active orogenic zones. The Cenomanian transgression, which is so clear in the most diverse regions of the earth, including the Paris Basin, seems to be the reaction of tectonic movements that raised the bottom or compressed laterally the oceanic trenches occupying the emplacement of mountain chains in course of formation, particularly in the Pyrenean and Provencal zones of France. But it is very evident that there is no direct correspondence between the Pyrenean folds and the transgression of the Paris Basin; it is the world balance sheet of the reduction through folding of the deep trenches that determined a transgression. In an isolated sea, or in a lake, it is the discharge or the relation between evaporation and precipitation which determines the water level rather than the variations in basin volume.

In this particular case, we again find the influence of the climate, which, after all, is responsible for the variations of glaciers. Variations of climate may also directly affect the nature of sediments produced—an effect that should not be attributed to deformation. A change of climate may change the nature of the materials brought to the sea or the nature of the rock-building organisms that invade it, thus giving the illusion that a change in depth occurred. But this influence is especially marked when we seek to interpret terrestrial morphology; a renewal of erosion or, on the contrary, an alluviation due to a change of climate should not be attributed to a displacement of the base level or to an uplift or a localized subsidence (Chap. 2).

Daly[1] has shown that, even in the absence of any deformation of the solid earth, the eustatic variations of sea level should not be of a uniform amplitude over the whole surface of the earth; for example, the displacement of masses of water trapped in the ice caps of the polar regions modifies the field of gravity and deforms its horizontal surfaces. But calculation[2] shows that these inequalities are slight and that the variations in sea level in very distant regions differ by only a few tenths of their value.

However, when we consider disturbances of such great magnitude, we must take into account the conditions of isostatic equilibrium (Chap. 14). In particular, the formation of an ice cap involves a progressive sinking of the overladen region, and its melting will be followed by a progressive rising. Although such progressive sinking is no doubt due to deformation of the solid crust, it seems logical not to consider such isostatic readjustments as actually constituting tectonic deformations; the latter normally result from the active intervention of internal causes, whereas the re-establishment of isostatic equilibrium does not. However, the corresponding deformations may appear under quite varied aspects.

One of the simplest examples is the isostatic readjustment of Scandinavia, which began after the melting of the Quaternary glaciers. Scandinavia is a region that has long been stable and may be considered as being particularly rigid; the central region has been uplifted about 100 m since the arrival of the sea, and certainly much more since the period of maximum glaciation, but no zone of flexure or fault separates it from the regions that were not reached by the glacier and which were not uplifted; the adjustment takes place along a width of about 1000 km. Thus there is neither fault nor appreciable deformation of the rocks.

In Scandinavia, the readjustment required some tens of thousands of years, which is slow in relation to the disappearance of the glaciers (however, this may not be slow in relation to the time required for their formation), but relatively rapid in relation to tectonic movements. But the readjustment of a smaller zone might take considerably longer.

Isostatic readjustment may be caused by the formation or disappearance of ice caps or by the processes of erosion and sedimentation. Theoretically, an overall variation of sea level should also be accompanied by an isostatic readjustment that would probably be expressed in the long run by a difference between the apparent variation of level in isolated islands, on the border of the continents, and along interior seas. But since this readjustment requires a certain delay, we should expect to observe in the first place the eustatic variation of level, which was probably only progressively changed by the readjustment. The readjustment would nullify the first variation for an interior sea, but would let it persist for an isolated island and would reduce it in a variable relation along the shores. Since the same phenomena apply for each eustatic variation, the laws of apparent displacement of sea level would theoretically be quite different in widely separated places.

Isostatic readjustment may be accompanied by complications of still another order. With the deep magma at a constant viscosity, the smaller the structure, the more time required for the re-establishment of equilibrium. We may then expect that certain types of irregular overloads will first produce a general readjustment of regional character; the deformation that will permit each of the elements to be individually compensated will take place later at a very slow rate. For example, a series of relatively light granitic masses would be followed shortly by a regional compensation that would determine the mean altitude of the region. Later, local deformations might be produced that would bring about the individual compensation of each of the granitic massifs. As has been indicated (Chap. 14), it is very possible that most of the Mesozoic beds in the Paris Basin were folded in this way, judging from the magnitude of gravity anomalies they produce.

The Bray structure consists essentially of a localized flexure that runs northwest–southeast and which attains an amplitude of up to 1000 m, the difference of level being taken up by a slight dip of the southwest panel. Gravimetry indicates a strong positive anomaly (15 milligals) to the northeast of the flexure, due to heavy rocks that cannot be more than 4000 m deep. When the Mesozoic beds were deposited, there must have been regional, but not local, compensation of these heavy rocks; the action of the flexure corresponds to the passage to a local compensation. It is possible that many less important folds in the chalk may have a similar origin. The delay with which these movements were produced is not due only to the viscosity of the deep magma, but doubtless in great measure to the rigidity of the earth's crust, which is capable of supporting, without yielding to, the shearing force that results from the juxtaposition of compartments that are not individually compensated. It is possible that the re-establishment of local equilibrium may have been produced only after the deformation was triggered by another phenomenon, such as a distant reaction to Alpine movements that may have merely produced some fractures, or a supplementary effort which, by itself, might have been incapable of producing the slightest deformation. In this way, we might explain the age of these movements in the Paris Basin, which seem to be related to the Alpine movements.

So here we are touching upon the problem of the role of active tectonic movements of deep origin in producing deformation outside of orogenic zones.

But before tackling this problem, it would be well to emphasize the number and variety of the movements that may be produced outside the influence of the active tectonic movements and whose role is perhaps less than might have been supposed at first sight. However, there are movements that do not fit into the explanations that have just been offered and whose cause must be sought. Their most striking aspect is generally vertical displacement, the amplitude of which may vary rapidly over short distances, faults or flexures taking up the differences of level thus determined.

Since the principle of isostasy determines the mean elevation of a region, the vertical displacement of a zone with a given area expresses a variation of the mean density of the earth's crust, but does not imply the intervention of hypothetical vertical forces. For example, in the Colorado plateau, which is several hundred kilometers in extent and which has been uplifted some 2000 m since the Cretaceous, isostatic equilibrium seems to have been reached.

It is very difficult to imagine what phenomenon could have produced a change of density of the earth's crust over such an area. In certain cases we may suspect the intervention of eruptive phenomena, such as the formation of a laccolith, even if it has not been reached by erosion, or, on the other hand, the collapse of the roof of an underground reservoir that fed volcanic eruptions. But generally, in the absence of any indication, we must remain in doubt. The vertical displacement of extensive regions is perhaps the one phenomenon that presently accepted theories least enable us to explain and whose interpretation constitutes one of the criteria by which we should judge new theories that might be proposed.

When it is a question of less extensive compartments that may be alternately uplifted or lowered, we can no longer affirm that each one of them is individually compensated; isostatic equilibrium is perfectly compatible with quite notable relative displacements. In fact, numerous regions are characterized by the action of faults determining a series of horsts and grabens, among which are Syria, Lebanon, and Palestine, or, more generally, the area of the African trenches and certain parts of California (Coast Range). Frequently, especially in California, the study of sediments in the different compartments makes it possible to reconstruct a very complex history, certain compartments rising and sinking alternately in relation to others, their relative characters, moreover, changing with time.

Although we cannot disregard the fact that such phenomena can be produced, it is not necessary to assume changes in density of the earth's crust; it is much more natural to explain these movements by the intervention of exterior forces, which must be horizontal, since they can scarcely be vertical.

We have seen in Chapter 11 how a trench located between two faults (usually reverse faults) seems to result from a stretching force. Moreover, there are often to be found, not just isolated trenches, but systems of horsts and grabens whose explanation must be very analogous. At times, there are also found isolated faults or, in the sedimentary cover, "double faults" such as those of the Marne[3] (Wassy and Gondrecourt faults). These two parallel faults, located in the midst of the tabular region of the Paris Basin, define a sunken belt 1 km wide; their throws are moderate, with lesser changes of level outside the structure. We have seen that such a structure probably expresses the repercussion within the cover of a single, slightly inclined fault in the basement.

The most important deformations of Alpine age in the Paris Basin (taken in a broad sense) seem to be connected with compression faults; the subsidence of the Rhenish trench, and the accompanying uplift of the Vosges and the Black Forest through isostatic compensation, is the very type of structure that seems to be due to stretching. It is known that, in the Triassic, nothing interrupted the continuity of the basin between Germany and France; the uplift of the Vosges–Black Forest region introduced a feature that seems altogether new and which doubtless appeared before the Cretaceous.

The uplift of the Morvan region, which belonged originally to the marginal part of the basin, seems to constitute a distant reaction to the Alpine movements, as are the faults of the Limagne system that border the basin on the west. The Limagne faults, which have a lesser amplitude, are structures comparable to the Rhenish trench. The dip of such faults is difficult to establish; it is probably less at depth than in the flat-lying surface formations, in which the faults tend to multiply and to approach the vertical.

We have seen in orogenic zones that, where the horizontal displacements reach large values, certain vertical faults are seen to have a considerable horizontal displacement. It is possible that, in zones of horizontal beds, where we are led to interpret the different systems of faults and subsidences as resulting essentially from horizontal movements, the number of faults involving a horizontal displacement is also higher than it is ordinarily assumed to be. In the Lorraine ferriferous basin (Homécourt), certain fractures without any vertical throw exhibit striated slickensides that no doubt indicate a horizontal displacement whose value cannot be determined. However unusual such fractures may be, they have made possible a quite important horizontal deformation, which it is ordinarily impossible to recognize.

Often, however, faults that have a considerable horizontal displacement also involve a certain vertical throw, at times of variable sense. They may have placed opposite one another portions of the earth's crust that differ in composition and whose positions of isostatic equilibrium do not correspond to the same altitude of a reference bed. It is hard to imagine how a fairly large horizontal displacement could eventually be reduced to zero along a fault; thus, we may expect faults with horizontal displacement to be very continuous or to join other structures. However, if the vertical component of the displacement has been obscured, the chances are that the fault will escape observation or that the horizontal displacement will be divided among a great number of small structures whose existence will be difficult to establish. The study of the horizontal displacement of faults in nonfolded regions is even less advanced than in folded regions.

Our study of the different manifestations of tectonic forces on the surface of the earth remains of necessity very incomplete, since we are in almost complete ignorance of the behavior of the ocean bottom. The folded zones and the quiet or simply faulted regions that form the continents occupy only one-fourth of the earth's surface. With respect to the other three-fourths, which is hidden by the seas, we are completely ignorant of how tectonic deformations manifest themselves. The discovery of great rectilinear structures that seem to correspond to faults on the bottom of the Pacific, between California and the Hawaiian Islands (p. 000), casts a first gleam of light upon this problem.

As regards nonfolded continental zones, we have shown that horizontal movements appear during the initial stages of a certain number of deformations, as in folded zones. Deformations due to stretching constitute one of the original characteristics of these nonfolded zones; other structures seem to result from sliding along transverse faults.

Should we generalize the interpretation of these examples and say that the tectonics of nonfolded regions is dependent on horizontal displacements resulting essentially from stretching forces, whereas folded zones are produced by compression forces? Doubtless this would be too absolute a solution. The vertical displacements of broad areas should, in fact, have a different origin; such displacements imply a transformation of the earth's crust at depth, whose precise nature it is generally impossible to determine. There is no reason for rejecting the possibility that analogous transformations may also have been produced in other cases; thus we are justified in hesitating between different explanations.

Notes and References

1. Daly, R. A., Swinging Sea Level of the Ice Age, Bull. Geol. Soc. America, vol. 40, pp. 721–734, 1929.

2. Goguel, J., *Contribution à l'étude des variations glaciaires du niveau des mers* (in preparation).

3. Abrard, R., and Corroy, G., *Etude de la double faille de la Marne et des régions voisines,* Bull. Serv. Carte Géol. France, vol. 30, no. 165, pp. 17–24, 1927.

CHAPTER TWENTY-TWO

In Search of an Explanation

Hypothetical character of theories on the deep causes of tectonic deformation—Geophysical data; isostasy; thermal regime; question of initial
temperatures; indications of seismology on internal structure—Origin of
tectonic forces; hypothesis of an extraterrestrial origin; hypothesis of vertical uplifts; hypothesis of a horizontal compression, its origin—Hypothesis of cooling, its modalities—Notions of mobility of elements of earth's
crust—Wegener's theory—Forces susceptible of acting horizontally; Epstein, displacement of the pole—Principle of theory of convection currents
—Instability resulting from superposition of a solid rock on the same rock
in the molten state—Effect of horizontal branches of currents—Absence
of effects of inertia—Continuous or discontinuous movement?—Distribution of ascending or descending branches—Various hypotheses on the
deep structure of a mountain chain and origin of roots (in the Airy sense)
—Role of downward dragging of roots.

OUR STUDY of the different aspects of tectonic deformation has been, up
to now, essentially descriptive and analytical in nature. It could not be otherwise, since we are observing only one aspect of the phenomena, the superficial
aspect, whereas from all the evidence the deep aspects are very important; the
essence of the causes of deformation must reside in depth. The descriptive
method that is imposed upon us brings tectonics closer to the natural sciences,
which describe the living world, but the descriptive method is employed in
tectonics for very different reasons. On the one hand, there is the wealth of
forms, the spontaneity of the living world, and, on the other hand, our ignorance of a whole aspect of the phenomena under study, probably the most
important, which prevents us from basing our conclusions upon a determinism
whose accuracy is beyond question.

348

However, we are not entirely without indications of the deep structure of the earth and its prevailing conditions of equilibrium. But these data are fragmentary and hazardous and are far less accurate than data obtained from geologic observations made at the surface. The synthesis that we may perhaps attempt presents only the degree of probability of the less well known of the elements that we bring into the picture; consequently it can hardly serve to support direct geologic study. On the other hand, from the point of view of geophysics, it is essential for our comprehension of deep structures, upon which the conditions of deformation on the surface furnish information of prime importance.

In order to discuss such a synthesis, we are obliged to introduce a greater proportion of hypothesis than has been necessary so far. Thus, it should be well understood that the conclusions made in the present chapter do not lay claim to the same degree of certainty as those of the preceding chapters. The very variety of theories that have been successively proposed is sufficient to show this.

What data do we have at our disposal upon which we can base our concept of the internal structure of the earth? Clearly, any proposed structure must permit us to explain all the evidential statements relative to tectonic deformations presented in the foregoing chapters. This structure should also account for volcanism and the formation of rocks at depth (plutonism), both under present conditions and under those of the past (Precambrian). Geophysics supplies us with a certain amount of data, the most important of which are grouped within the theory of isostasy. We must also take into account what we know of the thermal regime and the very precise indications furnished by seismology.

It would be satisfying to be able to present our concept of the present structure of the earth in the broader framework of a cosmogenic hypothesis, but it is evident that we know so little about the origin of the terrestrial globe that such considerations are of little help. Nevertheless they do play a quite important role in certain of the theories before us.[1]

We have already shown the essential consequence of isostasy. With a time constant of the order of 10,000 years, the elevation of the surface is established such that the vertical pressure is constant at a given depth, provided the depth is greater than 50 or 100 km. The adaptations required to restore this condition imply that the material at such a depth has the mechanical properties of an extremely viscous fluid. The earth's crust is distinguished from this viscous "asthenosphere" in that it is endowed with rigidity, but we are in no way obliged to assume a clear-cut boundary between the earth's crust and the asthenosphere.

Let us repeat: Isostasy implies nothing regarding the structure of the earth's crust, whose thickness or composition (acid or basic rocks, sial or sima) may vary in any manner whatsoever. The same is true for the "degree of regionality" (introduced by Vening Meinesz in geodesic calculations), which expresses the capacity of the earth's crust to support stresses and measures the degree of interdependability between adjacent compartments. The interpretation of belts of negative anomalies, whether in terms of the hypothesis of "buckling" or any other analogous hypothesis, essentially introduces this interdependence, owing to which the zone of anomaly is maintained at a level below the equilibrium position by the action of adjacent compartments.

The hypotheses used by the geodesists for their calculations of corrections can in no way be considered as representing the actual structure of the earth's crust. But the comparison of the results of measurement makes it possible, within the framework of any hypothesis under consideration, to determine the most probable value of the essential parameter.

The study of the thermal regime of the earth shows an independence between what takes place on the surface—where solar radiation, atmospheric movements, and radiation toward intersidereal space control the distribution of temperatures—and the thermal regime of the earth's interior. The latter is characterized, on the one hand, by the flow of heat that escapes through the earth's crust by conduction and which corresponds to a progressive elevation of temperature with depth of about one degree for each 30 m (geothermal gradient) and, on the other hand, by the evolution of heat due to the decay of radioactive materials dispersed throughout all rocks. If, in a 50-km thickness of rock, the radioactive content were comparable to that measured for granites, the heat evolved would be equal to that lost by conduction. But the radioactive content of basic rocks, especially ultrabasic rocks, is much smaller. In the granites, it does not seem that the radioactive content is the same at the center of batholiths as that found in samples usually taken at their periphery.

The study of the thermal regime is perhaps the most difficult field in which to work without the aid of a cosmogenic hypothesis; the theoretical calculation of the cooling period of a body the size of the earth, and which has the properties of superficial rocks, leads to time constants far in excess of the few billions of years that nuclear physics and astronomy lead us to consider as the maximum age of the earth. To the degree that we consider the earth as entirely solid, it might almost be said that the original distribution of interior temperatures has remained almost unchanged without influencing the conditions prevailing near the surface. This distribution would depend only upon what goes on in the few hundreds of kilometers from the surface down. Determinations at the surface would tell us nothing regarding the thermal regime of the interior.

However, another hypothesis may also be considered plausible. Within the earth's interior, heat transfers took place, and are perhaps still taking place, according to a mechanism other than simple conduction; these heat transfers were, or are, much more easily and rapidly achieved.

Since the time of Laplace, most authors begin with the hypothesis that the earth was initially at a high temperature and probably cooled progressively. But the reverse process, in which a globe is formed in the cold state and is progressively heated by the radioactive bodies that it contains, has also been considered under the name of "planetesimal hypothesis"; it enjoys a certain favor in the United States.[2] This hypothesis, however, raises a difficulty. From cold and originally dispersed matter, considerable heat is emitted while it is being concentrated to form a mass the size of the earth. Owing to the speed of its fall alone, an aerolite reaches the earth at a high temperature. It has been calculated that the temperature could reach some tens of thousands of degrees; even assuming that each of the successive layers had time to cool while it still constituted the surface, the compression of the central part by the increasing weight of the successive beds would again raise its temperature to more than 1000 degrees. So it seems that the earth must have been at a quite high temperature from the time of its origin. Later cooling, through the surface, and the emission of heat by the radioactive bodies must have balanced each other, in part, and determined a very moderate geothermal gradient.

However, Joly[3] sought to explain the periodicity of tectonic phases in terms of a cyclic thermal regime based essentially on the alternation of phases of solidification of submarine basalts, during which the heat is very slowly dissipated and the temperature rose, and in terms of phases of melting, during which the accumulated heat is dissipated rapidly. But in order to explain that a noncyclic, intermediate order of equilibrium is not established, he had to call upon other hypotheses, to which we shall have occasion to return later, but which seem largely arbitrary. The thermal evolution of the earth, at least as long as we bring in conduction only, would lead to a state of equilibrium and cannot produce periodic phenomena.

At first sight, it would seem that volcanism, through the deep phenomena that are its cause, should bring us important information concerning the geothermal gradient. But the volcanic regions are visibly exceptional. The geothermal gradient in them is generally much higher than elsewhere; that is, at a given depth the temperature within volcanic regions is much higher than in normal regions. Even volcanoes that are close together may emit lavas that are very different chemically. So the deep phenomena of volcanism are very localized. The activity of volcanoes proves the existence of reservoirs of molten rock at depth, but we know nothing concerning the origin of these reservoirs. It is also accepted that all reservoirs that produce other than basaltic rocks are of local origin and are the result, at least in part, of the re-fusion of earlier formed rocks. As regards the basalts, which present a very great uniformity of composition throughout the world and which constitute a very large proportion of the tonnage emitted, opinions are divided, but it seems impossible that there exists a continuous layer of liquid basalt. Moreover, we do not know the origin of these liquid basaltic masses, some of which are discharged at the surface. In any event, we must exclude the possibility that a vitreous basalt may become fluid following a lowering of pressure that would result from the opening of a fracture that reached the surface. A fracture could not open to such considerable depths unless it were immediately refilled by a fluid balancing the greatest part of the rock pressure, otherwise this pressure would close the fissure again by plastic deformation. After having been filled by the basalt, during eruption, the pressure at the base of the chimney would differ little from that due to the weight of the adjacent solid rocks.

The study of the propagation of vibrations emanating from earthquakes furnishes indications of the mechanical properties of successive layers. Let us enumerate them in the order of increasing depths. In the first tens of kilometers we have been led to distinguish successive layers, which are characterized by an increase in the speed at which waves are propagated through them and whose depths have been calculated on the assumption that their boundaries are probably horizontal surfaces. We have acquired the habit of designating them by geologic names, such as basaltic, intermediate, and granitic layers, which are justified by the agreement between the measurements in the field and in the laboratory, but we should not take these terms too literally. Not only the nature of these layers but even their individuality has been questioned.

The thicknesses found for these different layers differ greatly from one region to another. There are some indications of local variations, such as the increase of thickness of the granitic layer under the Alps and of the intermediate layer under the Sierra Nevada, but a great deal still remains to be done before we can state precisely the differences in the structure of the continental basement from point to point.[4]

Seismologists agree that corresponding layers do not exist beneath the oceans. The basement of the Pacific Ocean is probably basaltic; as regards the Atlantic, Ewing's last measurements do not confirm the existence of the intermediate or acid layer, the existence of which had been assumed earlier, just as it was assumed to exist under the Indian Ocean.[5]

All these layers are characterized by speeds that increase with the depth, which produces a refraction of the seismic rays toward the surface and makes it easy to identify them.

On the other hand, if the speed diminishes toward the bottom, we can hardly expect to record it by the measurement of travel times. Only the existence of a zone of silence at a determined distance from the focus may furnish an indication, but it can only be established by the comparison of the records of a great number of stations. However, it has been possible to recognize the probability of a slight diminution of propagation speeds at depths of about 80 to 100 km, determining a zone of silence at some fifteen degrees from the focus (1700 km).[6]

At lower levels, the variation of speed with depth seems to be everywhere the same. It is accepted that geographical differences no longer make themselves felt. The instantaneous velocity, insofar as it may be determined as a function of depth by the study of the propagation times at different distances, increases up to 2800 km. The most recent investigations do not confirm the existence of discontinuities in the velocity that had been accepted by various authors at depths of 800 to 1500 km. The increase of velocity, which is continuous, seems to be due to the increase of pressure with depth, which influences both the density and the elastic constants, except perhaps between 400 and 900 km. The measured speeds seem to correspond to those measured for basic or ultrabasic rocks, but it is difficult to specify whether they are in the crystalline or vitreous state.

In the absence of discontinuity of velocity, there is no reason to imagine several layers of different compositions. It is possible that the relatively rapid variation of elastic constants between 400 and 800 km is due to a physical transformation, for example, to the appearance of dense minerals that are stable only under high pressure and which replace less dense minerals. For the simple substances that he has studied under very great pressures, Bridgman[7] has shown the role that polymorphic transformations can play; it seems that in the case of a magma of silicates transitions between minerals are susceptible of playing an analogous role.

After all it is not to be disregarded that, from 100 to 2800 km, in what we call the mantle, the material is almost homogeneous. But it is equally possible that a change of composition, more or less progressive, may take place between 400 and 900 km.[8]

Beyond a depth of 2800 km, in what is called the *core,* the properties of the material become very different. The transverse waves that characterize a solid have not been detected below 2800 km. So the material below this depth probably possesses the properties of a fluid at this depth. In order to indicate astronomical constants of the earth (mean density, moments of inertia) we are led to attribute a higher density to the core than to the mantle. Many geophysicists assume, in particular by analogy with the mean composition of meteorites, that the core is composed essentially of iron in the liquid state. It would then be fascinating to assume this bath of molten iron to be in chemical equilibrium with the mantle of overlying silicates;[9] in such an equilibrium, comparable to those that metallurgists make use of, the noble metals (but little oxidizable) should pass into the ferrous bath, and the oxidizable metals, or lithophiles, should pass into the silicated scoria.

At the present time, there is a tendency to attribute (Bullard, Elsasser) the origin of the terrestrial magnetic field to electric currents produced by displacements of the fluid, conductive matter of the core.[10] An entirely different interpretation has been proposed by G. Cagniard.[11] The material composing the core would not differ from that of the overlying layers of the mantle, either in density or elastic constants; thus, it would be solid but endowed with a high electric conductivity. The Foucauld currents, due to the action of the magnetic field, would reduce the longitudinal waves and some of the transverse waves; the only wave observed would then be a transverse wave, polarized in the sense of the magnetic field. But this hypothesis does not take into consideration the waves reflected at the surface of the core, which are actually observed.

In other respects, the properties of the core, still poorly known, contribute little to our understanding of the movements of the earth's crust. Let us recall that if the foci of earthquakes are situated, in general, within the thickness of the earth's crust, which is rigid, they may descend much lower along determined inclined surfaces in certain regions.

The problem that presented itself to structural geologists—long before we had reached the notions regarding the interior structure of the earth that have just been indicated—was essentially that of imagining the origin of the forces whose action is observed in mountain chains.

The earth is isolated in space; the radiation that it receives from the sun, even if it produces all the movements of the hydrosphere and of the atmosphere, does not seem capable of penetrating to a great depth. So it seems that we must call upon interior forces. Attempts have been made to explain tectonic deformations as being the result of extraterrestrial phenomena. Arnold Heim,[12] transposing the theory of Chamberlin and Moulton on the origin of the solar system, assumed the passage into the neighborhood of the earth of a heavenly body that was heavy enough to produce very high tides, capable of modifying the rotation speed of the earth. He wondered if the interior strains that would result could not explain the formation of mountains. This hypothesis has never been subjected to a precise mathematical analysis; it seems that it could explain only a very brief deformation and not the slow and prolonged movements that we record. One of the arguments that Heim offers in support of a cosmic origin of folding concerns the fact that the sedimentary cover is often much more folded than the basement upon which it rests; however, we know today that this is due to tectonic flow. Arnold Heim made an analogy between this hypothesis and the *traineau ecraseur* "crushing sledge" of Pierre Termier. But it seems that Termier's crushing sledge was only a continental block dragged over the folded zone.

Of course the foregoing comments do not apply to such abnormalities as the "meteor crater" of Arizona, which seems to mark the point of fall of a meteorite. Despite this isolated attempt, it is far within the interior of the earth that we should seek the origin of the forces that built the mountains.

Since one of the most striking characteristics of mountains is their elevation, it was natural to think at first of vertical forces that probably determined "craters" or "axes" of uplift (Leopold von Buch, Thurman). The dip of sedimentary beds on both sides of the "axes" appeared to be a result of the uplift. Long before the theory of isostasy showed how difficult it would be to account for such forces of vertical uplift, another idea appeared, one that has not stopped developing since—namely that horizontal compression may buckle strata and thus fold an initially horizontal stratified series. As early as 1788, James Hall used a very elementary experiment to demonstrate the possibility of such a mechanism. It would take too long to retrace here the successive stages through which this concept of horizontal compression has passed as it has progressively supplanted the idea of localized vertical movements.

We have seen that the re-establishment of isostatic equilibrium indicates that the asthenosphere has the mechanical properties of a very viscous fluid and that this should make possible both the horizontal displacement of a part of the earth's crust and the re-establishment of the equilibrium through vertical movement, assuming, however, that a horizontal force acts upon the earth's crust. However, the origin of this force poses a difficult problem.

The essential role of horizontal compression, however, is not unanimously accepted today. Partly to avoid the difficulties raised by the origin of horizontal forces, certain authors (Haarmann, and, to a certain extent, Gignoux) have tended to consider uplifts as being the essential fact of orogenesis. It is the gravity slides of sedimentary beds on the sides of swells thus produced that would explain folding and, in a more general way, all the indications of compression observed there. But Haarmann proposes no explanation of the origin of these deep intumescences or "geotumors."

In this alternative recourse to mutually engendered horizontal and vertical forces, the principle of isostasy appears to us as the safest guide. To assume vertical forces capable of seriously disturbing the isostatic equilibrium amounts to relying upon an entirely unknown cause. We have insisted on the difficulty constituted by the regions that rise or subside, which can be interpreted only by a deep transformation of the earth's crust, becoming lighter or heavier. To explain the formation of "geotumors" important enough to constitute the essential fact of orogenesis, we would have to assume transformations of the earth's crust of a very great magnitude, which would be a return to an idea expressed by Pratt in 1855, according to which the formation of mountains would result from a swelling of the earth's crust.

Van Bemmelen[13] took up the matter in a modified form, attributing the cause of tectonic deformations to a geochemical evolution connected with the diffusion of ions and atoms and expressed by the granitization of originally basic rocks, which would result in a strong diminution of their density. Isostatic readjustment would then be accompanied by important uplifts (for the Pyrenees, the author suggests the figure of 10 km), following which gliding tectonics would take place, involving great masses and even affecting the crystalline crust. Beginning with more or less vertical uplifts, isostatic readjustment would explain the somewhat tangential tectonic structures that are to be observed on the surface.

Such a geochemical evolution, taking place in a discontinuous manner both in time and in space, is an entirely gratuitous hypothesis in view of the present state of our knowledge. The diffusion of matter, to which the author assigns such a magnitude, represents, after all, mass displacements that would be subjected to the control of gravity, and it is hard to visualize where the required mechanical energy would come from. The exothermal reactions that the author assumes in metamorphism or the radioactive heat that he infers do not seem to constitute an adequate source of energy. It does not appear that the explanation of orogenesis proposed by Van Bemmelen can be retained.

If the origin of vertical forces seems to us quite gratuitous, it is possible, on the other hand, to propose various hypotheses to explain the origin of horizontal forces. For each of these hypotheses attempts have been made to determine the distribution of these horizontal forces and, consequently, the behavior of the structures they might produce.

The theory of contraction by cooling of the earth, proposed by Elie de Beaumont, has long enjoyed great favor. It is by no means evident, as J. Coulomb has recently emphasized, following Jeffreys,[14] that the cooling of a globe that is originally at a high temperature should produce compression at the surface; on the contrary, the first stage of cooling will produce tension. But once the crust has reached a temperature in equilibrium with the radiation received from the sun, and if the cooling gains in depth, the volume of the interior matter of the crust diminishes; if the crust has become rigid it should adapt itself to this change of volume, which it can do by wrinkling or folding.

In a completely gratuitous manner, Elie de Beaumont accepted the idea that, during this reduction of volume, the earth's crust would tend to assume the form of a pentagonal dodecahedron. The theory built upon this notion has encumbered the literature for several decades.

Following W. Lowthian Green,[15] whose theory had been precisely stated by Albert de Lapparent, the idea was at times entertained that, by diminution of its interior volume, a flexible sphere should show a tendency to form a tetra-

FIGURE 201. *Possible position of the tetrahedron in relation to terrestrial relief (the projection used represents the greater part of the earth, not a hemisphere).*

hedron, whose shape it was sought to recognize in the arrangement of the continental masses (Fig. 201). Even if completed by the hypothesis of a twisting of south ridges, toward the east, this image is not very satisfactory, and above all, measurements of the intensity of gravity in no way confirm this hypothesis, which should be abandoned.

Also, laboratory experiments have been used to indicate the manner in which structures due to contraction are distributed on a sphere. Several authors have deflated a rubber ball covered with paraffin. More recently, Walter H. Bucher[16] studied the rupture of a sphere whose surface was subjected to stretching, using such materials as paraffin on rubber or glass in which water was frozen. The results present no analogy with the network of structures at the earth's surface.

This lack of correspondence is easily explained: The earth's crust is certainly very far from being homogeneous; the distribution of weak zones and resistant zones plays an essential role in the behavior of the structures. And on the other hand, it is not at all certain that the crust is so independent of the interior part of the earth that we can envisage a system of horizontal stresses prevailing throughout the whole of the crust, excluding the unknown effect of the evolution of the interior parts.

The wedge theory of Rollin T. Chamberlain[17] is only a variant of the contraction theory. No longer assuming mechanical independence between the crust and the interior part of the earth, it accepts the premise that in an overall contraction, more marked in the interior than at the surface, oblique fractures should appear near the surface, determining a sort of wedge that would be both uplifted and compressed horizontally. This theory seems hardly reconcilable with the idea of isostasy.

But the most serious objection, which aims at the very principle of the hypothesis of contraction, concerns the magnitude of contractions. We have seen that it is possible, with some plausibility, to doubt the very existence of progressive cooling of the earth, which evidently would leave no place for the idea of contraction. In any event, there is no doubt that a notable portion of the heat lost at the surface comes from radioactive bodies. Moreover, if we take into account the heat emitted by the work of gravity in the contraction of the earth,[18] we find that the contraction could only reduce a meridian by 10 km in 100 million years, which seems altogether insufficient to explain the formation of the known mountain chains.

For the last several decades, the hypotheses have been oriented in a different direction. The existence of an asthenosphere, that is, a layer sufficiently fluid to permit the rigid crust to achieve isostatic equilibrium over a long period of time, should also permit horizontal displacement of the crust, or of parts of it, relative to the interior part of the earth. A number of theories derive from this general principle, which differ either in the amplitude accepted for the horizontal displacements of the crust (or the consequences of these displacements) or by the origin of the forces responsible for these displacements. Moreover, these two points of view are independent, and the nature of the horizontal displacements accepted by a given author may be incompatible with the forces inferred by the same author. So none of the theories proposed can be either accepted or rejected in one block.

The idea of notable horizontal displacements of parts of the earth's crust was introduced at once in its most extreme form by Wegener[19] along with the theory of continental drift. Later, a certain number of precursors were discovered.[20]

Wegener's theory implies an essential difference of constitution between continental and oceanic areas. Having accepted that the first involves only acid rocks (sial), the author assumes that the sima (analogous to basalt) behaves as if plastic, both under the mass of the sial of the continents and under the oceans, with the exception of a thin, stiff film that seems to play no mechanical role. We must remember that it had been long believed that basic rocks were more fusible than acid rocks, whereas the opposite is now widely accepted. So the plasticity of the oceanic sima, essential for Wegener's theory, now appears extremely doubtful.

In order to establish the essential difference between continents and oceans, Wegener insisted on an interpretation of the hypsographic curve that differs considerably from that given above (p. 316), according to which the two most frequent levels correspond respectively to the continental and oceanic areas, without taking sedimentation into account.

These points (in truth, very debatable) being accepted, and the continental masses being considered as capable of having been displaced, all the theories on continental drift have in common the notion of a progressive separation of America from Europe and Africa, a notion suggested by the similarity of the coast lines and by the very real analogies of geologic constitution between the parts under consideration.[21]

In addition, Wegener, but not Taylor, accepts the idea that Madagascar, Peninsular India, Australia and Antarctica were originally joined to South America and Africa.

If we accept the possibility of such continental displacements, which amount to several thousands of kilometers, the horizontal contraction evidenced by folded mountain chains no longer raises any great difficulty, either because it takes place along the front of a mass that is being displaced following reactions of the deep magma—such was probably the case for the Andes, America as a whole being assumed to have a displacement toward the west—or because a mountain chain forms between two continental blocks (for example, the Alps between Europe and Africa).

But it is useful to specify (the contrary opinion seems to be quite common) that it cannot be a question of a shock, in which the energy accumulated under kinetic form in the masses undergoing movement would be dissipated in the crush zone. Kinetic energy varies as the square of the velocity and is absolutely negligible at velocities that are at most on the order of a meter per year, compared to the energy necessary at each instant in order to overcome the viscosity of the asthenosphere; if the force that produced the movement were suddenly removed, the speed acquired would be lost in a fraction of a second. So the crushing of an orogenic zone can be due only to the direct action of forces that tend to displace the continental blocks.

Wegener assumes that the arcs of eastern Asia were probably left behind by the continent as it moved toward the west. However, according to Taylor, the movement of Asia and Europe was probably to the south and must have buttressed against Africa and Peninsular India; the arcs of eastern Asia probably formed along the front of the moving mass, which seems more satisfactory to one's mind.

Whatever the detail of the movements we imagine, the area occupied by the continents may vary, either following the compression of the orogenic zones or inversely by incorporation of the matter contained in the geosynclines formed on the edge of the continents. Among the hypotheses proposed to explain the limited area initially occupied by the sial, let us point out the one according to which, at the time of the separation of the earth and the moon, the latter must have carried away a notable portion of a sialic crust originally complete.[22] But we could just as well consider the moon as an independent planet captured by the earth.

Most of the numerous arguments assembled by Wegener are, in fact, devoid of any importance. In particular, the repetition of precise measurements of longitudes has not yet indicated any variation attributable to drift. Of the many arguments gathered together by Wegener there stand out only those concerning the paleogeography and, in particular, the distribution of climates in the Carboniferous and in the Permian. The distribution of deposits of the same age, containing either a flora of tropical character (Europe, United States, Northern Asia), or a cold flora (with *Glossopteris*) associated with glacial formations (South America and South Africa, India, Madagascar, Australia), is incomprehensible in view of their present position. However, this can be clarified if we assume that the continents with *Glossopteris* were in contact with one another around a pole; at the same time, this leads the deposits with tropical floras to the vicinity of a great circle which should represent the equator of the epoch. It is always difficult to compare the results furnished by different disciplines; thus, we hesitate, in the absence of any positive geophysical argument, to say that the paleoclimatology of the Carboniferous is sufficient to impose the notion of continental drift. In any event, there is no reason to retain the other details given by Wegener, such as the detailed chronology of recent displacements of the pole, and so forth. Quite recent paleomagnetic studies seem to give new arguments, but much further work is still necessary.

But if nothing is to remain of the picture set up by Wegener of continental drift, his theory has probably been useful in that it has obliged geophysicists and geologists to consider the possibility of notable horizontal displacements of certain parts of the earth's crust, displacements that are a necessity in order to explain the genesis of mountain chains.

The role played by the oceanic areas in such displacements remains still unknown. It seems doubtful that, as Wegener would have it, they constitute zones free from resistance, permitting the free displacement of continental areas; certain oceanic areas (such as the center of the Pacific), which appear to be rigid from the point of view of isostatic compensation (Hawaiian Islands), should also be rigid as regards horizontal displacements. On the other hand, the observation of nature today gives us no indication of the degree of independence between the two margins of the great fractures along which huge masses of plateau basalts were emitted (Deccan and Angara). So it seems premature to attempt a reconstruction of the horizontal movements that may replace Wegener's.

It is no less necessary to examine what forces are susceptible of acting upon the earth's crust to displace fragments of it. We must also study the causes susceptible of displacing the pole in relation to the continents or in relation to the mass of the earth itself. If we imagine the continents as rafts floating in a denser magma, the form of the earth's field of gravitation introduces a force tending to drag the continents toward the equator (Epstein). But this force is very weak and barely amounts to a few millionths of their weight. Moreover, neither the hypothesis of continental drift nor the behavior of mountain chains gives the impression that they result from a force dragging the continents toward the equator.

Various authors have assumed a displacement toward the west, related to the rotation of the earth, but have not been able to establish the mechanics. The braking effect upon the ocean tides by the continents is evidently quite insufficient to displace the continents any more than the winds or the ocean currents. Wegener assumed such a displacement toward the west, although we can also conceive of continental drift without this phenomenon.

Joly assumed that the earth's crust as a whole slips toward the west in relation to the interior of the earth, whose different parts were thus probably alternately protected by the sial covering of the continent, in the shelter of which they reheated and, after having been fused, were exposed to cooling beneath the ocean areas. On the basis of such mechanics, he hoped to explain the cyclic character of the fusions and resolidifications of the basalt that were considered as being the cause of orogenic movements. But it seems hardly possible to explain this displacement toward the west in terms of mechanics. Moreover, the very recent measurements of the thermal flux at the bottom of the Pacific have given exactly the same value as in the continental areas, all of which does not seem very favorable to Joly's theory.

It is possible to show that the winds and ocean currents, which are not symmetrical on both sides of the equator, modify the kinetic movement of the earth and may entail a very slow displacement of the pole, the speed of which today might be of the order of 25 kilometers per million years.[23] Not only may such a displacement have played a part in displacing the climatic zones, but it seems capable of having involved certain stresses in the earth's crust, as Vening Meinesz has shown.[24] If the pole is displaced, the form of the earth, flattened by centrifugal force, should adapt itself to the new direction of the axis of rotation. The difference of length between the equator and a meridian amounts to 70 km. The adaptation should involve both a change in horizontal dimensions of the earth's crust (involving an extension or a compression according to location) and a change of form of the interior mass, which may involve the displacement of material capable of exerting drag forces at the base of the earth's crust. Vening Meinesz has assumed an important displacement of the pole at the beginning of the consolidation of the earth. He has investigated the behavior of the shear zones that probably originated then, which could have constituted directing lines for subsequent deformations. If the pole is still being displaced today, stresses may result; two quarters of the earth (bordered by a meridian and the equator) are compressed, and the other two are stretched. But these stresses are probably so weak that it is doubtful that they can be transmitted through the whole crust. Moreover, it does not seem that the distribution of tectonic structural events at a given epoch present the behavior that this explanation would lead us to foresee. The study of the magnetism of Paleozoic rocks[25] seems in fact to indicate such a displacement of the pole has taken place continually since the Precambrian.

We have just reviewed the different forces susceptible of acting horizontally upon the earth's crust. However, none of them seems sufficient to explain either continental drift or tectonic deformations. The latter, moreover, do not present, in plan, the geometric behavior that would cause us to foresee the distribution of either of these forces. Finally, in order to have such forces come into the picture, we would have to accept the idea that the stresses that they produce may be transmitted horizontally through the earth's crust for thousands of kilometers, through regions that are not undergoing deformation, to the zone in which the active tectonic movements are taking place, which is by no means evident. Finally, it would be hard to explain the relations between volcanism or plutonism and tectonics if the moving force of the latter were one of the forces that have just been considered.

Many geologists and geophysicists have the feeling that the solution should be sought along a different path. Tectonic deformations and, eventually, continental transfers should borrow their energy from internal phenomena.

On first examination, the energy balance sheet is entirely compatible with such an interpretation. The earth loses annually about 10^{28} ergs in the form of heat dissipated through its crust (that is the equivalent of a permanent power of 30 billion kilowatts). The mechanical energy dissipated by earthquakes has been estimated by Gutenberg and Richter at one tenth of this figure, or even less.

The origin of the internal energy thus dissipated is to be sought, on the one hand, in the heat lost in the course of the eventual cooling of the earth, and on the other hand, in radioactivity, through the medium of the release of heat that it produces. Without being able to give accurate figures, it is certain that the heat dissipated at the surface comes from masses at high temperatures; it is thus theoretically possible, from the thermodynamic point of view, that mechanical energy is produced during the transfer; to particularize, such could be the origin of the energy dissipated in earthquakes. The attempts made to evaluate the energy absorbed by the formation of mountain chains,[26] (taking into account the long duration of their genesis) show that the available energy of interior origin is usually superabundant.

But if from the global point of view it is relatively easy to show that the internal phenomena and, in particular, the thermal evolution of the earth may be the cause of the movements and deformations of the crust, it is more difficult to specify the exact mechanics of the phenomena. Lacking direct information we can only formulate hypotheses, thus conceiving a model that we endeavor to submit to the test of calculations. If the results are satisfactory, we shall have shown that the mechanics under consideration are possible, but we shall by no means have shown that they actually take place. No matter how much imagination is employed in order to conceive the mechanics of deep phenomena, there is no doubt that things are in reality even much more complicated; thus, it is not a question of choosing among the solutions proposed, but of considering them as landmarks, which, at most, might suggest the type of phenomena that enter into the picture.

Heat may produce either the expansion of a rocky mass or an increase of volume much more notable by fusion, leading to an uplift of the surface by the action of isostasy. This phenomenon seems to have taken place, but the changes of level that it is susceptible of producing are too slight to furnish an explanation of tectonic deformations, inasmuch as we would not understand why the contribution of heat and the expansion would be uneven in time and space. Haarmann calls upon cosmic phenomena (which are not precisely stated) rather than simple thermal expansion, to explain the genesis of his geotumors. However, this could not explain the origin of horizontal forces in the earth's crust. On the other hand, the hypothesis of subcrustal convection currents, for which it is possible to conceive quite numerous variants, seems susceptible of furnishing a much more satisfactory explanation.

Isostasy shows that there exists a contrast between the mechanical properties of the earth's crust, which is rigid, and its substratum, which behaves as if viscous; that is, the substratum yields in the long run to mechanical stresses, however slight they may be (asthenosphere). Moreover, we know that such a long-term viscosity does not prevent matter from reacting as if solid—that is, as if it were elastic—with respect to brief mechanical impulses, as in the transmission of seismic waves.

On the other hand, we know that there are two very different modes of heat transfer. In conduction, the material remains immobile, and the heat is propagated from point to point. In fluids, convection may be produced, that is, a circulation of the fluid, which carries with it latent heat. The moving force of convection currents is furnished by the difference between the density of the hot material and that of the cold material. The first tends to rise and the second to sink. The transfer of heat from below upward is easily done, but not the reverse; if we try to heat water on the surface a thermal stratification is produced and the cold water that remains below is heated by conduction only very slowly. On the contrary it is enough to observe water heating in a stewpan to see the hot water rising from the bottom to the surface, heating the whole mass.

The mechanical equilibrium of a fluid does not necessarily correspond to a uniform temperature. We know that gases (and, to a lesser degree, liquids and even solids) increase in temperature when they are compressed without exchange of heat. The equilibrium of the atmosphere corresponds to a distribution of temperatures equal to those that would be attained at the prevailing pressure at each height by a mass of air being displaced vertically (adiabatic equilibrium). In the atmosphere, the convection currents are not at a constant temperature, but are produced by rising masses of air at a temperature that, during the course of the movement, remains above that normally prevailing at the same level, whereas for heavy descending currents, the temperature is slightly lower.

In an analogous manner, convection currents in an ascending or descending liquid mass are characterized by the difference between their temperature and that which would normally prevail at the same height by virtue of adiabatic equilibrium.

For a given temperature difference, convection currents produce a more rapid transfer of heat than does simple conduction. That is, by convection, the same transfer of heat may take place with a much smaller temperature difference.

In order to produce convection currents, the resistance opposed by the viscosity of the fluid must be overcome. Considering the enormous value of the viscosity of the asthenosphere, as indicated by the slowness of isostatic readjustment, the possibility of subcrustal convection currents is not at all evident a priori. But theory shows that the hindrance caused by a specified viscosity diminishes if the dimensions of the currents increase; such currents are possible with the viscosity calculated for subcrustal layers if the currents are very broad (about 1000 km), and if they are very slow (less than a meter per year), the differences of temperature in relation to adiabatic equilibrium being only some tens or hundreds of degrees (Fig. 202).

The model on which such calculations can be made does not necessarily represent reality; but it is sufficient to have established that a certain type of current is possible for us to be able to accept that others are equally so and that, in general, the process under consideration is to be taken into account.

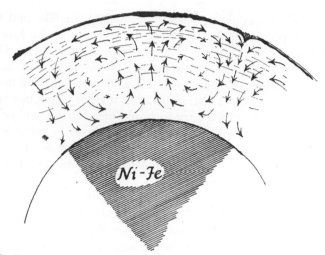

FIGURE 202. *Diagram of convection currents in the silicate mantle.*

We can attempt to render this notion concrete by seeking to represent the physical state of the material in the earth's crust and in the asthenosphere. In the earth's crust, practically all the minerals are crystallized. At a depth of around 100 km, if the temperature regularly increased, all the minerals would be fused in spite of the effect of pressure. So, as we penetrate down into the earth's crust, we should find not only changes of chemical composition, which we express in a somewhat symbolic manner by the superposition of basic, intermediate and acid rocks, but also changes of physical state that will be shown by a diminution of density. Is it to such a passage into the molten state (or vitreous, if preferred) that we should relate the diminution of the propagation speeds of seismic waves pointed out above?

Moreover, it is evident that the transition will not take place at the same level for all the minerals of a rock and that, through a considerable thickness, the material is probably formed of crystals in equilibrium with a "molten magma." According to the proportions of the different phases, the overall mechanical properties of such a system may vary considerably; but they are dominated by the extreme viscosity of most of the molten silicates, a viscosity further increased by the pressure. Besides, we cannot reject the possibility that slow changes of form under the action of even weak stresses, whose possibility characterizes the asthenosphere, may be due to recrystallization in a solid medium.

Leaving aside this hypothesis, the superposition of crystallized rocks on molten rocks of the same type, which are thus less dense, is not theoretically stable from the mechanical point of view. Fragments of the crystallized rocks should thrust deeper into the molten rock or the latter should rise into the fissures of the solid rock if the viscosity does not prevent these equilibrium ruptures. But it is conceived that a local superheating or an increase in the proportion of volatile materials dissolved in the magma (the fumarolic gases, water, carbon dioxide, and others) may lower the viscosity and thus trigger volcanic phenomena. These then appear under the direct dependence of the variations of temperature affecting the base of the earth's crust.

If we imagine subcrustal convection currents, the amount of heat at the base of the earth's crust should be very irregular, whereas the flow of heat lost at the surface varies only slightly. Calculation shows that the latent heat produced by the crystallization of molten rocks (or on the other hand, by the fusion of crystalline rocks) constitutes a means to regularize the heat dissipated toward the exterior by conduction through the earth's crust and to mask to a very great extent the irregularities of the supply of heat of internal origin at the base of the earth's crust. A calculation made on the basis of plausible hypotheses shows that the supply of heat originating at depth would have to cease completely for a hundred million years in order for the heat dissipated at the surface to be reduced by half. On the other hand, a great increase in the amount of heat of internal origin at the base of the crust over a million-year period would scarcely have disturbed the geothermal gradient in the vicinity of the surface.

The system of convection currents should involve not only ascending and descending branches but also horizontal branches uniting the preceding. These horizontal branches should exert horizontal impulses upon the base of the earth's crust, which may explain the fact that displacements or compressions follow a horizontal direction.

It seems, then, that the hypothesis of convection currents opens very great possibilities for explaining all the data that tectonics enables us to collect. We must also take into account the changes in the gravitational field, which should result from the existence of heavy (descending) branches and light (ascending) branches; the surfaces of equal pressures will not coincide with equipotential surfaces, and the elements of the sial crust may thus be subjected to horizontal forces and eventually present the appearance of an isostatic disequilibrium.

Let us note a further particularity that calculation enables us to establish in a definite manner. On the scale of our experiments, we are accustomed to seeing inertia (the tendency of bodies to continue in their state of motion) play an important role. However, on the scale of sub-crustal convection currents, inertia plays no important role; the velocities are so slight and the resistances due to viscosity are so strong that the movement would stop in a few millionths of a second if the forces ceased to act. That is, the development of events depends at each instant on the forces present, but not at all on the previous distribution of velocities. In the same manner, it can be shown that the complementary forces of acceleration (Coriolis forces) due to the rotation of the earth, which influence the winds and determine the direction of cyclones and anticyclones, play no appreciable role in determining subcrustal currents. In the latter, then, no eddies or periodic oscillations can exist, although these phenomena play an essential role in the convection currents that we observe in water or in air.

The various authors who have concerned themselves with this question have naturally sought to bring some accurate data into the picture that we have just sketched. These data are at times contradictory, and we are going to find ourselves in the presence of very different hypotheses.[27]

What is the rhythm of these currents? For certain geophysicists (Vening Meinesz), these currents were probably produced during the initial phase of consolidation of the earth, after which they ceased. They probably played a role in the building of the continents, but did not furnish the motive force of subsequent tectonic deformations. We shall put this concept to one side.

The simplest image that can be envisaged, in particular when we are seeking to establish even the possibility of the phenomenon,[28] is that of currents functioning in a permanent order in a continuous manner. But the rhythm of tectonic deformations, even in the midst of their action, as we have shown in Chapter 17, even if we reject the concept of brief isolated periods of orogenic activity, hardly seems to correspond to such a continuous movement. Thus, various authors, in particular J. Joly and D. Griggs, have developed the idea of movements that are discontinuous in time.

According to Joly, convection plays a somewhat secondary role, and the rhythm of these phenomena is determined essentially by the alternations of fusion and solidification of deep basalts, which, it seems, cannot be explained on the basis of simple thermal considerations. We have seen that the hypothesis of a slipping of superficial beds, in which the continents probably played the role of insulator, does not appear to be retainable either.

According to Griggs,[29] on the other hand, the cyclic character of convection currents would be due essentially to the fact that they affect solid material, that is, they deform only when a certain threshold of stress is exceeded. In a long preparatory phase, during which the deep layers heat progressively while the upper parts cool, the differences of density would progressively increase until the stresses overcome the resistance of the material. In the course of the movement, the difference of density between the hot ascending branches and the cold descending branches passes through a maximum producing a relatively rapid movement; the movement would then cease as soon as the normal stratification of the densities was established, the heavy cold material being at the base and the hot light material at the top. As a result of the extremely slow rate of conduction in a solid medium, the initial distribution of temperatures is probably not re-established for a very long period. Griggs estimated that the duration of repose would be approximately ten times that of the "orogenic storms," which would not necessarily be simultaneous in different regions. As the result of a calculation that indicates, at most, only an order of magnitude, he estimated that the period of repose might last for 500 million years. He suggested that the inclined surfaces along which the foci of deep earthquakes are localized around the periphery of the Pacific were probably due to shearing in a zone in which the action of currents produced particularly high stresses.

Griggs formally assumed the material to be solid. It is somewhat futile to discuss the physical state of this material (which lies, let us remember, at depths of 100 to perhaps 2900 km). The terms solid and liquid indicate, by definition, an ordered arrangement of atoms for the former and a disordered arrangement for the latter. Notwithstanding the fact that, in molten silicates, atomic structures seem to exist in relatively well-determined positions, a very viscous liquid—a glass—holding in suspension a large proportion of crystals or crystalline structures susceptible of changing form by migration of ions, can hardly be recognized by its overall mechanical properties, which alone are accessible to us. But if we study the theoretical problem of the cooling of a mass (fluid or solid) the size of the earth,[30] two conclusions are immediately evident. Through the mechanics of convection, the fluid mass would cool relatively quickly (on the scale of geologic time) and would then have reached the temperature of solidification. On the other hand, in a solid, conduction would be so slow that in the three or four billion years that seem to represent the age of the earth, practically nothing of the latent heat of the interior parts beyond a few hundreds of kilometers would have reached the surface. That is, from the moment when the crystallization of the material was sufficiently advanced, the latent heat of solidification could no longer be dissipated, and, *a fortiori,* the material could not cool below the temperature of solidification. So it seems probable that if the earth has ever been molten the temperature should be at every point approximately that of an incipient solidification.

It is conceivable that, if convection currents tend to be produced, friction at their boundaries may slightly heat and partially fuse the material and greatly diminish its mechanical resistance (even bringing it to such a state that it may be injected as a liquid into the earth's crust and produce volcanic phenomena there), whereas in the center of ascending or descending currents, the material could remain practically solid. So perhaps we should not imagine convection currents as harmonious fluid movements but as the stirring of a half stiffened material that may be liquified in certain places under the effect of friction. Many irregularities recorded on the surface might result from the fortuitous action of such phenomena, the details of which evidently escape our analysis.

We do not even know at what level this sort of convection current prevails. It seems evident that they cannot simultaneously stir up the very dense fluid core (NiFe?) and the silicate mantle, which has completely different properties. Certain authors, Griggs in particular, assume that these convection currents prevail between the top of the asthenosphere (50 to 100 kilometers) and the limit of the core (2900 km). This requires that the change of mechanical properties indicated by the variation of seismic speeds between 400 and 900 km be due not to a variation of chemical composition but to a physical transformation, such as a polymorphism affecting certain constituents. We can only form hypotheses concerning the ways in which this transformation would influence the action of the currents—that is, variation of temperature due to the latent heat, eventual delay in the transformation, and more or less sudden character of the transformation.

There has also been under consideration the hypothesis of currents affecting only a lesser thickness, 1200 km according to Vening Meinesz; we could also consider currents between the base of the earth's crust and 475 km, but their action would seem mechanically more difficult to explain. Finally, there is nothing to prevent our imagining several convection zones, for example, one in the core (which would be at the origin of the terrestrial magnetic field) and one in the mantle, or one between 50 and 475 km and another between 900 and 2900 km, but such a hypothesis would evidently be quite gratuitous.

The question of the depth of the convection regime is directly connected with that of the distribution of the ascending and descending branches. It is accepted, as a result of experiments by Bénard, that convection cells that tend to form in a liquid (with an ascending current in the center, descending on the edges) have a width approximately three times the depth. But inertia (due to eddies) plays a notable role in such experiments, whereas its role is absolutely nil in terrestrial currents; thus, it is evident that this proportion may not be applied to the latter. Nevertheless, we should expect a certain correlation between the width of the cells and the depth.

When we wish to submit convection currents in a sphere to calculation, we must assume a simple form for them that can be represented by a mathematical formula (spherical harmonics), but there is evidently no reason for the form to be the same for real currents. However, a calculation made by Jeffreys,[31] confirming results obtained earlier by Vening Meinesz, presents as the most probable in the thickness of the mantle a distribution of currents corresponding to harmonics of the third and fourth orders. Let us point out that one of the harmonics of the third order corresponds to the division of the sphere by three rectangular diametral planes into eight triangles, four of which would correspond to the ascending currents and four to the descending currents; but other arrangements are equally possible.

Holmes[32] thought that the position of the continents might have a determining influence upon the position of ascending currents. The continents, in fact, present a thickness of some tens of kilometers of acid rocks (sial) that are richer in radioactive elements than the basic rocks; at their base, the temperature should be several hundred degrees higher than at the same depth under an oceanic basin. The horizontal branches of the currents would then tend to break the continent into fragments, separating its parts from each other and producing peripheral mountain chains. The extent to which such arrangements are actually realized is a matter of personal opinion.

Griggs has formulated a very different hypothesis.[33] As a result of experiments on scale models, he thinks that a horizontal current may, under certain conditions, exert its forces upon the sial crust and compress it upon a part of its initial area at the emplacement of a descending current branch. According to these same experiments, an ascending current might, under certain conditions, drive the fragments of the light crust situated at its emplacement toward the periphery. The author suggests that the continents were probably formed by such a mechanism, starting with an originally continuous crust of acid rock. Moreover there is no reason for assuming that both of the mechanisms did not play a part, that of Griggs in the Precambrian, and that of Holmes later on, once the continents were formed. We see that the hypothesis of convection currents is susceptible of many variants, which certainly have not yet all been developed.

We can retain the idea that a phenomenon of this kind is physically very probable. The principal difficulty that it raises is to explain by some sort of polymorphic transformation (in a mass of homogeneous chemical composition) the variation of physical properties between depths of 400 and 900 km. In spite of this difficulty, of all the hypotheses that have been proposed to explain the origin of tectonic deformations and, eventually, of horizontal displacements of continents, the convection-current hypothesis is the only one that seems worth retaining.

Quantitative calculations indicate velocities between a centimeter and a meter per year and a cycle that lasts at least a few tens of millions of years, perhaps even hundreds of millions. These orders of magnitude seem quite in harmony with our knowledge of the geologic history of mountain chains.

But owing to its very flexibility, this hypothesis does not seem susceptible of leading to precise rules regarding the position of orogenic zones or their distribution in time. On the contrary, it is to geologic analysis that we must turn for information upon the great lines of the history of convection currents.

It seems logical, under these conditions, to try to place the hypotheses that we are obliged to form regarding the deep structure of mountain chains in harmony with this theory of convection currents. It makes us foresee a dragging of the earth's crust at its base above horizontal branches and, eventually, a carrying downward at the emplacement of the descending currents, toward which the horizontal currents converge. Finally, the action of convection currents may explain great variations in the flow of heat at the base of the crust, which will be felt at the surface only in greatly attenuated amounts. In addition, the inequalities between ascending and descending branches change the position of the geoid (that is, the position of sea level) in relation to the continents in isostatic equilibrium; these inequalities may be expressed locally by transgressions or regressions, under conditions as yet unsatisfactorily investigated.

Since the theory of convection currents can no more furnish an indication on the scheme of tectonic structures than can any of the other hypotheses on the deep causes of orogenesis, it is through observation that we should seek to systematize our tectonic schemes. We shall not review all the doctrines aimed in this direction by various authors (principally German), who have exploited perhaps too systematically the way opened by E. Suess.

As an example, Kober's[34] scheme may be analyzed. It would be of little interest to discuss the differences between his scheme and that of other authors. The Alps are generally selected as a classic type of mountain chain, since they are by far the best known and doubtless the most complex. Generalizing a few scattered observations, Kober assumes that the model mountain chain should normally involve two branches (joined together or separated by an intermediate compartment), in which the structures are tilted in opposite directions toward the exterior of the mountain chain. The western Alps present only one half of this model.

Kober generalizes at the same time the nappe structure of the Alps, as it has been established in Switzerland, by putting the three zones in parallel, Helvetic nappes (Externides), Pennine nappes (Metamorphides) and Austro-Alpine nappes (Centralides); it is hardly necessary to emphasize how much such a systematization is open to discussion. Is it possible to put in parallel Helvetic nappes with Pennine nappes when the former present only gliding Mesozoic cover and (in France) pass to the simple folds of a cover that has slipped on a basement usually unchanged? Is it not imprudent to postulate the general character of the Austro-Alpine nappes when their existence is established at most only in the eastern Alps?

The difficulties become much more serious as soon as we try to apply the scheme to other mountain chains. There is no need to recall the grave errors precipitated by the desire to find in all mountain chains a superposition of nappes of Alpine style. Kober's system also led him to exclude the Pyrenees from the Alpine edifice and to include them simply among the reactions of the Alpine orogenesis in the foreland.

However fascinating the picture may appear that Kober gives of an orogenic edifice, and however convenient it may be from the didactic point of view, by furnishing a framework into which local descriptions can be arranged almost automatically, such a synthesis runs the risk of being misleading if it leads to imposing a ready-made framework for an orogenic structure being studied. The originality of this structure is liable to be misunderstood.

The intimate structure of most mountain chains is still too little known, it seems to me, for the moment to have yet arrived to establish a systematic classification. We may even wonder if the Alps, with the considerable development that nappes attain in them, do not constitute an exceptional type of mountain range, or at least a relatively rare type. In any event, the wealth and variety of structures that nature offers us is such that we risk misunderstanding it in reducing it to any sort of system. It is better to analyze and describe the greatest possible number of examples in order to deduce the general mechanical principles according to which nature works rather than, by reducing them to a system, risk being misled concerning the variety of types to which these principles lead.

In any case, we observe only the superficial part of an orogenic structure to the depth of some thousands of meters reached by erosion. In Chapter 18, we noted the difficulty involved in trying to visualize the constitution of deeper zones by comparison with more deeply eroded old mountain chains, such as Precambrian chains. Between the depth directly accessible to observation in the tectonic edifice and that in which we can imagine the action of convection currents, there extends a wide domain upon the structure of which we are reduced to hypothesis.

It would perhaps be betraying the thought of authors such as Argand and Staub to discuss the manner in which they extended the outline of certain overall sections downward as if it were a question of very formal hypotheses. But we cannot completely avoid it, even if we make only simple suggestions, because other authors have taken up the problem systematically.

The study of the superficial part of dislocations imposes upon us the notion of a certain transverse contraction, the value of which has varied according to the interpretations in fashion. Although figures of 200 to 1000 km have been advanced for the Alps, gliding tectonics today leads to much more moderate evaluations.

On the other hand, the law of conservation of volume requires that this contraction correspond to a thickening of the crust which should determine the mean altitude through the action of isostatic equilibrium, taking into account what has been carried away by erosion. Besides, it is hardly possible to express this correspondence quantitatively, since the uplift of the surface for a given thickening of the crust depends upon the difference of density between the crust and the asthenosphere, whose value is very largely hypothetical.

It may be more or less accepted that the thickening of the part of the earth's crust that constitutes the "root" of the mountain chain, in the sense as used by Airy (not to be confused with the roots of nappes) should represent a much greater volume, namely, five to ten times that of the visible part of the chain.

For a basement mountain chain whose structure is interpreted as resulting from a crushing of the basement due to a great number of fractures, there is no difficulty in harmonizing the horizontal compression and the thickening of the earth's crust which determines the mean altitude of the region by the action of isostasy. It was in this way that I evaluated the initial length of a belt in the Pelvoux massif as being 120 km, but which now measures only 65 km (Fig. 203), through the geometric study of the different structures. If we accept the fact that the top of the crystalline basement was originally at a depth of 5000 m and that the sial crust was 35 km thick (compensation depth of 40 km), the compression, in the ratio of 65:120, must have brought the thickness to 64 km. The mean altitude, which is approximately the mean altitude of the top of the crystalline basement, is about 2400 m; the base of the crust should then be at about 61.6 km. The isostatic equilibrium is verified

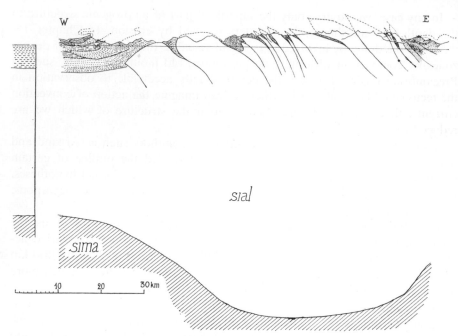

FIGURE 203. *Diagram of the total deformation of the sial crust in the Pelvoux region. On the left, thickness and initial position of the crust.*

on the condition that the difference of density between the asthenosphere and the earth's crust is on the order of 0.3, which is in conformity with the hypotheses usually formed. However, let us remark that we might just as well assume a lesser thickness of the crust, with a greater difference of density. It is self evident that in such considerations there are no grounds for taking into account the tectonics of the cover but only the movements of the basement that provoked it.

The problem is more difficult if the basement itself is involved in a system of nappes, such as the Pennine nappes. It depends on the manner in which the roots are interpreted and also on the way in which the impulses to which the crust is subjected are represented. According to classic theory, it is considered as undergoing a compression that crushes a weaker part. In certain sections (Fig. 204), Argand, who accepted such a crushing of a weak zone

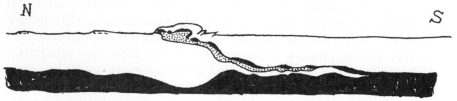

FIGURE 204. *Diagrammatic section of the Alps (according to Argand).*

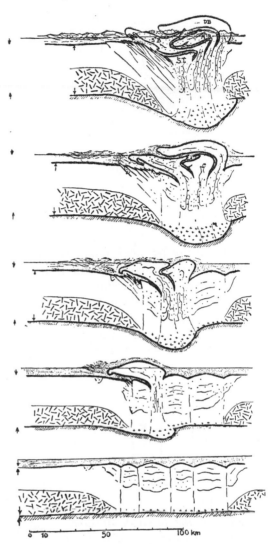

FIGURE 205

Series of sections explaining dia-grammatically the formation of the Alps. Goguel, J., Introduction à l'étude méchanique des défor-mations de l'Écorce Terrestre, Mém. Carte géol. France, 2nd. ed., Paris, 1948.

between rigid jaws, calculated the prolongation of the basement of the fore-land engaging and passing under the basement of the other jaw, which he expresses in a picturesque manner, saying that Africa passes over Europe. Perhaps he did this to express the idea that the material of the nappes was, so to speak, raked over its deep basement. Isostasy prevents our accepting the idea that one of the basements is engaged under the other, outside the folded region, but nothing would prevent its being accumulated in any manner whatsoever under the folded region.

In the series of sections reproduced here (Fig. 205), I have tried to show how the whole crust could, as a result of its crushing, produce such nappes.

Kober's section, reproduced as Fig. 206, also expresses the accumulation

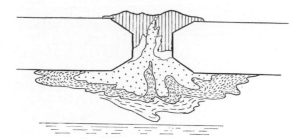

FIGURE 206

Diagram of the structure of an orogene. [After Kober, Die Orogen Theorie, Fig. 9, p. 54.] The plastic material, pressed between the two rigid jaws, escapes downward to constitute roots.

of the material in the root of the mountain chain; it seems that, according to Kober, the "orogenes" destined to fold are distinguished essentially from the resistant "kratogenes" by the plasticity of the lower part of the earth's crust, which spreads out to form the root.

In these diverse interpretations, the root—that is, the thickening of the crust—results from compression, in the same manner as do the deformations nearer the surface. Recently, a number of authors have proposed interpretations according to which the root was probably formed directly by some sort of drag in depth. Thus, it might be easy to explain the manner in which the roots of nappes plunge in depth as if sucked in, such that it is impossible to observe the synclines that should logically separate them (See Gignoux,[35] Ampferer, Umbgrove). Naturally, the interpretations that may be applied to this general principle differ on numerous points.

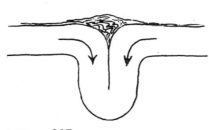

FIGURE 207

Diagram of the behavior of superficial formations in a buckling of the earth's crust according to the hypothesis of Vening Meinesz. [After Hess, Gravity Anomalies and Island Arc Structure, Proc. Amer. Phil. Soc., vol. 79, pp. 71–95, 1935.]

According to Vening Meinesz, and, to a certain degree, Umbgrove, who collaborated in the establishment of his theory of "buckling" (Chap. 14, Fig. 182), and Kuenen,[36] who illustrated it by experiments on models, this was probably essentially a lateral compression that must haave determined a sort of enormous syncline of the entire thickness of the earth's crust, in which the superficial formations were probably at once compressed upon themselves and carried toward the depths (Fig. 207).

Griggs,[37] as the result of his experiments on models (Figs. 208 and 209), which were built in such a way as to conform to the rules of similitude, reached the conclusion that, in the action of deep convection currents on the earth's crust, the suction of the crust at the emplacement of the descending currents played as important a role as the drag of the base by the horizontal currents. Contrary to most authors who have concerned themselves with convection

FIGURE 208

Experiment by Griggs, designed to produce the structure of an orogene by the action of currents circulating in a viscous liquid upon a plastic material floating on its surface.

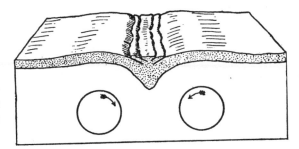

currents, he does not think that the forces exerted upon the base of the earth's crust need to be transmitted over a great distance in order to finally produce a localized crushing.

Daly,[38] has offered interesting suggestions on the mechanism of orogenesis. In 1925, Wegener's theory was only beginning to spread, opening a whole series of new ideas, which Daly was endeavoring to investigate. While seeking the moving force of horizontal displacements, he thought he could attribute it to gravity, by assuming a dip of the earth's surface. This was in contradiction to isostasy, and the author seems to have abandoned this idea later. But his description of the orogenic structure is independent of the cause of continental translations and contains suggestions of the highest interest. Daly starts out with his remark, which we have referred to several times, that the rocks at the base of the solid crust, because they are crystallized, should be denser than the immediately underlying asthenosphere, which is formed of the same rocks in a vitreous state. Except in certain cases, those in which discharges of basalt may be produced as surface flows, the mean density, should be lower than that of the asthenosphere. But in a compressed orogenic zone, when these low parts of the crust sink into the asthenosphere, they should have a tendency to descend lower and lower, since they are denser. The compression force is only exerted on the upper part of the crust, which is formed of light rocks (such as sedimentary rocks and sial), and it is this part alone that undergoes crushing, while absorbing much less energy than would the whole crust in an analogous deformation (Fig. 210).

We may even wonder if the sinking in depth of heavy rocks of the base of the crust does not furnish a motive force that might be responsible, if not for

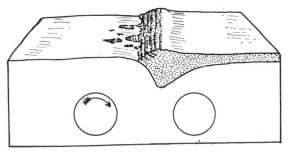

FIGURE 209

Another experiment by Griggs with the same apparatus. One of the drag rollers being stopped to simulate a dissymmetric convection current, the substance floating on the surface is pushed laterally.

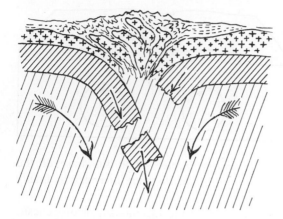

FIGURE 210

Diagram showing how the descent of the crystallized sima into the less dense molten sima may facilitate the crushing of the upper part of the crust. [Inspired by a suggestion of R. A. Daly.]

the appearance of the orogenic structure itself, at least for the continuation of its deformation. Not only would this explain the sucking into depth of certain more superficial fragments of the crust, which confers so special a character upon certain root zones, but the progressive crushing of the orogenic edifice would appear to us on the whole as a self-driven process. Even without going quite so far, Daly's suggestions make it possible to reduce greatly the estimate that we are able to make of the energy furnished by other phenomena, such as convection currents, in the orogenic edifices. They also make it possible to explain the localization, often along a very narrow belt, of the deformed zone between blocks that remain unaltered, which evidently constitutes a difficulty for any theory implying a transmission of orogenic forces through the earth's crust along a great distance.

However fascinating it may seem, this theory has one defect, namely, that it rests entirely upon the assumption that the asthenosphere is formed of molten rock, which has by no means been established.

But on comparison with Griggs's theory—he considers the material of the asthenosphere to be crystallized—we realize that the two theories lead to analogous results. After all, it makes little difference whether the convection currents carry a crust downward in spite of a density somewhat less than that of the asthenosphere or whether this crust descends spontaneously once the movement is triggered, owing to a slight excess of density, if the effect upon the upper parts of the crust is to be the same.

In some way or other, the formation of the root by an active downward carrying movement seems more satisfactory than its genesis by a simple horizontal compression of the crust. This movement takes place, of course, within the framework of isostatic equilibrium and is accompanied by lateral compression. The best example to be found of such a phenomenon is doubtless furnished by the skin that forms on milk; it wrinkles, then forms a fold that sinks into the liquid under the action of the very weak forces exerted by eddies in the milk.

It seems that it is to a plan of this type that we must seek to relate the movements that we are endeavoring to reconstruct by observation of the high parts of mountain chains.

Moreover it is not certain, let us repeat it once again, that the plan arrived at for the most studied mountain chain, which is the Alpine chain, should be applied without modification to the older chains. Since metamorphism and granitization appear to be normal in a mountain chain at a sufficient depth, the Precambrian chains perhaps differ from Tertiary chains only in the deeper level reached by erosion. Perhaps the concept of the interior structure of the earth that we have used to explain the genesis of the Alpine chains should be adapted to explaining the oldest chains. A less advanced cooling of the earth, allowing notable volumes of molten material to continue to exist, or simply a thinner crystalline crust might perhaps make possible orogenic deformations accompanied by an intense plutonism under conditions in which they would be impossible today.

If we should accept such a difference of prevailing conditions, the concepts of Daly, relative to the instability under diverse forms of a crystalline crust on a molten asthenosphere, would apply to the Precambrian. Daly's concepts could, it seems, easily explain the contraction of the sialic crust upon itself, which has produced continents at the same time as the intensity of eruptive phenomena. Later, each of the great convection movements expressed on the surface by the formation of a mountain chain probably greatly cooled the corresponding parts of the interior of the earth, now become almost entirely crystalline.

Perhaps behind the history of the successive episodes that we are trying to reconstruct, we shall be able to discern the great lines of the evolution of the earth which should lead it from an origin still enigmatic but whose date we now know, to a maturity that should see progressively reduced the manifestations of interior activity.

The concepts that we have just sketched are still largely hypothetical. But whichever one is finally retained, there is no doubt that the history of the movements that have affected the earth's crust will provide us with data essential for the overall knowledge of the earth. It places us face to face with a scale of time and dimensions that obliges us to modify profoundly the empirical notions furnished by our experience. On this scale, we foresee a whole interior life of the earth and perhaps an evolution that may infinitely enrich and enlighten upon many points the static picture that geophysics is endeavoring to set up.

These movements of internal origin, insensible to the scale of time of our current experience, and which manifest themselves apparently only in the vibrations of earthquakes, interfere with all the aspects of a geologic history, determined in great part by superficial phenomena that are dependent upon solar radiation and upon which the presence of life imprints particular characteristics.

These slow waves of dislocation that periodically prevail at the surface of the earth constitute, with the presence of life, one of the two most characteristic phenomena of our planet. Through them is affirmed the solidarity between the surface, occupied by living beings, and a deep structure upon which physicochemical phenomena, still poorly understood, confer a rhythm of activity of its own.

Notes and References

1. There is a good summary of most of the theories proposed, as well as a detailed bibliography, in Hume, W. F., Terrestrial Theories, a Digest of Various Views as to the Origin and Development of the Earth and Their Bearing on the Geology of Egypt, Geol. Survey, Government Press, Cairo, 1948.

2. Developed principally by T. C. Chamberlin and F. R. Moulton. See T. C. Chamberlin, *The Origin of the Earth,* Chicago Univ. Press, 1916.

Chamberlin, T. C., The Growth of the Earth, Carnegie Inst., Yearbook, no 25, pp. 372–387, 1927.

3. Joly, J., *The Surface History of the Earth,* Oxford, 1925.

4. Gutenberg, B., Crustal Layers of the Continents and Oceans, Bull. Geol. Soc. America, vol. 62, pp. 427–440, 1951. This summary does not take into account Ewing's final results on the absence of an intermediate layer in the Atlantic.

5. See: Minutes of the Meetings of the Committee on Physics of the Earth's Interior, Aug. 1951, Ann. de Géophys., vol. 8, no. 1, pp. 112–132, 1952.

6. Gutenberg, B., On the Layer of Relatively Low Wave Velocity at a Depth of about 80 km., Bull. Seismolog. Soc. America, vol. 38, pp. 121–148, 1948.

7. Bridgman, P. W., Polymorphic Transitions and Geological Phenomena, Amer. Jour. Sci., vol. 243-A (Daly volume), pp. 90–97, 1945.

8. Birch, F., The Variation of Seismic Velocities Within a Simplified Earth Model in Accordance with the Theory of Finite Strain, Bull. Seismol. Soc. America, vol. 29, no. 3, pp. 463–479, 1939.

9. Perrin, R., *Quelques remarques à propos du noyau terrestre de la lithosphère et des théories géologiques,* Bull. Soc. géol. France, vol. 18, 5ᵉ ser., pp. 199–206, 1948.

10. See, for an overall view and for the bibliography: Elsasser, W. M., The Earth's Interior and Geomagnetism, Rev. Modern Physics, vol. 22, pp. 1–35, 1950.

11. Cagniard, C., *Sur la nature des ondes séismiques capables de traverser le noyau terrestre,* Acad. Sci. Paris, Comptes-rendus, vol. 234, April 21, 1952, p. 1705.

12. Heim, Arnold, Energy Sources of the Earth's Crustal Movements, Sixteenth Internat. Geol. Congr., Washington, vol. 2, pp. 904–924, 1936.

13. Bemmelen, R. W. van, *Mountain Building,* The Hague (Nijhoff), 1954.

———, The Geochemical Control of Tectonic Activity, Geologie en Mijnbouw, new ser., vol. 18, no. 4, pp. 131–144 (bibliography), 1956.

14. Coulomb, J., *Tensions engendrées dans le globe terrestre par son refroidissement,* Ann. de Géophys., vol. 1, fasc. 2, pp. 171–188, 1944–1945.

15. Green, W. L., *Vestiges of the Molten Globe as Exhibited in the Figure of the Earth,* Volcanic action and physiography (part 1), London, 1875; (part 2), Honolulu, 1887.

16. Bucher, Walter H., The Pattern of the Earth's Mobile Belts, Jour. Geol., vol. 32, pp. 265–290, 1924.

———, *The Deformation of the Earth's Crust,* Princeton Univ. Press, 1933. (See especially pages 115–124.) Bibliography of earlier experiments.

17. Chamberlin, R. T., The Wedge Theory of Diastrophism, Jour. Geol., vol. 33, pp. 755–792, 1925.

18. See reference 1, Chapter 1, Goguel, J., Introduction . . . , 1st ed., p. 97; 2nd. ed., p. 103.

19. Wegener, A., La genèse des continents et des océans. Théories des translations continentales (translation of the 5th German edition), 236 pp., Paris (Nizet and Bastard), 1937. The first German edition was published in 1915.

20. Placet, R. P. François, Où il est montré que devant le déluge l'Amérique n'était pas séparée des autres parties du monde, third edition, Paris, 1688.

Pelligrini, A. S., La création et ses mystères dévoilés; l'origine de l'Amérique, Paris, 1859.

Taylor, F. B., Bearing of the Tertiary Mountain Belts on the Origin of the Earth's Plan, Bull. Geol. Soc. America, vol. 21, pp. 179–226, 1910.

———, The Lateral Migration of Land Masses, Proc. Washington Acad. Sci., vol. 13, no. 29, pp. 445–447, 1923.

21. Du Toit, A. L., Our Wandering Continents, Edinburgh-London, 1937.

22. The theory that the moon broke away from the earth, the Pacific Ocean marking the scar left by its departure, has been considered by numerous writers, the first of whom seems to have been R. Owen in Key to the Geology of the Globe, Nashville, Tenn., 1857.

The astronomic theory, based at once on the effect of centrifugal force for a rapid rotation and on the vibration due to resonance with solar tide was developed by G. H. Darwin in: On the Precession of a Viscous Spheroid and the Remote History of the Earth, Trans. Roy. Soc. London, vol. 170-A, pp. 447–538, 1879–1880.

Darwin, G. H., Problems Connected with the Tides of a Viscous Spheroid, Trans. Roy. Soc. London, pp. 539–593, 1880.

H. Jeffreys, in successive editions of The Earth denied, then accepted, and finally rejected again the possibility of the phenomenon.

The identification of the Pacific as the scar left by the departure of the moon is essentially due to O. Fisher, author of On the Physical Cause of the Ocean Basins, Nature (London), pp. 234–244, Jan. 12, 1882.

See also Pickering, W. H., The Place of Origin of the Moon: The Volcanic Problem, Scottish Geogr. Magaz., Edinburgh, pp. 523–535, Oct. 1907; and Jour. Geol., vol. 15, pp. 23–38, Chicago, 1907.

The incidence of the phenomenon on the discontinuity of the sial layer has been pointed out by B. Gutenberg in Die Veränderungen der Erdkruste durch Fliessbewegungen der Kontinentalscholle, Gerlands Beitr. z. Geophys., vol. 16, pp. 281–291, Leipzig, 1927, and by Mohorovicic, S., Über die Konstitution des Erd- und Mondinnern, Astronom. Nachrichten, Kiel, vol. 200, no. 5271, pp. 245–250, 1924.

Mohorovicic, S., Das Erdinnere, Zeitschr. Angewandte Geophys., vol. 1, pp. 330–383, Berlin, 1925.

———, Über Nahbeben und über die Konstitution des Erd- und Mond-Innern, Gerlands Beitr. z. Geophys., vol. 17, pp. 180–231, 1927.

The question has been raised again with doubtless illusory details by Escher, B. G., Sur l'origine de la forme asymétrique de la surface de la terre et ses conséquences sur le volcanisme de la terre et de la lune, Bull. Volcanol., 2ᵉ ser., vol. 8, pp. 23–39, Naples, 1949.

23. Goguel, J., Déplacements séculaires du pôle, Ann. de Géophys., vol. 6, no. 3, pp. 139–146, 1950.

24. Vening Meinesz, Spanningen in de aardkorst tengevolge van poolverschuivingen (Summary in English, French, and German), Nederlands. Akad. van Wetensch., Verslagen, Amsterdam, 1943.

25. Runcorn, S. K., Paleomagnetic Comparison between Europe and North America, Proc. Geol. Assoc. Canada, vol. 8, pt. 1, pp. 77–85, Nov. 1956.

26. See reference 1, Chapter 1, Goguel, J., Introduction . . . , Chapter 23.

27. Let us point out here that Bowie, after having made a contribution of first importance to the theory of isostasy, by developing and applying Hayford's hypothesis,

thought he had found in this theory an explanation of orogenesis. However, this does not seem to be the case. He understood that the re-establishment of isostatic compensation requires currents of material in depth, but for them not to displace the base of the crust (assumed by Hayford to be at a constant depth), he further assumed that these currents could be situated in the thickness of the crust itself and could explain orogenic deformations. However, it is easy to see that the distribution of pressures would by no means explain the appearance of the currents assumed by Bowie. If displacements of materials are possible at a certain depth, they will evidently tend to produce an isostatic readjustment in relation to this same depth of compensation and not in relation to a deeper level.

The distrust that certain American writers show regarding the hypothesis of isostasy is aimed in fact at this particular theory, not at the principle in general.

28. See reference 1, Chapter 1, Goguel, J., *Introduction* . . . , Chapter 7.

29. Griggs, D., A Theory of Mountain Building, Amer. Jour. Sci., vol. 237, pp. 611–650, 1939.

30. Goguel, J., *Note sur le refroidissement du globe,* Ann. de Géophys., vol. 4, fasc. 3, pp. 253–258, 1948.

31. Reports of the Sessions of the Committee on Physics of the Earth's Interior, Ann. de Géophys., vol. 8, fasc. 1, pp. 112–132, 1952.

32. Holmes, A., The Thermal History of the Earth, Jour. Washington Acad. Sci., vol. 23, pp. 169–195, 1932.

33. Griggs, D., A Theory of Mountain Building, Amer. Jour. Sci., vol. 237, pp. 611–650, 1939.

34. Kober, L., *Die Orogentheorie,* Berlin (Borntraeger), 1933.

35. Gignoux, M., *Méditation sur la théorie de la tectonique d'écoulement par gravité,* Univ. Grenoble, Lab. Géol., Trav., vol. 27, pp. 1–34, 1948.

36. Kuenen, Ph., The Negative Isostatic Anomalies in the East Indies (with experiments), Leidsche Geol. Mededeel., vol. 8, pp. 169–214, 1936.

37. Griggs, D., A Theory of Mountain Building, Amer. Jour. Sci., vol. 237, pp. 611–650, 1939.

38. Daly, R. A., Relation of Mountain Building to Igneous Action, Trans. Amer. Philos. Soc., vol. 64, no. 2, pp. 283–307, 1925.

————, *Our Mobile Earth,* New York (Scribners), 1926.

INDEX